The Garden
of Janus

The Garden of Janus

Carlos Rojas

Translated from the Spanish by
Cecilia Castro Lee

Madison ● Teaneck
Fairleigh Dickinson University Press
London: Associated University Presses

Associated University Presses
440 Forsgate Drive
Cranbury, NJ 08512

Associated University Presses
16 Barter Street
London WC1A 2AH, England

Associated University Presses
P.O. Box 338, Port Credit
Mississauga, Ontario
Canada L5G 4L8

The paper used in this publication meets the requirements
of the American National Standard for Permanence of Paper
for Printed Library Materials Z39.48–1984.

Library of Congress Cataloging-in-Publication Data

Rojas, Carlos, 1928–
    [El jardín de Atocha.   English]
    The garden of Janus / Carlos Rojas ; translated from Spanish by
Cecilia Castro Lee.
        p.   cm.
    ISBN 0-8386-3672-1 (alk. paper)
    I. Lee, Cecilia Castro, 1943–   .   II. Title.
PQ6633.O594J3713   1996
863'.64—dc20
                                                                96-5290
                                                                CIP

PRINTED IN THE UNITED STATES OF AMERICA

Contents

Introduction

CECILIA CASTRO LEE

THE Garden of Janus, a novel by the Spanish writer Carlos Rojas, is a narrative of a narrative. It tells the story of fiction in the making. In it, Cervantes becomes a fictional character joining his own creations, Don Quixote and Sancho Panza. Embedded in the Cervantine world of fiction, Rojas's fable is a heartwarming story that retraces the mysterious avatars of Cervantes. *The Garden of Janus* becomes a mythical, magical journey into the depths of Cervantes' soul through dreams, memories, and enigmas. At the same time, the novel recreates the true flavor of everyday life during the Spanish Golden Age. As we follow Rojas's characters through the streets of Madrid, the country roads, taverns and inns, the snowy landscapes of Esquivias, or the sunny beaches of Algiers, we feel the rhythm of Cervantes' times. In this introduction I will review some of the historical background of Cervantes and a few of the features of his masterpiece which may serve to bring forth some of the special qualities of Rojas's narrative art in the *The Garden of Janus.*

Carlos Rojas was born in Barcelona in 1928. He earned his doctoral degree at the Universidad Central in Madrid, and he is the Charles Howard Candler Professor of Spanish Literature at Emory University. Rojas has published twenty novels, and as an art critic he has four books and numerous articles on the Spanish artists Picasso, Dalí, and Goya. Rojas was awarded the Mirror of Spain Prize in 1984 for his book, *El mundo mítico y mágico de Picasso* (The mythical and magical world of Picasso). Another art book, *El mundo mítico y mágico de Salvador Dalí* has been translated into English under the title *Salvador Dalí: Or the Art of Spitting in Your Mother's Portrait,* 1993. As an interpreter of history, Rojas has written several books on themes related to the Spanish Civil War and the cultural aspects of Spanish history. *Diálogos para otra España: Una llamada a la conciencia de todos,* 1966, (Dialogues for another Spain: A call to everyone's conscience) is an important book that offers valuable insight on Spanish culture and thought. He has also written books on the works of Ortega, Unamuno, and Machado. Rojas is a respected scholar and a distinguished fiction writer in the academic community throughout the United States and the Hispanic world.

Since early in his career as a novelist, Rojas has provided new paths for the Spanish novel. In the late fifties and early sixties Rojas openly opposed the realistic novel of the post-war period because, in his view, it did not respond any longer to the aesthetic and intellectual needs of the readers; instead he promoted a more imaginative, artistic, intellectual, and universal novel. Rojas experimented with narrative techniques such as stream of consciousness, multiple point of view, flashbacks, and foreshadowing. He has always aimed toward expanding the boundaries of reality through oneiric experiences, myths, fantasy, and magic. Although firmly grounded in the Spanish narrative tradition from Cervantes, Unamuno, and Valle Inclán, Rojas is closely aligned with other European writers who have given the genre of the novel a depth of thought, and an awareness of history and universal concerns. Some of his thematic obsessions are his quest for meaning and identity, the morality of human actions, and the nature of artistic creation. His fiction is an art of fabulation in which myths and art are interwoven with history within compelling stories. The reader who approaches Rojas's texts is invited beyond the surface to see meanings within different levels of reality. Furthermore, Rojas has a subtle sense of humor based upon paradox and irony.

Rojas initiated his career as a writer with his novel *De barro y esperanza,* 1957 (Of mud and hope). Two of his main novels during the sixties were *Las llaves del infierno,* 1962 (The keys of Hell) and *La ternura del hombre invisible,* 1963 (The tenderness of the invisible man). The publication of his novel *Azaña* in 1973 represents an important moment in his career, generating public interest as well as recognition from the literary critics who awarded him the Planeta Prize. He was granted the National Prize of Literature in 1968 for his novel *Auto de fe,* and in 1977 he received the Ateneo de Sevilla Prize for his novel *Memorias de José Antonio Primo de Rivera.*

The trilogy of Sandro Vasari gained Rojas great popularity and is considered a landmark of his work. Several doctoral dissertations at major universities and scholarly articles have been written on these three novels. *El valle de los caídos,* 1978 (The valley of the fallen) establishes an imaginary dialogue between Goya and a writer in the twentieth century. In this fable, Goya's paintings are transformed into narrative form to prove once more that the "dream of reason produces monsters," and that history repeats itself in an endless circle. The second novel of this trilogy is *El ingenioso hidalgo y poeta Federico García Lorca asciende a los infiernos,* 1979 (The ingenious gentleman and poet Federico García Lorca ascends into Hell), for which Rojas received the prestigious Nadal Prize, dramatizes Lorca's life. Lorca, the poet who feared death as the loss of individual consciousness and identity, finds himself condemned to eternal wakefulness retracing every moment of his life. Lorca's fable takes the reader to the turbulent times at the beginning of the Civil War, and by calling forth Lorca's lyrical and dramatic poetry the reader descends into a Dantesque inferno. *El sueño de Sarajevo,* 1982 (The dream of Sarajevo) represents a great moment in Rojas's art of fabulation. Ekphrasis, intertextuality, and metafiction are some of the different layers of this fantastic and humorous tale which may be considered an epic of Western civilization.

The unfinished trilogy of the gardens includes *El jardín de las Hespérides,*1988 (The garden of the Hesperides) and *El jardín de Atocha,* 1990 (The garden of Janus). In both works, Rojas explores the mystery of artistic creation in relation to the human reality of the artist. Spanish painters Salvador Dalí and Diego Velázquez are the protagonists of the first garden, and Cervantes, "The Prince of Wits," is the main character of the second garden. *Yo, Goya,* 1990, and *Proceso a Godoy,* 1992, both published by Planeta in its "Memory of History" collection, are his most recent novels. It should be noted that several of Rojas's works have been translated into German, Russian, Lithuanian, Bulgarian, Hungarian, and English.

Critics have made valuable observations with regard to Rojas's narrative art. "Rojas's fictional world," says Spanish critic Ignacio Soldevila "is one of the most original, powerful and cohesive in contemporary Spain" (339). Rafael Sánchez Torroella compares the richness of Rojas's style to Picasso's *Guernica* and to Dalí's multiple images of his paranoiac critical method. Canadian critic, Kenneth Golby, studies Rojas's visual imagery and points out that Rojas "demonstrates masterfully that it is possible to provide food for both the mind and the senses leading us to *see* intellectually" (169). Rojas has acknowledged the importance of art in his own literary creation:

> My debt with art has always been much greater than what I can learn, and I am still learning—as Goya once said—from literature. There is a certain wisdom in the vision of the eyes incomparably superior to the verbal representation of the world. The few times that the best literature approximates the highest artistic qualities, it has done it in terms of plastic images. Let us think, for example, on the chapter of the windmills

in *Don Quixote,* as a paradigm of the visual and baroque transformation of reality through circumstantial appearances. ("Entrevista," 372)

Carlos Rojas has lived in the United States since 1960, but every summer he returns with his wife and children to his native soil of Catalonia for an encounter with his roots. His summer home in the heart of the Pyrenees Mountains could very well be his spiritual refuge. I dare say, that the Pyrenean landscape, with its striking beauty, represents for Rojas his own mythical and magical spot in the universe. His novel, *El sueño de Sarajevo,* offers delightful descriptions of this land in luminous visual images. Furthermore, it is very common to find in Rojas's novels special places full of magic and fantasy in which the characters and the reader are transported out of the boundaries of this world into sublime moments, as if conquering a paradise of absolute beauty and peace. These epiphanies in his fiction, inspired by nature and by art, reveal Rojas's existentialist view of mankind. His characters represent postlapsarian man, struggling with the world and with themselves, but constantly seeking to regain here on earth the once lost paradise.

The two characters created by Miguel de Cervantes in his immortal novel, *Don Quixote of La Mancha,* have become part of the collective unconscious of Western civilization symbolizing, among many other things, the poetry and prose of our existence. Throughout the years, the figure of this noble Knight has personalized the highest ideals of mankind; he is the courageous man who dares to transform reality to suit his dreams. That is the nature of his madness. Sancho Panza, on the other hand, represents man's ability to cope with reality knowing very well that he cannot change it. Therefore, with his feet on the ground the practical Sancho struggles for survival while demonstrating an understanding of our human nature. On the other hand, Don Quixote, "The Knight of the Sad Figure," toils to bring back that golden era of yesterday, in which brotherly love, freedom, and frugality were the norm. Together, both characters tell the story of what it means to be human.

Century after century, Cervantes' masterpiece has shed light on the meaning of existence and on our obsessions with our own identity, free will, honor, justice, love, death, and immortality. Different periods of history have seen in *Don Quixote* different aspects of the hero's personality according to the spirit of the times, the prevailing value system, and the aesthetic principles peculiar to each. For the contemporaries of Cervantes *Don Quixote* was the most amusing book of the seventeenth century, and its success was extraordinary. The readers of Cervantes' time enjoyed the wit of the parody of the chivalry books, engrossed as they were with these fabulous stories. The eighteenth century appreciated the satire and the psychological insights found in Cervantes' novel, while the romantics of the nineteenth century identified themselves with the rebellious spirit of Don Quixote. They perceived him as a tragic hero, a Christ-like figure, a victim of society's evils. "The German Romantics," says Manuel Durán, "were the first ones to give a deeper and most comprehensive reading to Cervantes' works: they recognized *Don Quixote* as the prototype of the modern novel, a perfect model for all modern fiction as it reconciles the epic and the dramatic genres with the framework of modern artistic sensibility" (177). Cervantes has left a remarkable imprint among Spanish writers of all times. For Miguel de Unamuno, in *The Life of Don Quixote and Sancho,* Don Quixote represents Spain itself: the drama of its history with its glories and defeats. The philosopher Ortega y Gasset, reflects on Cervantes' lessons on narrative technique and the significance of *Don Quixote* in the shaping of the modern novel. For Ortega, "Every novel bears *Quixote* within it like an inner filigree" (*Meditations on Quixote,* 16). The rich panorama of Cervantes' novel does not cease to address the concerns of readers and writers of our twentieth century and of our postmodern world.

It is not surprising that Rojas would create a fable of Cervantes since he has always shown great admiration for Cervantes and his masterpiece. In his article in 1987, Kessel Schwartz analyses the impact of Cervantes on Rojas's fiction at different levels of intertextuality, and stresses that "with the exception of Goya, Rojas refers most persistently to Miguel de Cervantes and his writings, to the importance of the man and his works in the literary world, and to Cervantes as determinant in Rojas's own development as a novelist" (70). Aside from innumerable incidental references and comparisons using Cervantine imagery, Schwartz sees a profound identification of Rojas with Cervantes' ideology and with his ethical and political beliefs, and he also sees an affinity in their paradoxical interpretation of reality and the complexities of authorship. Cervantes' ideas about history and art, his understanding of human nature, and his yearning for a better world are deeply rooted in the fictional and nonfictional writings of Carlos Rojas.

In *The Garden of Janus,* Rojas uses as a narrator an unnamed twentieth-century writer who eagerly speaks to Cervantes, wherever he may be in the paradise of eternity, seeking to understand the enigmas of Cervantes as a man and as a writer and hoping for answers to his own quest. The narrator addresses him as "Your Grace" in a very respectful, yet intimate and affectionate manner:

"Here, page after page and paragraph after paragraph, I try in vain to conjure you. But my incantation fails, because Your Grace never responds" (*The Garden of Janus* 120). Through the narrator's words Cervantes is led to recollections of his past as he attempts to make his last confession. Marcel Proust's involuntary memory and his kaleidoscopic vision are vehicles used by Rojas toward the recapturing of a past now gone. The novel's collage-like structure is woven like a rich tapestry threaded with entangling dreams, recollections, and reflections.

The title, *The Garden of Janus,* refers to a mysterious garden in the land of Atocha in old Madrid, where, as a child, Cervantes would go for strolls with his younger brothers and sisters. In this garden, there was a two-faced statue of the Roman deity, Janus. This garden becomes a mythical and magical place in the novel, for there the ghosts of Don Quixote and Sancho Panza meet their creator, Cervantes, at one of the most critical moments in their lives. The novel is set precisely in the ten-year lapse between 1605 and 1615, the decade that separates the publication of the first and second parts of *Don Quixote*. For Rojas, these ten years of hesitation are one of the greatest mysteries in the life of Cervantes, comparable to "the dark night of the soul" of the mystics. For reasons unknown, Cervantes does not say much about this intriguing interim, which Rojas describes as "the most prodigious of the entire human comedy" (124). In his novel, Rojas aims to unravel and unveil this enigma. What made Cervantes wait ten years before completing the second part of *Don Quixote?* What conscious or unconscious forces kept him from writing the second part? Was he afraid of failure after having enjoyed fame? Had he become disillusioned with the world and its elusive glories? Had he gone mad or did he need to lose his reason to be able to write? The literary dilemma, to write or not to write, becomes for Cervantes, as well as for Rojas and for any other writer with an authentic vocation, the crucial dilemma between existing or ceasing to exist. These existential complexities of Cervantes are thoroughly explored in Rojas's novel, for we see the poverty in which he lives despite his fame, the diverse trials which make him unable to believe in his success, and his fears and metaphysical pondering during these ten years prior to his death in 1616.

Yet, there is still another mystery in the history of Spanish literature which Rojas explores because it profoundly affects Cervantes and determines the composition of the second part of *Don Quixote*. A contemporary of Cervantes, who has never been identified, hides himself behind the pseudonym, Alonso Fernández de Avellaneda, and writes a sequel to Cervantes' first part. He publishes it in 1614 just one year before Cervantes publishes his own second part. The "Apocryphal Quixote" is a novel of inferior quality and it includes a prologue full of insults to Cervantes. Angry at this theft and feeling abused, Cervantes decides to complete his unfinished second part, far surpassing his earlier efforts. In his prologue to the second part, Cervantes shows an example of his ironic style when he mocks his adversary, Avellaneda:

> This gentleman must be suffering greatly, seeing that he does not dare to come out into the open and show himself by the light of day, but must conceal his name and dissemble his place of origin, as if he has been guilty of some treason or act of lese majesty. (*Don Quixote II*, 506)

The Garden of Janus is conceived as a novel of intrigue and mystery. A crime has been committed and the guilty party must be found and tried. Rojas weaves his plot like a detective through intricate and surprising revelations about Cervantes and his contemporaries, Góngora and Lope, as he tries to unmask Avellaneda. Throughout history, this plagiarist has been a name without a face, a nobody, whose intentions have yet to be determined. In his novel, Rojas raises questions about the imposter's intent: Was he, whoever he was, trying to destroy Cervantes and keep him from writing his second part, or was he, on the contrary, provoking him into writing it? Was he acting alone or was he protecting someone else's identity? What role did Lope and Góngora play in this act of treason? Since Avellaneda succeeded in awaking Cervantes from his lethargy, Rojas concludes that the world owes Avellaneda, not for his poorly written second part, but for Cervantes' great work.

The impact of Cervantes' delay in completing his second part creates an existential dilemma for Don Quixote and Sancho in the pages of *The Garden of Janus*. The troubled ghosts feel that their author has left them in limbo as he postpones the telling of their adventures. Anxious to truly live, they beg their master to continue writing. At the same time, the ghosts have the premonition that someone else, an imposter, is writing a continuation of their story, leading them through the nightmare of a fake existence and, eventually, to madness.

Cervantes' encounters with his characters in the mythical garden of Janus bring to mind Unamuno's encounter with his fictional character, August Pérez, in *Niebla (Mist)*. In both cases, the characters are aware of being products of their author's imagination and a projection of their creator, but at the same time they claim freedom to fulfill their own destiny. "I want to live, I tell you, to live and to be myself," says Augusto to his author, Miguel de Unamuno. "It cannot be, my poor Augusto . . . It is already written. It's in the books. Your fate is sealed and you cannot live any longer." Augusto then sentences his creator to death: "Very well, my lord creator, Don Miguel de Unamuno, you will die too! God will cease to dream you!" (226). In the final analysis, the author's fame and immortality are achieved only through his characters and in the minds of the readers.

Metafictional reflection and narrative discourse are tightly woven in *The Garden of Janus*. For Rojas, narration and metafiction are as inseparable as the proverbial heat and fire. In a recent interview, Rojas explained the intricacies of this process:

> I wrote *The Garden of Janus* because I had thought for a long time about the ten years that Cervantes let pass after the extraordinary success of the first part before writing the second part of *Don Quixote*. My own pondering became another fable, *The Garden of Janus*, which in turn was forcing me into a double reflection about my own narrative reasons and the assumed reflections on the part of Cervantes. In essence, I do not know if I wrote my novel because I had meditated so much, perhaps too much, about those years in which Cervantes refused to write his novel or if I indulged in those meditations so that from them I would conceive *The Garden of Janus*. ("Entrevista," 369)

Another feature of the *Garden of Janus* is the parodic motifs such as the scene with the ghosts in the garden. In his recreation of Cervantes and his characters, Rojas imitates Cervantes' language and style as he portrays the distinctive personalities of Sancho and Don Quixote. Modern parody is understood as the transformation of a text in order to create a new synthesis and does not imply a satire or mockery (Hutcheon 20). Rojas's intent is not to ridicule his characters; on the contrary, by means of the parody he confirms the vitality of the Cervantine characters and offers a subtle tribute to their author. The dialectics of the ghosts and their creator, Cervantes, in the mythical garden also includes a parody of Unamunos's *Niebla*. Cervantes addresses his characters who are challenging him into writing:

> I thought I had freed myself from you and from the book that brought me so much pain. You are only shadows of shadows, reflections of what existed solely in some mountain fastness of my spirit. The hidalgo replied, 'Even so, more is said about us than about your Grace.' (31)

Cervantes is not satisfied with only a satirical reply to Avellaneda in his prologue. He needs to prove beyond any doubt that his is the only true story of Don Quixote. To do so he uses one of Avellaneda's characters, Don Alvaro de Tarfe, who in Avellaneda's novel had the opportunity of meeting the fake Quixote and Sancho. Cervantes proves him wrong and Alvaro de Tarfe has to change his mind: "Let me affirm once more that I did not see what I did and that what happened to me didn't happen" (*Quixote II* 72 928). Rojas brings Alvaro de Tarfe into his story in order to demonstrate Cervantes' ingenuity.

Rojas quotes Nabokov in the epigraph for his novel as the point of departure for the imaginative flight of *The Garden of Janus*. Nabokov's clever idea captures the essence and the spirit of Rojas's fable. The Russian novelist proposes a battle between the two Quixotes, the real and the fake, to settle the matter of identity. "How splendid it would have been if instead of that hasty and vague last encounter with the disguised Carrasco, who tumbles our Knight in a jiffy, the real Don Quixote had fought his battle with the false Don Quixote" (*Lectures on Don Quixote*). Inspired by this image, Rojas proposes other duels in the course of the story and embellishes them with visual imagery and dramatic qualities. In a dream, Cervantes sees himself dressed in full armor on the verge of a battle with Avellaneda in order to defend his honor and the authorship of his book. Another challenge in this fable is the one between the narrator, who is also a writer, and Cervantes himself. The narrator maintains that every writer in the Spanish language, including himself, is indeed another Avellaneda since everyone attempts to measure up to Cervantes. Ultimately, all the quarrels, duels, and challenges in this fable are reduced to Cervantes' battles with himself as he tries to reconcile his dreams with his humanity.

When Cervantes was born in 1547, the Spanish Empire was at the pinnacle of its power and fame. In Nabokov's words, "its worst troubles and its best literature began at the end of the century"(6). Two important historical events were of great significance for Cervantes. One was the defeat of the Turks in the sea battle of Lepanto in 1571, in which Cervantes fought and was wounded. The other was the defeat of the Spanish Armada in 1588. These two events, only sixteen years apart, set two distinct moods within Cervantes. The euphoria of the glories of Lepanto is followed by disillusionment and deceit. The altruistic spirit of the Renaissance that united the people of Spain under the ideals, God, country, and king gave way to the tormented baroque spirit. Therefore, it is understandable that

Don Quixote may be seen by some as an archetype of the Renaissance and by others as the symbol of the baroque.

In this novel Rojas depicts the contradictions and ambiguities of this period of Spanish history. In the shadow of the Inquisition and the traumatic autos-da-fe, people from all walks of life devour the pages of *Don Quixote* to amuse themselves with the Knight's misfortunes. The owner of an inn entertains his guests by reading the adventure of the windmills, while some young nuns read it secretly in their cells, and even the King himself states that "your book is worth more than my Kingdom."

In this novel the characters of Lope de Vega and Luis de Góngora are developed through their relationship with Cervantes. Both Lope, father of the Spanish theater, an inquisitor, the Phoenix of Wits, and, as Cervantes called him, a "Monster of Nature," and Góngora, the famous and erudite poet of the Spanish baroque period, enter the story as friends and confidantes of Cervantes and as possible Avellanedas. The novel presents them in their humanity with their weaknesses and contradictions, rather than in their celebrity as writers.

The life of Cervantes was full of hardships and incredible misadventures. As Rojas recreates Cervantes' personality, he brings forth his sorrows and frustrations, which are balanced by a serene attitude toward life. Rojas emphasizes Cervantes' strong convictions as a man of arms and letters. This double destiny is symbolized by the two-faced deity, Janus. Above all, Cervantes loved his freedom, but his family life was difficult to reconcile with his yearnings for adventure, his long trips, and the several times when he was imprisoned. After twelve years away from home, Cervantes seemed like a stranger to his own parents. Later on, his wife Catalina would sadly remark: "We are husband and wife, but we have lived more apart than together since the day of our wedding" (61). In his youth he loved two women who bore him children—La Zeffirina, an Italian girl, mother of Promontorio, the son that he would never see, and Ana Franca who gave birth to Isabel, the daughter who never loved him. During his five years of captivity in Algiers, Cervantes attempted to escape several times before a ransom for his freedom was finally paid to his slave-master. In *the Garden of Janus,* Rojas takes the reader through adventures and incredible happenings in exotic Algiers, land of the homosexual Azán Bajá.

Cervantes completed his last novel, *The Wanderings of Persiles and Segismunda*, just a few days before his demise. In the prologue for this posthumous work, aware of his impending death, Cervantes makes his final farewell to his friends, to his readers, and to this world: "Adieu to gaiety, adieu to wit, adieu to my pleasant friends, for I am dying, yet hoping to see you all again happy in another world" (Durán 175). Cervantes envisions himself as entering an Eden of serene happiness and love. In *The Garden of Janus*, Rojas leads Cervantes to a paradise made to conform with his dreams. The novel reaches a climax with the realization that life, in spite of its adversities, is worth living: "Perchance your entire life, although stitched with threads of bad luck and woven with mishaps had been for the better." (211).

The Garden of Janus can be appreciated on various levels, from the mysterious and historical setting, to the mythical and fantastic episodes, to the metafictional inquiries on the relationship between an author and his characters. Furthermore, the three parts of the novel, "The Garden," "The Tapestry," and "The River," correspond to concrete places in the story which develop into mythical settings within the ambiance of a fable. Ultimately, these aesthetic places come to symbolize different stages in the vital and mythical cycle of the protagonist on his journey towards self-discovery.

The special challenge for the translator of a rich text such as *The Garden of Janus* brings much personal satisfaction. I have tried to capture the spirit of the Spanish text by faithfully reproducing the style of the original Spanish version. Some sections of "The Golden Age" reflect the awkward syntax of the language of the time. Also, some legal documents have been translated keeping the redundancies of style of the original.

I would like to acknowledge my appreciation to student assistants, Julie Estes and Laura Higgings, for their invaluable assistance in this translation project, and my gratitude to The West Georgia College Foundation for providing me with these students. I would also like to thank West Georgia College for its financial subvention and for the color print for the jacket. I would like to thank the author, Carlos Rojas, for his encouragement in this endeavor. Special thanks are presented to my husband, Carey, and to my children, Susana, Phillip, and Sara for their support and understanding. I dedicate this effort to my children and to my husband.

WORKS CITED

Cervantes, Miguel de. *The Ingenious Gentleman Don Quixote de la Mancha.* Translated by Samuel Putman. New York: The Viking Press, 1949.

Durán, Manuel. *Cervantes.* New York: Twayne Publishers, Inc., 1974.

Golby, Kenneth. "Stylistic Unity in The Sandro Vasari Trilogy" in C. Lee and C.

Soufas, *En torno al hombre y a sus monstruos.* Potomac, Maryland: Scripta Humanistica, 1987.

Hutcheon, Linda. *A Theory of Parody.* New York: Methuen, 1985.

Lee, Cecilia Castro. "Entrevista al escritor Carlos Rojas." Boulder, Colorado: Anales de la literatura española contemporánea, 18, 1993.

Nabokov, Vladimir. *Lectures on Don Quixote.* Bruccoli Clark: Harcourt Brace Jovanovich, 1983.

Ortega y Gasset, José. *Meditations on Quixote* (1914). Translated by Evelyn Rugg and Diego Marín. New York: Norton, 1961.

Rojas, Carlos. *El jardín de Atocha.* Barcelona: Debate, 1990.

Schwartz, Kessel. "Cervantes and the Fiction of Carlos Rojas" in C. Lee and C. Soufas, *En torno al hombre y a sus monstruos.* Potomac, Maryland: Scripta Humanistica. 1987.

Santos Torroella, Rafael. "*El sueño de Sarajevo* y los montruos de la razón". Introductory Address. Barcelona, 1982.

Soldevila, Ignacio. *La novela desde 1936.* Madrid: Alhambra, 1980.

Unamuno, Miguel de. *Novela/Nivola.* Translated by Anthony Kerrigan. Princeton, N.J: Princeton University Press, 1976.

The Garden
of Janus

How splendid it would have been if instead of that hasty and vague last encounter with the disguised Carrasco, who tumbles our knight in a jiffy, the real Don Quixote had fought his crucial battle with the false Don Quixote.

—Vladimir Nabokov, *Lectures on Don Quixote*

The Garden

"Everything is the same as when I was a child," you say to the ghosts.

You tell us how, in 1561 or 1562, you found by chance the house and garden, while you were strolling with your younger brothers and sisters. They had not yet started to demolish the walls of Atocha by Puerta Cerrada nor to destroy the inns, the tile sheds, or tents which flanked them along the creek bank, where now meadows and foal-pastures follow in succession. For a short while, your father, that unlearned bloodletting quack, had tried vainly to establish himself in Madrid as a surgeon. By then your family had lodged for a couple of weeks in a sinister, dark inn, like so many others you would later know, when you were not in jail. On sunny holidays, you were ordered to take your brothers and sisters to the fountains of El Prado, or you would enjoy yourself wandering through the esparto-grass fields among the white hawthorns. This took place so long ago that you may have the feeling that it happened to someone else, or perhaps that it had been painted on a lost panel that you saw only once before you cast it into oblivion. In those days, virtuous ladies still remained at home. Or they might venture to church on Sunday all covered in dark veils, like Moorish women.

"Years passed through the garden almost without touching it, like rain through air. Atocha is a land of prodigies, or so Your Grace said just yesterday, without going back any further," interrupts the Squire in profile astride his donkey. He looks at you from under his grayish, bushy-browed frown, his hazel eyes staring intently. We understand that this man, his donkey, the halter, the packsaddle and the crupper are nothing more than apparitions. If we ceased imagining them, they would melt in the afternoon light, as would the puny Hidalgo, halted by his side and raised high on tiptoes in the stirrups of his nag. More than the Squire himself, you answer those eyes, so rich and brown that they seem ironically real in a ghost.

"Atocha is truly a place of marvels. Legends tell that St. Luke himself carved the Virgin of the sanctuary and that another apostle brought it from Antioch. No one knows who the apostle was, and it is better not to confuse the issue by trying to clarify it. More recent traditions report that before Madrid fell into the hands of the Moors, a nobleman called Gracián Ramírez buried the image to protect it from burning or from sacrilege. With the city lost, the man retired to his home in Rivas from where he would begin the fortunate reconquest of Madrid. On the eve of the battle Gracián Ramírez carried out the Vigil of Arms and at the break of dawn, as soon as he had received communion, he beheaded his wife and daughter to save them from outrage, should he perish in action. When the day was won and Our Lady returned to her sanctuary, the hero prayed, deploring his hastiness. At that moment, his victims came back to life at the foot of the presbytery. They did not return headless but all in one piece, although a very thin scar, brighter than red-hot coals, crossed each of their throats from ear to ear."

"Such miracles are lesser marvels, next to a house like this," the Knight joins in. "It is so spacious and delightful to the senses, yet it is still not known whose it was and why it was abandoned," as Your Grace saw fit to tell us. "Nobody claims it either, even though it holds treasures like that tapestry and the mirror that faces it. All of which is too excessively unreasonable for reason to grasp it."

"Not to mention the bust of Janus on its Peguerinos granite pedestal. The one that was already here when I came with my brothers and sisters," you add, glancing at the double forehead of the sculpture. "My brother Rodrigo, may he rest in peace, was the first to discover it through the briar patch and the gate. 'In spite of being identical, each of the two faces of this man resembles you more than it resembles the other,' he told me, while Luisa and Magdalena nodded in agreement. 'They are your very image,' exclaimed the girls. 'If the stone could speak, it would do so with your voice.'"

"Even in the cut of the beard, Your Grace turns out to be identical to that double-faced king of a deck of cards—Janus, or whoever he may be," the Squire remarks, without removing his glance from your eyes. "The three of you wear it combed to a point with drooping mustaches."

"When Rodrigo, Luisa, and Magdalena pointed out the resemblance, I thought they were crazy. Only Juan, too young to speak, kept quiet and stared at me from Luisa's arms. Barely thirteen or fourteen, I had not had the time to know who I was. With the passing of time, I learned to recognize myself in the faces of Janus. Or, rather, to better say it, I realized that I had reached manhood and then grew older to copy his faces. It was my destiny."

"Your double destiny," the Hidalgo clarifies, leaning on the pommel of the saddle, bent over, astraddle his raw-boned horse.

"Let it be double, then."

You concealed what happened the previous autumn, when Magdalena was at death's door, though one could read it in your eyes as truthfully as it is transcribed here. You went to the convent of the Carmelites of Alcalá to tell your sister Luisa—the Prioress Luisa of Bethlehem in the Holy Order—that Magdalena was weakening. The Prioress received you in the orchard, extending her withered hands. *"May God be with you. What has brought you so suddenly?"* The same autumn sun that whitens Madrid and gilds Salamanca whitewashed the walls half-covered with acanthus. Beneath the acacias and next to the noria, pushed by a young nun for the lack of a donkey, moisture seeped through the earthen jars. You kissed each other's cheeks, and you gave Luisa the sorrowful news. The Prioress listened very silently, staring at the cobblestoned path that divided the recently plowed plots. Shaking her head she promised to pray for Magdalena, even though everything was in the hands of the Almighty. Then she became absorbed in thought while you, Señor, evoked once again that afternoon of your childhood in the house of Atocha. Pensively and loudly, you were reminiscing how you and Rodrigo raised the single-log crossbar of the door. With a squeaking of hinges, the door swung, and suddenly you found yourselves before the mirror, the tapestry, the bench, and the chest. That was the same chamber, lit by high windows, that you would show to the ghosts of those who were first figments of your writer's imagination and then probable visions of your insanity. It was a kind of insanity similar to mine, when I insist on sharing these pages with you and your apparitions. I am invisible to your eyes, and the three of you would be deaf to my voice if I were to call your names.

In the house lingered a suffocating silence—an atmosphere kept tight for entire eternities, maybe since the beginning of creation, at the awakening of the newly born world. The Sierra breeze had to air out the chamber before you could enter, close together in awe. Covering a wall from the carved, vaulted ceiling to the marquetry of the floor, the mirror gave the final touch to your fear. On that faded, tarnished glass, you saw yourselves, unsteady and hesitant, as though transformed into your own parody, divested of the reality of the flesh. On another wall a tapestry as large as the mirror cast its reflection in front of your eyes. It showed an embroidered maze of events, places, and figures that you would learn to decipher only in part with the passing of time. *Someone who must have known us before we existed portrayed us in that wall hanging,* you told Luisa in the orchard of the convent. *There they embroidered our lives in relief, as well as our parents'. You might not believe it, but at one*

*end of the tapestry I recently found the Peasant and the Knight of
my novel, astride their saddles. At another point they might have
anticipated this very moment, as you and I think of poor Magdalena,
and your novice keeps pushing the noria.*

Her hands crossed over her habit, Luisa was frowning and staring
as if you were speaking in a strange language, a gibberish from
which she could only make out, after much reflection, some lost
names and absurd statements which amounted to nonsense. *We
learned about your book in this house of prayer, and I believe that
several sisters even read it on the sly,* she smiled. *But now you are
making fun of me talking about that place in Atocha. Neither as a
child nor as a grown woman was I ever with you in a house that
had Janus in its garden. Needless to say the canopy and mirror you
describe never existed. Are, you mocking the world, after having
suffered so many of its hardships and injustices?* You bowed your
head and scuffed your boot against the cobblestones. In a way, your
sister's reply did not surprise you. You and Luisa continued to speak
of Magdalena's calvary, though in a rather different way. Both of
you seemed resigned to her death, as if it had happened in another,
very distant autumn, already embroidered in the tapestry. Restless,
you abandoned yourself to your inexpressible fears. Suddenly, you
felt a burning hurry to flee the convent, as though trying to escape
from your own self. As soon as you could, you bade Luisa farewell,
kissing her hastily. As you turned the corner of Imagen Street, you
stopped and collected yourself before the house where Luisa, Rodrigo, and you were born. Though not Magdalena, because she
came into this world later in Valladolid. Then you took the post
chaise to return to Madrid. As you crossed the flat banks of the
Henares River, by Don Manuel Azaña's estate, a low breeze combed
the sunflower fields.

*The statue that you discovered must be exceptional. No one knows
of another of Janus, but his double profile abounds, crowned with
laurel, on Roman coins,* Don Luis de Góngora, that poet-priest, lame
and resentful, had once told you, under his yellowish and pharisaic
smile. At the comedians' tavern, a place of gossip if ever there was
one, you snacked on some flaky, crusted meat pastries and a pitcher
of light red wine from Yepes or Valdemoro. Predictably, Góngora
knew everything and put forward his erudition with weary indifference, as something inherited at birth with his lameness and his
crooked ankle. *At the Imperial forum there was a chapel to Janus
that would open its gates at war time and close them with the coming
of peace. No one knows the reason for that rite, though Janus was
the double deity of departures and arrivals. Or, in other words, of*

beginnings and ends. Also, the Romans believed him to be the god of gods and father of the Dawn. In the XIV book of The Metamorphoses, Ovid speaks of a temple to Janus next to the frozen fountain of the Naiades. Those verses of his are immortal. You ought to know them: Naiades Ausoniae gelido rorantia fonte. His elbows on the table and his red satin cloak hanging from his shoulders, Lope kept quiet. Resting his face in his palms, he made a gesture somewhat austere and reflective. After much trouble and many scandals, Lope de Vega y Carpio had learned to feign the appropriate expression for a minister of the Holy Office, the best suited countenance to an Inquisitor. He probably inherited his demeanor, as one of his uncles had enjoyed the same position and privilege. Perhaps he was losing track of Góngora's words and found himself reminiscing over verses from the rhymes honoring his notorious relative: *Beware of Carpio! They are roasting meat, Carpio burns more than fire!* But knitting his brows, so finely drawn over his mocking eyes, he suddenly exclaimed: *By my troth, I cannot remember the house that you are describing, although I know that quarter of Atocha very well!*

Then he silently broke off a piece of pastry that he did not even taste. At that point you, Señor, might have thought with me that the hands of that former libertine and dashing swordsman were as pale and delicate as a woman's. *The strangest thing is that we are talking about the same spot, between the cliff, the sanctuary, and the inn,* proceeded Lope. *When I was young, I had a mistress in that corner of Atocha. My heart is in my throat when I remember our affair. She was Flemish, and her husband traded cloth from Cambray, fine lace from Brussels, narrow lace edging, entre-deux de croisee, taffeta, and grenadine. We first crossed paths one Easter afternoon, when the couple was strolling arm-in-arm in El Prado. From that day on, I never let up until I had determined where she lived and then laid siege, sending her a messenger with billets-doux and sonnets as soon as her husband would leave to sell his lace. To tell the truth, I did not fall in love with her but with her breasts, may Saint Agueda bless and preserve them, since she is patroness and protectress of the female bosom. I have forgotten her face, although I believe she was a blond with green eyes, but I cannot drive away the memory of her cleavage, imprinted in my mind from the moment I saw it in her low-cut dress in El Prado, before the palace of the Dukes of Maqueda. Women from Flanders and Picardy are less modest than our ladies when blessed with such charms. I could not wait to see and kiss hers, and then die from my own unbearable delight. I cut the story short to confess that I almost went mad contemplating the beauty of her breasts, when she finally* received me in her bedroom, as soon as I had removed her three-corked soled Valencian chopines, her stockings, her skirt, her bodice, and her shirt. If in my frenzy I had anticipated a bosom worthy of Friné, exposed, hers transcended all imaginable beauty, including that of the playful fawns of the Shulamite. I do not want to shout it from the rooftops, but I suppose she desired me as much as I did her. In the frolic of the spirit and the excitement of the body, all it took was for me to hold her breasts in my palms and to kiss them fervently for her to begin moaning and twisting like heather on fire, calling to me in her incomprehensible tongue. That morning I could also see for myself something that I had thought just gossip among soldiers and buglers upon their return from her land. Like all Flemish women, my lady had her sex slanted. I had to cover her on the bias, lying from southeast to northwest and taking her all stretched out from northeast to southwest. One adjusts immediately to that particular position, and it even increases the pleasure, as you enter the turbulent sea of panting and sinning. Our love affair lasted one year without her husband ever discovering or suspecting it. It goes without saying that, in order to encourage his blessed innocence, I bought the silence of the entire inn. I also required the services of two musically inclined lads. As we indulged in the pleasures of fornication, I made one play the pan pipe, behind the bedroom door, while the other would sing some of my poems. Although my rhymes, by contrast, dealt with death and the corruption of the flesh, they excited me so that she would come into my arms up to twenty times before I could hurl myself down the precipice of satiated pleasure. I am talking about the sonnet which goes:

> This head, when still alive, had flesh and hair
> Over the architecture of its bones,
> Imprisoning the eyes which it enthroned,
> Eyes that looked and were captured by their stare.
> Here was the rose of her mouth, unaware
> How soon to be wilted, kisses of stone.
> Here were the emerald eyes, so bright they shone,
> The color that captured souls in their snare.
> Here lies, in the end, now, she who once held
> The beginning, the joy of all movement.
> Here, of all faculties, harmony dwelled.
> A kite in the wind is your wonderment.
> Now, beauty, where such presumption once swelled,
> Even worms have nought but disparagement.

On the next Easter Sunday, the couple moved to Paris where the husband would go to iron the underwear of His Most Christian

Majesty. I would not see my beloved enemy again. She always swore to me that she was a Catholic, but I still pray for her salvation. I hope she did not deceive me and was not, instead, a Lutheran. God forbid!

Lope concluded his remembrance of times past with a sigh and even pretended to wipe away a tear lost in his eyelashes. Góngora's already thin smile became discolored and more fleshless. As for you, Señor, you would not take seriously the account of that love affair, accustomed as you were to the wanderings of the Minister of the Holy Office. With the same swiftness he would go from madrigals to treachery or from salaciousness to piety. Nor did we know if the amorous adventure was really true or Lope only assumed it to be so as he spun it. Silently, Góngora must have scorned Lope, but this did not prevent his admiring him. With equal sincerity Your Grace would feel now disgusted with, now dazzled by Lope's many contradictions. Not to mention how it must have annoyed you to realize that, younger, he could outlive you. The Inquisitor interrupted his reflections by finishing off his sorrowful speech: *All of my story is apropos of what you were saying, although it became entangled with sweet memories. Never did I see in Atocha a house with Janus in the gardens. Truly and by my faith, I assure you.*

When taking leave, Góngora said that the enigma had an easy solution; together, the three of you should go to Atocha. Even though Lope and Luisa denied the existence of the villa, the orchard, and the statue, Magdalena had mentioned this place in her last words. While you and Catalina were keeping watch at her bedside, she woke from a long lethargy, sitting up on her elbows with the gesture of an enlightened visionary, and yelled at you: *The empty house is calling me, and the two faces of the stone man are looking at me. I do not want to go alone. Come with me, please! I beg you!* Before you could answer, she fell back on her pillow, her eyes closed. That was during a cinnabar sunset, almost like the ones that inflame the Algerian summer sea. She died in her sleep at dawn, as a young partridge pecked at the window.

You would never return with her to the garden of Janus. But you did return in a not too distant future that you could not have foreseen, with that pair of ministers, just as Góngora had advised you. Two weeks later, the three of you went to Atocha with Micaela Luján, Lope's mistress. You, Señor, would guide them, walking tall and at a good pace despite your cane. To everyone's amazement, you found the house and the statue of the god immediately, amid the maple trees and bushes in the salmon and blue afternoon. We would imagine an absent-minded Góngora, silently ruminating over one of his extravagant and incongruous poems, where foam is the graying hair of water, indecisive love hesitates between purple or red snow, or a white lily is compared to a field of myrtle, as cottage cheese to a diamond. But his thoughts must have been different when, resting his lean hand on your back, he whispered: *Are you certain that we see what it is and not what you imagine?*

"Perhaps I was brought to this garden by my insanity," you abruptly say to the ghosts of your creation. "You are nothing but the shadows of my madness. I would need only to regain my mind to dispel you."

"If your highness is right, why don't you try to recover your senses?" asks the Hidalgo, leaning on the pommel while holding the reins in his hands. "Like the Almighty calling for the universe to be, say *Let my reason be* and see if we disappear."

"We and our horses!" the Servant concludes, smiling in that blue-black beard of his that time has not yet touched.

"Why not the house, the orchard, and the two-faced statue?" you exclaim, exasperated by something you cannot control. "Why not the Court, the Throne, Castile, the Kingdom and its seas? What does the world have to do with my dreams, I wonder?"

"According to you, the world envies and admires you. No one speaks of anything but your book, as in former times the war against the Turks and the Britons was the main topic of conversation," the Knight argues. "If you really lost your sanity, in your frenzy you made people know us better than Your Grace yourself."

"And what does Your Excellency think of the case?" intervenes the Squire, shaking his massive head. "Do you also know us better than you know yourself?"

"There was a time when I thought so. I would evoke the iris of your eye, the sweat and leather smell of your saddles, and even the humming of the brooks where you rested by their banks, at the foot of the oaks. I had never before so clearly imagined all that I was writing, even though the end of the book turned out so differently from the way I conceived it. But today I look at you, and sometimes I can hardly recognize you."

"Why not? We are the same, although we came out of the pages of your book, as one goes from the farm to the field or the wheat field to the vineyard. We might be shadows. But at least I call a spade a spade." The Peasant muddles us with his wild reasoning.

"How could I know who you are, when I am only sure that I would never have seen you had it not been for the loss of my mind?"

"We are as real as daylight," the Squire insists. "And who knows if you, Señor, are nothing but our ghost, while you suppose us to have emerged out of your folly."

"I left you in my novel, once I finished it. Having returned you to your nameless town, I thought I had freed myself from you and from the book that brought me so much pain. You are only shadows of shadows, reflections of what existed solely in some mountain fastness of my spirit."

"Even so, more is said about us than about Your Grace," persists the Hidalgo. All skin and bones, his voice sounds in his chest like an echo.

"The same year it was published, they put out six editions of my novel and thirty thousand copies in Spanish have been sold already. It was printed in Madrid, Valencia, and Lisbon. They say that soon it will come out in such different and distant places as Brussels and Barcelona. They also made you, Sir Knight, and your Squire, speak in other languages, as if the flames of Pentecost had descended from heaven to your foreheads, because they translated my fable into English and French. I dare say that sooner or later they will put it into all languages, and I hope to see it in Arabic and Italian, the only ones that I read besides my own."

"Pride would blind you with so many happenings," the Knight smiles. "Considering your vanity, I pity you."

"I do not live in pride but in perplexity. After an infinity of misfortunes and humiliations, this recognition has a glimmer of unreality. I would not have anticipated it nor would I have believed it, even if some saintly Discalced monks had previously sworn it to me. In your assumed madness I made you say in my fable that various magicians, some favorable and some contrary to your deeds, divided and shared the world. Now I conclude that the same happens to me. A sarcastic warlock must have created this mirage so that I deceive myself into believing it true. One day another enchanter will wake me, and everything will turn into ashes for the wind to sweep away."

"And will we also be banished then?" asks the Squire in a tone bordering on anxiety.

"You, too. You are only reflections of the nonexistent. As I said before."

"If we are shadows, there is no gale strong enough to sweep us away."

"Truly, there is not. And each day I admire you more for your discretion and good sense," the Hidalgo praises the Rustic, before turning sharply toward you. "It is no small irony that you invented my madness and today you seek to copy it as if it were contagious, taking the folly to extremes I never reached."

"I imitate you? I mimic the madness that I supposed yours?" you hesitate, perplexed.

Perhaps now you remember María Mercedes del Calvario and the night with her at that inn with its trained vine and canary. The same hostel where she slipped stealthily and silently into your bed *... if I cannot possess you I am not going to buy you either. Go away and leave me alone.* It was then that María Mercedes del Calvario whispered in your ear that her deceased godfather, a hard drinking and lustful canon, thought you went mad as soon as you quit writing but you were of sound mind when you narrated the wanderings of your unbalanced knight. Nevertheless, the inn, its trained vine, the night, and the whore belong to your past and also to this future other book, where in due time we shall find them anew.

"Your madness is worse than ours. Who but a lunatic, mad as a hatter, would call as witchcraft the fame and success your book gave you? If the works of chivalry dried up my brain, you were touched by your own novel. There you recorded the story of my insanity, the same insanity which you so dutifully imitate."

"My master has you there!" cries the Peasant. "You are not a fool because you see us and speak to us but because you term as magic what really occurred. I still wonder if you are not sane only when you talk to us. But you lose your mind again as soon as you leave Atocha. Mind me, sir, for perhaps I am hitting the nail on the head, and I found the true evil for its cure. When you least expect it, you stumble onto the truth. And, as my old grandmother used to say, there are only two kinds of people, those with knowledge and the simpletons."

He bursts out laughing, echoed by the Knight. As they laugh themselves into fits, their saddles almost touching, it is worth seeing how close they are and yet how different. If the former Peasant would have gladly given up his life for his Master, he could also abandon him, sick and dying—*The empty house is calling me, and the two faces of the stone man are looking at me!*—distracted by the aroma of a golden pigeon soup and a frosted pastry. After losing him, he would weep desolately, but a generous bequest in the will, for example, a herd of Merino sheep or an irrigated orchard, would soon console him. Suddenly, Your Grace seems to tire of living and writing in a world where real beings and ghosts diminish and grow paler, though your readers already call you the Prince of Wits. You would like to believe that Master and Servant will vanish in the air if you truly try. You close your eyes to forget them and steel yourself to erase them. Your heart would beat in your breast like a tamor's club as you half-open your eyes. Now breathlessness doubles them

over their saddles and mitigates their merriment, next to the bust
of Janus. Everyone else must imagine the Knight and the Squire
with the same clarity you perceive them at this very instant. More
than weaving a novel, Your Grace taught the world to conjure a pair
of shadows. If you had been born blind—let's say, blind and king,
not to force you to panhandle in a fantasy as you sometimes had to
do in life—you would never have spun your narrative nor would
the ghosts have appeared in the orchard of Atocha.

"You may laugh at me, but, crazy or not, you owe me your fleeting
existence. If I were not here, you would fade away because no one
else can perceive you. And not even I would be able to see you if
I had killed you at the end of my book before printing it. You last
because in my words I gave you the imaginary gift of a pretended
life."

Exhausted, you fall silent. A stork crosses the sky and the air
brings a sweet fragrance of rockroses. At times, it is very hard to
pierce your self-absorbed silences. Perhaps you are thinking that
some day you will return to the empty house in search of this precious and precise moment in the tapestry, while you are bickering
with your ghosts and a perfumed smoke—trimmed bushes burning
on some terrace—joins its scent with the blooming rockroses. *Are
you sure that we see what it is and not what you imagine?* Góngora
had asked you, his chaplain's hand shaking on your shoulder but
his expression as unalterable as ever. With the always doubtful effu-
sion that a prioress could allow herself, Mother Luisa of Bethlehem
denied the existence of the house. She also told you that several of
her nuns had read your book on the sly, and you concluded that she
was letting you know that she had also read it, thoroughly. Coming
back from Alcalá at dusk, you find your wife in Magdalena's bedroom. They had both fallen asleep, and Catalina was resting openmouthed in an armchair. They had lit the kitchen grate, and at the
chopping block your servant Miguel Cortinas was dicing celery.
*Señor, you will get a kick out of this story they are telling in the
market,* he said, without looking up. *Glancing from the balcony of
the Plaza Mayor, His Majesty sees a boy sitting on a bench with a
book in his hands. Suddenly, the chap falls down, rolling around
balled up and laughing himself into tears.* "Go and find out what is
happening to that poor wretch," *the King orders one of his yeomen.*
"If he has gone crazy, as I fear, send him the Palace doctors. I hate
to see someone else in pain, because it festers my melancholy." *In
time the messenger returns, caught in the same fit as the boy.* "By
heaven and the entire celestial hierarchy!" *the Monarch exclaims.*
"Have you lost your wits, too? Is all Madrid drifting into insanity?"

*As soon as he catches his breath and is able to speak, the courtier
replies that the youngster is quite lucid. If he was laughing so much,
it was from the pleasure of reading Your Grace's novel. He had only
to recite a few passages to send the King's messenger into the same
bout of merriment. Relieved, Don Filipo Hermenegildo lets out a
sigh. Then he says:* "I know the book, and I nearly threw up my
cap and danced when I read it. Nothing is wrong here. We can go
on a hunting spree to El Pardo. The season is open, and I have a
craving for a nice young rabbit roasted in its own blood with green
onions. Give twelve copper coins to that jovial lad to pay for the
favor he did me by not going crazy. May God and the Most Gracious
Virgin Mary of Gracia be always praised."

"Your Grace spared us from death in the true chronicle of our
deeds, or you forgot to kill us when concluding it," muses the Knight.
"Consequently, we will never know if we would be here or not, had
you buried us in former times. What is written is written, and no
one can relive a moment past."

"A plague upon it! A man is worth as much as he owns, and he
owns as much as he is worth! My master means that you left us in
limbo, where, even being who we were, we are still no one because
you will not go on with the next part of our story. It is not fair to
keep us suspended between heaven and earth for so many years,
as if we were the tomb of Mahona, the big liar."

"Mohammed, not Mahona," his Master corrects him. "The Mahona is a Turkish boat."

"Let it be Mohammed. I know what I am saying. A smart man
sees with half an eye and gets the picture in few words."

"I will never finish the second part of my novel, despite the con-
siderable progress I had made before I ceased writing it. The sor-
cerer who will wake me up one day and warn me of the futility of
this fame that now comes with my poverty played a new sarcastic
jest on me. I wrote my story, the same story you tend to call yours,
as a parable of deception. But the wizard made people take it as
buffoonery, and my readers inadvertently rejoice in my disillusionment. Nothing delights men more than their neighbor's sorrow. Perhaps that is why they go with almost the same eagerness to see the
juggler's circus and the auto-da-fe, when they burn heretics and
queers at the stake."

Judging by their expressions, the Peasant and the Hidalgo are so
surprised by your renunciation that they hardly listen after he re-
veals it to them. It is almost sundown in the pastures of Atocha, and
the acacia trees stripe the garden with their shadows. In that calmness the goldfinches sing over the murmuring of the creek.

"You may have learned by your own mistakes and stopped be-lieving in your own pursuits," replies the Knight, "but you have no right to deny us a future, simply because we are different from Your Grace. Nevertheless and in all truthfulness, I will add that a common destiny awaits the three of us."

"There is no such destiny," you object immediately. "There are just written words to be read backwards. The rest is ashes swept by the wind."

"I will not get into that. It is dark already, and soon we will vanish into the first night shadows," the Hidalgo answers. "Before we run out of time, Señor, I would like to ask if you ever considered the possibility of someone else writing the next part of your novel. Someone who wants to publish it under his own name. You are taking so long to complete your work that you leave it open to plagiarism."

By your gesture of disbelief, one would think you did not grasp half of his words—vaguely guessing what they mean and knowing you will be wrong in any attempt to interpret them. You used to experience the same confusion with Algerian Arabic or Hebrew before tuning your ear to their singsong idioms. Now you probably fear that the ghost is telling the truth, the sort of truth that deep down you prefer not to accept.

"Who would steal my book? Who would call his all I wrote, and dare to continue it? If you really mean it, your madness is greater in this orchard than in my novel. And so is the simpleness of your Footman, if he firmly believes such nonsense."

"Squire, not Footman," protests the Peasant. "I do not go on foot but on my donkey, and I do not take the bridle of anyone."

"Your anger surprises me, if life is ashes and books are words to be read backwards," smiles the Knight, ignoring the Rustic's complaints. "I do not know who is writing the continuation of our story. I cannot call his name or point him out with my finger. I have not seen his papers, nor would I be able to tell where he hides them. But I am absolutely certain that he and his work are as real as the coming night."

"Your Highness should know that while we awaited you here, wondering if you would finally come, we felt as if our hearts had been pierced with the same thrust of a lance," adds the crestfallen Squire. "*Someone who is not our author drafts the other part of his novel!* we cried together. *The copycat's book is just nonsense. Nothing but a fritter. But it may be printed before our true historian rounds out the tale of our wanderings.*"

"And shall I credit your ridiculous premonitions? Is your word the Gospel truth?" Excited, you go from anger to scoffing. "You are merely shadows of shadows in my story!"

"Men only mimic what they admire. Your Grace is not going to be disparaged if someone else continues the narrative of our adventures," mutters the Knight. "But, if you let the fraud get ahead of you, two impostors will rob us of our identity. You ought to conclude the novel as soon as possible, to establish who we are, my Squire and I, and to keep others from impersonating us."

"This is all dreams, dreams in the void! Lope would die laughing if he could hear us. He would not raise a brow over two garrulous phantoms, because such wonders do not amaze the ministers of the Inquisition. Instead, he would be in fits of hilarity remembering what he told me when I published the first part of my fable. *Only you could have overlooked the many errors in your book. Did hastiness or laziness prevent your proofreading it? Did you fear dying if you stared at your work, as if it were the petrifying gaze of old Medusa?*"

"This Señor Lope should not accuse you of hastiness when you are taking so long in putting a tail to the tale," the Squire cuts in. "If the impostor beats you to it, you will always regret your delay and the harm it is inflicting upon us. Then it will be as if you looked at yourself in a tailor's mirror to find a scarecrow dressed up in your clothes."

"As you grow older between these two narratives, the one by our historian and the apocrypha that we foresee, I find you smarter all the time," the Hidalgo once again praises his Servant. "Truths like yours sound so right that they have no place in that false biography of ours."

You may want to ask many questions of the specters. How did they sense that someone else was forging ahead with your novel when you had no idea of such plagiarism? Unable to foresee your own future through so many disillusionments, you probably dismiss the presages of the ghosts. Were these shadows meeting with another man in that very garden? Was it by any chance possible that a frequenter of the comedians' tavern or a brother of the Unworthy Slaves of the Holy Sacrament of the Altar—the writers' fraternity—came behind your back to mingle with these apparitions? Darkness prevents you from inquiring as Rustic and Master gently fade into the night. One would say that they vanish in the air as if erased with a sponge, while the moonlight outlines the double profile of Janus and blurs the trees. In the distance the hour strikes, and you shrug your shoulders in resigned acceptance.

You put on your spectacles to orient yourself better and proceed on your way home. At a good pace, you cross before the four Hermitages—the Evangelist's, Saint Cebrian's, Saint Catherine's, and Saint Palonia's. Between two houses of correction for women, those of Our Lady and Saint Nicholas of Bari, some muffled grim-looking men cram together. They watch you in silence, pausing in their gossip. Almost at the corner of Saint Eugenia, on the side of the Sisters of the Third Order, a dog starts following you. It sniffs at your steps until you reach El Prado. But as you turn onto the Amor de Dios or Passion Street it disappears as if you had dreamt it. One may wonder if it is going to hide in the tapestry of that empty house, turning from flesh into threads because the world was not made to its liking. Between the General Hospital and Passion Hospital two horses drink at a stone water trough. Wearing a big beret and wrapped in a long leather apron, a young man brushes them while a witch-looking woman gives him light with a lantern. Its rays whiten their faces, and they turn to stare at you, the way the muffled men did before, almost as if they are trying to recognize you. They both have the yellowish glance of bats in a barn.

Oblique reminiscences perhaps take you back to the time when the hospital was a refuge for beggars, before the Obregón brothers came to take care of the sick. Recently settled in Madrid and with your daughter already married to Sanz del Aguila, you walked these quarters one day with Lope de Vega. The Inquisitor knew the history of the city as well as he knew the Lord's Prayer, and he did not want to spare you from the exemplary life of Don Bernardino of Obregón. *That blessed soul would be your age if he were alive. At the time of the sack of Antwerp and the conquest of Portugal, being a young lad myself, I met him in Madrid. I envied his starched ruff, his white sleeve ruffles and his fashionable short silk cape.* The steep, narrow street of these abandoned ones smelled like fried food, while both Leche and Vernica Streets stank like a rubbish dump. A one-eyed tanner pulled a cart loaded with lamb-skins. The combined odors made us feel like we were drowning in a spoiled soup of fish and lamb. Lope pulled a fragrant handkerchief perfumed with sweet marjoram and benzoin out of his sleeve and put it to his lips. After kissing it like a relic, he shook it in the air to spread its scent or perhaps to bid farewell to his long-lost youth, gone with the starched ruffs. *They say a street sweeper inadvertently splashed Don Bernardino with mud and he, angry and quarrelsome, slapped him. It was a memorable day because, with blessed meekness, the sweeper replied: I appreciate the slap by which Your Grace honors and teaches me. A poor devil can always learn from someone of your distinction. Moved to tears, Don Bernardino embraced him, and that very morning he renounced his elaborate dress but did not withdraw from the world to live in prayer on raw grasshoppers. Instead, he devoted himself to his faith and his foundations. We owe to him the hospitals of the Court, the Convalescence, the Holy Brotherhood, and of course this one they call Obregón in his honor. I wonder if, in three centuries, someone will write that perhaps the street sweeper was Christ himself. Though I disagree; had he been the Son of God, he would have offered Don Bernardino his other cheek.* Perhaps you think about the slap that had such wondrous consequences as we go up the steep slopes of Alameda, Redondilla, and Gobernador. We leave behind the palace of Fúcares, the marketplace and the yard of the Abandoned Ones. The bells of Our Lady of the Novena are chiming when you reach your house on León Street, by way of San Juan's. Miguel Cortinas awaits you at the door, a lighted oil lamp in hand.

"Señor, you should not walk alone in Madrid at such late hours," he chides you in a low voice. "I was getting worried. Your wife, the mistress Doña Catalina, had a migraine and retired without touching her supper. I have prepared Your Grace a nice lettuce salad a la vinaigrette and half a young pigeon. Come in now, the night is growing cold."

✳ ✳ ✳ ✳ ✳

Barefoot and having already hung up your cloak, Your Grace—who already in life, and perhaps by a whim of irony reserved for semigods, they call, Prince, and besides, of Wits—, takes off your jerkin, your slashed linen doublet, your close-fitting breeches, your sash and your undergarments. Now you find a run in a stocking, and looking at it you may remember the four reales you owe Diego de Rojas, the hosier on Santa Polonia Street. You must pay as soon as possible in order to buy a pair of cool straw-colored summer hose. Now you may think of a possible passage for that book of yours, the second part which you seem to have abandoned, where the Knight, inadvertently providing entertainment for some dukes as if he were an organ-grinder's monkey, would be shamed by his poverty upon discovering another run in his stocking. Though naked, you are tempted to pick up a candle and make note of that trifle, which for a few moments appears so transcendental. Shaking your head, you change your mind. You decide to bury the incident in oblivion, where it will die or later germinate of its own accord. Abruptly, you speak to your invisible ghosts who would never materialize so far away from the garden of Janus. Loudly you reiterate:

"I will never finish the next part of my novel, even though I was halfway done when I dropped it."

Enveloped in a nightshirt, casting a gigantic, thin shadow against the canopy of the bed, you put your garments away in a small chest between the basin and the skirting board. Carefully folded and arranged, you neatly pile your short-sleeved woolen Turkish doublet, your shaggy three-quarter coat, your black woolen shirts, and your Castilian leather slippers upon your white undergarments and the uncut taffeta that you had inherited from your sister Magdalena. The scent of the camphor roots that Catalina had placed between the old shirts permeates the clothes. With the unpredictable swiftness of shifting figures in a dream, the fragrance takes you back to your wife's house in Esquivias a quarter of a century ago, that afternoon when you went to ask for her hand. It was winter and next to the rectory the fountain of Ombidales was frozen. Between the churchyard and the Palacios' apple-tree orchard, the bare poplars were whitening beneath the gray skies. The old woman, who in a few weeks would become your mother-in-law, welcomed you dressed in mourning for the demise of her husband, who was once the treasurer of the Brotherhood of the Rosary. Suffering from a bad cold, she stared at you with watering eyes, eyes that normally had a disconcerting steel-like gaze, the same gaze that her only daughter, Catalina, inherited. From time to time, while she was listening to you, she would pull a handkerchief from her sleeve and dab at her lids and lashes with its lace. The entire room was thick with the same smell of camphor that now perfumes the clothes in your chest.

As soon as you close the box with your good hand, you smile and think perhaps of those who accuse you of serious shortcomings and oversights in the first part of your novel, errors that you could have avoided with more care and some rewriting. *Did hastiness or laziness prevent your proofreading it? Did you perhaps fear dying before you finished it?* In contrast to that negligence, you keep your garments as neat and orderly as those of a nun. Who would guess, you wonder, that such clothes dress an old, one-handed soldier, hardened by so many of life's blows. As people say—and Your Grace has a finer ear for idioms and proverbs than a vihuela player or a baritone of the Court's choir—you cannot judge a book by its cover nor a friar by his habit. All of a sudden, your memory returns to former times, but not too long ago, when you and Catalina lived on Huertas Street before you moved to León Street. Your renown then was already extensive. At Mass people would stop you and ask when you would publish the next part of your novel, and what new adventures Don Quixote and Sancho would encounter.

Admirers that you did not know and would never see again would come to praise your genius and your work. Some were windbags who never stopped talking, while others were timid and abashed at their own daring. A lackey wearing a wig and a pectoral brought you a letter on a gold platter from the French ambassador. His Most Christian Majesty's envoy requested your permission to pay his compliments in two weeks, on the first Sunday after Easter, for the sole purpose of expressing his devotion as a reader. Flattered and proud, you first accepted but later regretted not having used some pretext to avoid the meeting. You were embarrassed to receive such an exalted personage in your house in your mended shirt, your darned stockings, and boots that had been patched twenty times by Palomeque, the shoemaker. On the appointed day, *monsieur l'ambassadeur* arrived with two noblemen, compatriots then visiting Madrid: *le compte de la Fontaine baron du Château du Möise et sieur du lac du Bougrave* and *le duc de Lendru-Rollin compte des Bois de Neuilly*. They had all laughed and cried over the adventures of the Hidalgo and anxiously awaited their promised continuation. You, Señor, pretended to be your own servant and said that your master and mistress had been suddenly called to Esquivias, because Doña Catalina's father was dying from galloping consumption. In your apologies for your absence you amused yourself by bloodlessly and ironically disposing of your father-in-law, who actually never was, because he had already died before your wedding. You must have been a convincing actor, because the Frenchmen asked for paper, ink, and pen to write three letters expressing their profound admiration for *Don Quixote*. *Le duc de Lendru-Rollin* and *le compte de la Fontaine* also invited you, Señor, to be their guest at their châteaux, if you should ever happen to be in that part of *la douce France*. *Do not be concerned, Your Highnesses. I will certainly inform my master of your visit. I look after him and take as much care of him as if he were the pupil of my eye.*

Before blowing out the candle, you turn back the covers to snuggle next to your wife. She is sleeping on her back, and her tossing in the night has brought her nightgown up to her thighs. Now forty-five or forty-six, perhaps forty-seven, and having never given birth, you admire the still youthful freshness of Catalina's naked figure. You are eighteen years her senior, as she was barely eighteen when she married you in the parish of the Assumption in Esquivias. Even in those days, your graying beard and temples, which had been blond before, not to mention your crippled left arm, made you look more like her father than her husband. *You should cut off your arm up to the elbow and take it to the Christ of Lepanto in Barcelona,* Góngora will tell you years later. Now, at the age of sixty-three, people would take you for your wife's grandfather when you stroll together through El Prado on Sunday afternoon. You have lived apart longer than under the same roof since the morning of your wedding in an Esquivias of frosted fallows and bare hawthorns. Upon returning from your long absences, in prison or tax-collecting, you would never cease to marvel at the encounters with Catalina under the apple trees. She received you with the same casual, absent-minded smile that she would have had if you were just returning from an idle walk through her vineyards at the foot of the hill of Santa Bárbara. She would then give herself to you without complaint or reproach, although she had spent entire eternities not knowing if you were alive, buried by your debts, or perhaps dying with typhoid in the jails of Ecija, Castro del Río, or Seville, where you were quartered at one time or another, and not even knowing if you, the Prince of Wits, as you will be called in the future, were still in this Kingdom or had fled to the Indies. A flight you confessed you had once attempted to do in despair, until all those long waits and the red tape exasperated you to such an extent that with maddening anguish you renounced your project.

From the ardor in which Catalina gave herself to you, writhering and roaring like a furious beast, you could never tell whether she was satisfying her hunger after a long abstinence or enjoying the memory of a lover. A flash of jealousy struck and in vain, you tried to think of a man, as unknown as the one who, according to the specters of the garden of Janus, is now usurping your book, cuckolding you with Catalina on the very eve of your arrival. You had no child by your wife, even though occasionally, upon returning from your long wanderings, you hoped to find some little urchin at home, blond as yourself, running among the trees. Catalina and you never managed to get together at the right time, it seemed, because you had two children by other women and for some inexplicable reason—call it the persuasiveness of irrationality—you found it impossible to believe that your wife was sterile. With your slow and torpid memory, your reminiscences would soon shift into dreams. Perhaps you had never taken Catalina without the vision of other women blending with the body which you embraced. You would then evoke two of your mistresses—Ana Franca and *la Zeffirina,* the Italian girl who gave you Promontorio, your lost first-born. As if their images were portraits painted on three cards and shuffled by a cheater, you were always disconcerted by the uncertainty of who could be the true one possessed between the sheets.

Ego credo et inclino me tibi et omni pompae tuae. In nomine Patris et Filii et Spiritus Sancti, aequalis in se Trinitatis, you cross yourself before you go to bed. When you moved to Madrid, following the Court, it became impossible for you to know your wife in bed. Your unexpected ineptitude hit you as hard as would have the loss of your good arm after the disablement of the other by the sword at Lepanto. Your repeated failures, as you kept desperately trying for several more nights, crushed and humiliated you. Catalina, your executioner and testing ground, finally put an end to your torture by saying that battling the passing of time was as senseless as believing oneself to be immortal. She did not feel so young herself, and, besides, she recalled her confessor telling her that flesh becomes a sin for spouses if they do not enjoy it in order to engender children for the King or for the Church. Like crying over spilt milk was suffering for the loss of carnal pleasure, but both of you could be thankful for the love you had for each other even in such a humble dwelling as the one on Huertas Street. If you used to confuse the naked presence of Catalina with the absence of Ana Franca or *la Zeffirina,* a sinister fate would then make you yourself feel like someone different. With improbable but undebatable certainty, you would sense that she had spoken those very same words to another man, also prostrated by impotency in that bed. As a husband, you would be thus reduced to the image of an unknown and incapable lover whom Your Grace would reflect as if it were a human satire mirrored in shining copper. Although already resigned to the ravages of old age, such thoughts still fill you with jealousy. Besides, persistent and implacable, memory would replay your father's words upon your return from captivity: *We have not seen you for so long, my son, that we do not know for sure if you are you or if we have ceased being who we are.*

Thinking about your lost manhood and your questioned identity, you, the Prince of Wits, caress your sleeping wife's belly with your cheek. Although you are diminished like a child, desire overwhelms you in the darkness of the bedroom. Soft down tickles your cheek above your beard, and her obscure chamber must taste salty and sour as you lick it now, as if it were fried bread dipped in eggs and milk. For a brief moment, you evoke the toast that your mother used to make for you on Sundays in Alcalá, spread with virgin honey from the hills of Zulema. With Luisa and Andrea you would gather to share the slices in that kitchen on Imagen Street scented in winter with burning mimosa. Beneath the dark lids of your eyes, the house

of your childhood mingles with a Neapolitan *trattoria,* in the halcyon
days between the victory of Lepanto and your captivity, when you
were seriously considering settling down in Italy since your crippled
arm had put an end to your illusions of a military career. Then you
read the phrase chiseled on the rock wall behind the flames that
was to frighten you thirty years later: *Post tenebras spero lucem.*
As soon as all of the travelers had gone to bed and she had dried
the dishes and cleaned the stove, *la Zeffirina* came back to you. She
bent over to embrace you and you would feel that womb pressed
against your back where your first-born child was growing, a son as
lost now as if he had never been born. *I expect the light at the end
of the shadows.*

As soon as your book was released, you encountered the same
phrase on its flyleaf. It startled you, then, as if you were seeing the
past through a peephole. You ran to the publisher immediately and
asked him where on earth he had found such a motto. Amazed at
the impatience of a man usually so resigned, Juan de Robles
shrugged. The sentence simply reminded Juan de Robles of his
youth. He had seen it in the printing office of Pedro de Madrigal
when he was serving his apprenticeship under the old Madrigal's
widow. Now, memories, perfumes, and flavors burden your soul.
You notice that even in her sleep Catalina is quivering. In the silence
of her dreamed desire, and while she begins to moan, she twists her
hips, craving for your caress. Imploring your bite, the lips of her
sex start unfolding like two living petals. You must yearn to possess
her whilst you lick her like an old dog, blinded by age and hungering
for the forbidden sun of a former winter. To possess her as in the
past, upon every return from Andalusia. Or to possess her as in the
days that followed your wedding when you thought yourself resigned to living in Esquivias. In an Esquivias where you wanted to
lock yourself out of love for your wife in order to trim her hawthorns
and spend every Sunday afternoon with the Vicar of the Assumption
and the barber on Main Street playing cards while the light faded
on the grids of the window. Although your longings and hungers
are as intense as they were then, you despair over your consumed
manhood—your member as dead as your left arm—when you are
suddenly startled by Catalina's murmurings.

*Madu'a hazikna ko meyaga'at? Lama noladeti akara uvodeda?
Mi ha'ish hamitkare ishi? Why is it so tedious to grow old? Why
was I born barren and lonesome? Who is this man who calls himself
my husband?*

Now for an instant, Señor, you relive the day of the *auto-da-fe,*
when you thought Miguel Cortinas was speaking bastardized He-

brew to Catalina. But truly, we should not anticipate a day that belongs to another fragment of *The Garden of Janus*—the book, not the orchard. Nevertheless, memory quickly takes you, Prince of Wits, to another, more distant past: the time of your imprisonment in the baths of the infidels and your return from Italy. In that captivity you learned to pass from misfortune to fortune and from the threshold of freedom to the gates of death. No sooner would the Turks threaten you with impalement, than they would turn you loose to wander at will on the steep streets of the Sephardim ghetto, with enough money in your purse to buy the poems in which Don Sem Tob must have foreseen you three centuries ago, on this very night and in your own bedroom with Catalina. *A lass I kissed in my dreams, / fleeing the guests in her inn, / tasting lips touched with moon-beams, / sweetest that had ever been, / as moist as the mountain streams; yet bitter, passing with the wind.* Or those other poems where you learned to face despair with resignation. *I feel no sorrow, / in suffering there is less pain, / for in pleasure there is no tomorrow, / like wind, fleeting in vain.*

In the ghetto you got used to the Spanish-accented Ladino and even learned to speak it haltingly. There you met that old man who some believed was over a hundred and who had been born in the Jewish quarter of Toledo before the discovery of the Indies. Blind and seated at the threshold of his house, he would read the future to all comers, groping and feeling the sand in a bowl. *Macheti'ki hit'akhzer li gorali? What did I do to deserve this luck?* you asked him suddenly one day, before even greeting him. Sliding his fingers into the coarse sand, the diviner flattened it with his scrawny palms. *You are in as much trouble as a mouse in a hole, my lad,* he answered in the Ladino of times past. *But your name will live longer than you, longer than all of us. Your life might be dark, but your light will brighten all.* You left laughing and not believing a word of it. Much later, you would transform that blind seer into Cide Hamete—supposedly one of the authors of *Don Quixote,* among many other imaginary chroniclers—although you made your Cide a faceless, eyeless Moor and not a Jew. Thus, rolled the dice between life and words. Between the ghetto of Algiers and the orchard of Janus.

So many years later, face down on your bed, you try in vain to distinguish your wife's face in the dark. Dragged by the lust in her sleep, one of Catalina's hands creeps down through the sheets to touch her groin. *Why is it so tedious to grow old? Why was I born barren and lonesome? Who is this man who calls himself my husband? Madu'a hazikna ko meyaga'at? Lama noladeti akara uvodeda? Mi ha'ish hamitkare ishi?* And then: *I never missed him in all the years that he was gone. Now he has returned, and he is only a shadow.* Slowly, in the darkness, you translate. *Where are my old dreams from Esquivias? Where have they gone? Kol hashanim bahen lo haya imi lo chasar li. Wa'ata chazar We' eyno ela tzel. Ayey chalomotay me'esquivias? Ana ne'elmu?*

They call Esquivias a nest of hidden Jews, as they say that Toboso is a lair of authentic Moors and feigned Christians. The ancestors of Catalina, Palacios, and Salazares lost the faith of Moses, but they kept their tongue concealed with such fervor that even in her dreams she would only whisper it. More than by her disdain—*Who is this man who calls himself my husband?*—you are saddened by the thought of your remoteness from each other. You and Catalina live farther apart under the same roof than when you used to roam aimlessly through endless inns, jails, and streets. *Now he has returned, and he is only a shadow.* It is also true that time turned you into your own parody. In the eyes of others you are the mere reflection of someone they call the author of your novel. That famous, celebrated namesake of yours is almost like a stranger who is usurping your appearance and your privilege to remain in solitude with your back to the world. Several winters go by without people forgetting about your book, as you still fear and in a certain way expect, they keep asking your living copy when the next part of the novel will be given to the printers. Your own ghosts, the Knight and the Squire, believe they are speaking to your former self—their author and prodigious father—when you, Señor, visit with them in the garden of Janus. Although from time to time, as you are fusing with your double, you think that the drama of confronted mirrors will dissipate in the memory of others, you also deduce that the blind man's prediction has begun to be amply fulfilled. Except that now, far from enlightening you, the name that your namesake took away from you has darkened your mind and your being.

Ayey chalotomay me'esquivias? Ana ne'elmu? I suppose you never fathomed what Catalina would dream about in Esquivias. Perhaps you did not even want to think she was capable of dreaming. Instead, in another life you fell in love with the serene graciousness of that young woman, as distant now as an old half forgotten dawn. In those days, she had raven hair and her hands and face were as white as a swan's wings. With her clear gaze and her youthful laughter, she looked more Calabrian than Castilian. Shortly after requesting her hand and during your brief engagement, you would stroll with her on the path that led from Esquivias to Yeles and then through another wider and more yellow road to Cabañas, Olías, and Venta de Promutor. It was a white and golden afternoon, with the snow of the Gredos and Guadarrama Mountains shinning in the distance. As you passed by, Catalina would name the places, as if planting them among the olive groves. *That frozen creek meandering through the pastures is the Bobadilla. It crosses Casarrubuelos and dries up in July. But last Christmas it flooded its banks and reached the doors of Diego Ramírez's inn, where you are staying now. Who would believe it, seeing it so narrow and shrunken? Behind runs the Guadatén. It flows through Parla and Torrejón de Velasco. It is a trout stream, and it brings good carp. The ruins of the belfries and the abandoned hamlet that appear on the way to Yeles are from villages deserted long ago. They have kept only their names—Pozuelo, Palomera, Moratalaz, or Hontova—but I am also afraid that they will soon lose them.* She fell silent, plunged in thought. Then she said in a low voice: *I could not live far from here, without our vineyards, pastures, fallow fields, and woodlands. At least, not for very long.*

Your Grace, the Prince of Wits, inadvertently lied through your teeth then, promising Catalina that you would never take her away from home except for pleasant jaunts you would share with her in hackney coaches. Your words lead her through all of the lands of the Kingdom that you knew, from the rice paddies of Valencia to the estuaries of Guadalquivir, and even to places such as the forests of Galicia where you had never set foot. Those are thick forests, you said, where *Santa Compaña* sometimes appears among oak trees that six men cannot encircle with their arms and where people meet their own funeral procession. They see it as clearly as you and Catalina saw that herd of sheep and the shepherd who was keeping them. The deceptions piled one on top of the other as you proceeded with your delusions. Thus you promised yourself that you were ready to settle down in Esquivias, to tend the vineyards and market the wine. Deep inside, you must have thought it was the proper decision for a maimed man to seek refuge in Arcadia after having lost the dream of soldiering and having given up the dream of writing. Between Yeles and Seseña, with the mountains as witness to your happiness, you would live your idyll in a new Eden scented with rosemary. You were speaking with such a spirited conviction until all of a sudden you were stopped by the contented smile of Catalina and the brilliance of her love-filled eyes. That afternoon you took her in your arms and kissed her for the first time, wrapping her in the folds of your cloak to protect her from the rough, swirling wind. Like two little fish, the tips of your tongues passionately nestled and caressed. You desired her with love then, pressing her against your chest and your lifeless arm. Through the lashes of your eyes, tearing from the cold, you and Catalina saw the old shepherd standing next to the flock. Envious and smiling, he looked at you, shaking his chestnut head.

Halakach et chalotomay kelokcho et mohori? Gerartani me'esqui-vias. Weheve'tani halom le'ir haresha me'oreret ha'eyma. Et kol asher haya li kilita wehinchaltani et chovoteykha, oneykha, mapach nafshekha, wachalomot hashaw asher lekha. Did he take away my dowry with my dreams? You tore me from Esquivias. You brought me to this odious city. You squandered all that I owned and in return gave me nothing but your debts, your poverty, your disappointments, and your hopeless dreams, Catalina murmurs again.

It is all true, and flushing in the shadows, you probably curse your fate. But she also deceived you, and in addition, knowingly. Or at least she was not truthful when she kept hidden part of a past that you never asked her to reveal. You should have suspected that she was not a maiden when she kissed you as she did by the Bobadilla. On your wedding night, while the snow fell in Esquivias, you were surprised at being able to enter her with the same ease as a sword sliding in and out of its sheath. As you were relishing each other and Catalina moaned with delight, you decided to relinquish all questions concerning the honor she had lost before she met you. Whatever her past had been, you wanted to respect it, and you hoped that, God willing, the grapes would not turn sour. As a compassionate Christian, you would not be like those Algerian husbands who exhibit a beastly smile and show a bloody sheet out of the window as soon as they consummate their marriage.

Halakach et chalomotay kelokcho et mahori? Almost thirty years had gone by since your mother passed away at that tannery of Leganitos where she was rooming with Magdalena. Soon after her death, you bumped into Agustín de Cetina at the Government Bureau of the Exchequer. You had first met him when he was a young accountant apprentice in Seville, and you were dazzled by his privileged position. He was so high and mighty that he could almost demand a tax from the King and Queen. By contrast, you, Señor, just out of one of the Andalusian jails, pursued by harassing creditors, and having lost your friend and benefactor, Pedro de Isunza, on the same day that your mother died, were once again reduced to bitter poverty. *I live from hand to mouth, and we are almost starving,* you told Cetina. The powerful man nodded, stroking his beard. As soon as you concluded your complaints, he started talking to you very, very slowly about collecting the taxes in the Kingdom of Granada. It was no minutia, that debt to the Throne, being over two million maravedis. Two million four hundred fifty-nine thousand eighty-nine, he read from some papers in his office while adjusting his glasses after polishing them with a soft cloth. If you were to find a cosigner, Cetina would use his pull to have you commissioned to collect the taxes for the Crown.

Everything happened so fast and so fortunately that you could not help but suspect your joy. Like Polycrates, tyrant of Samos, you were frightened by your own luck. You would have delivered any offerings to fate to mitigate its perfidious, imminent treason. It is a fact that misfortune rides all winds, while happiness is slow in coming and always arrives too late, if at all. Through Agustín de Cetina, you were able to find a partner with a million and a half maravedis— only God knows what dealings he had with that man. He was Francisco Suárez Gasco, a neighbor from Tarancón, too affected and show-offy for your plain tastes. Another Official of the Exchequer, someone named Araiz and inimical to Cetina, badmouthed your guarantor. Although never brought to court, Suárez Gasco was suspected of having poisoned his wife, and afterwards his bad behavior cost him four years of exile from Madrid. Finally, after much red tape and many intricate maneuvers, on a hot August afternoon that could melt the stones of the streets, Araiz signed the document with the guarantee, though he insisted that you and your wife would have to back it with a large amount of your property.

You called Catalina to Madrid and briefly explained the difficulty to her. You were surprised by how swiftly she acquiesced and let you dispose of almost her entire patrimony. Together, you committed yourselves to account for the taxes you collected, down to the last penny. *That the parts both jointly, and each by himself and all in solidum, renouncing as expressly they did the authentic Presente tamen and Hoc ita, de Fidejussoribus, et de Duobus reis stipulandi et promitendi, and the benefit of the division and execution and the epistle from Divo Adriano and all other laws, privileges, and rights upholding those who commit themselves jointly, and in the manner expressed and validated by the law.*

Entire lines of the agreement that were to hurt you so much creep in and out of your consciousness. *They said that inasmuch as the gentlemen from the Government Bureau of Exchequer of His Majesty have appointed the above mentioned to go with his commission to the city of Granada and to other parts of the said Kingdom to collect taxes in the name of His Majesty and his Royal Bureau in the sum of 2,500,000 maravedis owed to His Majesty in taxes and other rents from the above mentioned Kingdom until the first quarter at the end of April of this year of grace, as it is declared in the said commission which said refers to and to which they referred.* You collected the taxes in Guadix, Baza, Motril, Salobreña, Almuñécar, Alhama, Loja, Vélez, Málaga, Ronda, and in Granada itself without any mishaps. From Seville you sent your first punctilious accounts to the Treasury. You even believed that your destiny had changed course and your future would be less bleak. At times you would dream of a future as the option between two impossibilities. You would either bury yourself for good in Esquivias or definitely escape to the Indies, with or without the wife that you had ceased loving, even though you still held her in the highest esteem. In the midst of such chimeras, misfortune struck you once more when a Portuguese—Freire de Lima—in whose bank you had deposited the collected taxes, disappeared with the funds. His flight ruined Catalina and plunged you back into ignominy, under the threat of a new imprisonment that, at your age, you might not have survived.

The memory of Freire de Lima brings to mind the memory of the unknown writer, whom the ghosts say is proceeding with your novel, while your wife sighs in her sleep and her hand slips from her groin onto the pleated sheets. Like someone who washes a dark spot off a wall with a wet sponge, you would like to forget the presumed existence of that stranger. To make him disappear you would only have to stay away from Atocha and your phantoms. However, you must admit in the depths of your conscience your inability to deny that man. You are as defenseless and lifeless in your attempt to forget the impostor as you are this very night in the sad effort to possess your dozing wife. In the wanderings of your mind, perhaps you give that pretender traits rather similar to yours. In the darkness, you might imagine him with your features and gestures as you begin to divide the two parts of your book. One part would be yours and the other his, if this is God's will. In other words, if the plagiarist exists, both of you will suffer the curse of Janus in his gardens. When you felt yourself to be two different men—one the victim of misfortune and the other the celebrated chronicler of *Don Quixote*—you only anticipated your fateful union with that impostor. Perhaps you have both crossed paths in Valladolid, in Madrid, or even in Esquivias. If you did not recognize him and suspect that he was making away with everything, it was not because you were too unalike but because you, Señor, resembled him so closely. After all, as Góngora says with his pale smile, no man on earth knows who he was, who he could be, or who he could resemble.

Right now you would like to silence your vivid imagination. To sleep without dreams face down on your bed. But rest and oblivion are denied you. You see the image of your double, tempting Catalina while you, Señor, not knowing what they plot behind your back, were rotting in jail or collecting taxes with a King's warrant tucked between your doublet and your shirt. *Then it will be as if you looked at yourself in a tailor's mirror to find a scarecrow dressed in your clothes.* One who could mimic you in such a way could also go to bed with your wife. Burdened by the fear of being caught *in flagrante delicto,* or perhaps plagued by unexpected remorse, the cuckolder would have been incapable of satisfying Catalina in some of their encounters. Other times she would surrender happily, ironically seeing in her lover the husband you were when you both loved each other. She would be carried away by the memory of your first kisses, in the wind off Guadarrama and with the ragged shepherd as witness to your joy. Overcoming your jealousy with weary sadness, you imagine your rival, that libertine, with his cheek against your wife's thighs, as you, The Prince of Wits, agonize tonight, waiting for the impossible. If you were the author of your dishonor and your apocrypha, your wife might wake up without even wondering why she was born sterile and lonesome or why tedium makes her feel like she is aging. She would smile at her lover in the dark, and perhaps she would chant that ironic madrigal which she used to sing in Esquivias accompanied by a lute. *Gentle child Narcissus / trapped by a cheating fountain. / Loving his own reflection / it led him to Erebus. / Lady with your lovely hair / and with such gracious spirit / Nearby fountains have a care / lest your eyes linger on it.* Little by little you, The Prince of Wits, doze off, lapping the soft hair between Catalina's legs like a ram craving salt kisses from the the crevices of the rock. Perhaps suddenly thinking of the run in the stockings, and the hosier of Santa Polonia Street you finally fall asleep.

I imagine that while asleep you dream that you enter your own book. Through the unwritten pages of the last part, the roads of La Mancha snake into the dusk. As if compelled, you follow your ghosts deep into the plains. *Where are you taking me?* you ask the Squire. He does not answer, nor even deign to turn his dark head. *Where is Your Grace taking me?* you persist, calling the Hidalgo. Perplexed, the ghost looks at you and then says: *You are going to encounter the one who is stealing your novel. The story cannot belong to both of you, and the time has come to settle the matter.* You assure him seriously that you do not know how to resolve it. As for the impostor, he need only swear not to continue the fight and to solemnly renounce that which he has already written. All of this regardless of whether you, Señor, proceed with the fable or leave it on the shelf indefinitely. The Knight smiles contemptuously. *Your*

Grace asks me to tell you how to solve the quarrel. You must be joking; a soldier always has an answer. He touches his right hand to the hilt of his sword. *I have a duel set with the copycat in one of these turns. As soon as we find him, I will let you borrow my blade so that with its blows you will prove to whom the telling of my adventures belongs.* You, Señor, were never a coward, and your courage has been proven before men and before history. In your dream, however, you are overwhelmed by a sudden, fearful reluctance. You argue that you are maimed in one arm, from your elbow to your wrist, and, besides, you are old. In such straits, why would you fight to the death with a stranger, even if he wants to steal half of your book? *He might also use only one arm, and the bad omens might weaken his courage, if he was made in your image,* the specter exclaimed, irritated by your objections. *Though, in faith, when I see you hesitating like this, I would almost prefer that you were not the narrator of my strenuous exploits.* You are about to reply when you encounter your double beneath some poplars. Weapon in hand, gripping the blade by the hilt, he awaits you in the middle of the road. The sun gleams on the edge of the sword, and your enemy seems to smile at you through a gray, once blond, beard. You almost see yourself when you stare at him. The likeness is so strong that you are almost afraid to hurt yourself by striking him. You seize the Hidalgo's sword, and he dismounts to second you when the impostor bursts into laughter. Guffawing, he yells: *Do not be foolish! If it is not worthwhile to die, why kill yourself over a novel? You and I are not who we believe we are, nor is this nightmare truly yours. We are in the waking dream of a third, who is about to take us to another book. Do not worry, and do not search for him in this feigned Mancha. His work is not yet published because he has not been born, and it will take him centuries to come into the world.*

From the day in which the French ambassador visits you with those two most illustrious gentlemen—*le duc de Lendru-Rollin compte des Bois de Neuilly* and *le compte de la Fontaine baron du Château du Möise sieur du Lac du Bourgrave*—your Grace and Miguel Cortinas always exchange identities to receive the foreigners who come to praise *Don Quixote,* which they have read in their own language. Since your servant is the father of a tailor, and the son charges him neither for the cutting nor the cloth, he easily passes for his celebrated master. As you dress more poorly—*the run in the stockings and the reales that you still owe the hosier!* —you soon get used to acting like your own valet. You both have such a knack with the switch that your visitors never notice the deceit. Also, by pure instinct, Miguel Cortinas learns to imitate you. If before he tended to be quiet and circumspect, when he takes your place, he becomes as pungent and loquacious as you. When he displays his Tuscan, as fluent as, or even better than yours, Your Grace cannot help but ask him where he learned it.

"If you want to, tell me. If you don't, don't. It is not my custom *ficcare il naso negli affari che non mi risguardano.*"

"As a young man, I served two years with a regiment in Naples. Even in this respect, I imitate my master. And one more thing, just in case there is any doubt and to round out everything, I recite from memory entire passages of your book. For instance: *In that blessed era all things were held in common and to gain his daily sustenance no labor was required of any man, save to reach forth his hand and take it from the sturdy oaks that stood liberally, inviting him with their sweet and seasoned fruit. The clear-running fountains and rivers in magnificent abundance offered him palatable and transparent water for his thirst; while in the clefts of the rocks and the hollows of the trees the wise and busy honey-makers set up their republic so that any hand whatever might avail itself, fully and freely, of the fertile harvest which their fragrant toil had produced . . .*

"That is enough, I believe you," Your Grace cuts in impatiently. "But tell me if those who know that you serve me ever inquire about my novel."

"Almost everyone wants to know if there will be a second part. I answer them: Perhaps it is still cooking over a slow fire and green wood. If there is one, the Knight will die in his bed at the very end."

"I never revealed my intentions to you," now intrigued, you smile. "How do you explain this apparent foresight?"

"My Señor, you must have created your Hidalgo as a man of flesh and blood. In such a case, you gave him the fate of a mortal, and because of the law of life, sooner or later you will have to lay your Knight on his deathbed."

For contorted reasons, his reply irritates you inordinately. Your servant deceives the foreigners, copying you so closely that you will have to mimic him to be even. It is inadmissible and incredible that he could be so conceited as to predict what his master has not yet conceived. In a wink, the insolent man is going to say that at the conclusion of the second part, your Hero dies after having recovered his reason and upon awaking from a dream of which nothing is known or which has been forgotten by the dreamer. *We are in the waking dream of a third man, who is about to take us to another book*. Perhaps he anticipates a brief agony for the Knight, while he bids his mourners to be prudent and sensible for there are no birds in last year's nests. Knowing that in lying to Miguel Cortinas you are lying to yourself, you reply:

"If I finish the weave I started, I will not make the Hidalgo die. On the contrary, I am going to prolong his misfortunes into a third part which will eventually close the novel forever."

One day while strolling up El Prado with Lope, you disclose to him in a fit of folly how you switch places and duties with your servant before your foreign readers. Frowning with those eyebrows that are so thin as to be almost nonexistent, Lope stops to confront you.

"It is hard to believe that someone is willing to look like you, even if he has no better fate than to be your servant."

We know that his changes of mood are as brusque as his frolicking and brooding and as drastic as his swings from piety to lust. But his insult is too gratuitous not to surprise you. Nevertheless, you are about to dismiss it with a shrug of your shoulders, when in spite of yourself you reply:

"Do I take that in offense and slap you or do I ignore it as a madman's babbling?"

"Take it as you please," Lope says indifferently. "But remember that I am now a clergyman. My faith forbids me the sword, and if you slap me with your good hand I will have to offer you my other cheek."

"I'll keep it in mind."

Forgetful of your presence, Lope falls into one of those withdrawn moods of which he sometimes sings in his verses. His silent reflections further whiten his natural pallor. When he suddenly turns to you again, all harshness has vanished from his voice. As you cross the Alameda, he even takes your arm, as if he were blind and would use you as his guide or as a living cane.

"You may wonder why I talk this way. I suppose I hurt my neighbor for the same reasons that I force myself to write. I exceed on both accounts because of my urge to feel that I am alive."

"To write in order to justify oneself, as they verify the purity of gold before they coin it, is not to write at all. I abandoned the second half of my book when I suspected that this was my only purpose. To write is to efface the world and humanity in order to create it anew in your own words."

"Perhaps such an imperative made us writers. But only in exceptional moments does it move us now," Lope exclaims, flinging his arms up in the air as if he were accepting banal and unnecessary reasonings. "As I grow older, I find that I write to prove that I am still able to dialogue in verse. Or to compose scenes according to the new art of comedy. The money that the theater brings in is almost superfluous as far as I am concerned. It is an unexpected profit given by sheer chance." After a pause, he suddenly turns to you and asks: "If you decide to continue your novel, will you do it to feel alive or to forget that you have lived?"

"If I were to proceed, I would do it chased like a mad dog by someone else's envy."

Your answer is so quick that it sounds shaded with distrust. You have the unforeseen suspicion that Lope might be the one trying to steal your novel. But his gesture of astonishment dissipates your doubts. The minister of the Holy Inquisition looks perfectly innocent.

"Someone else's envy? I'm afraid I don't understand you. What made you say that?"

"Let's say, the very disconcerting envy of just one man. Jealousy of someone else's good is only inspired by the powerful. By those who are sure of who they are and of the world that they step on and possess."

"Or by the visionaries of a future which they call their own. Whether in heaven or on earth," Lope adds thoughtfully.

"Or the enlightened ones; I grant you that. On the contrary, I have lost all my ambitions. They disappeared in the past, like water draining through a sieve. Even the memory of my dream of being a man of arms or a man of letters is going gray. Any day it will vanish like a breath into oblivion. As you once assured me, if the Turks impaired me for soldiering, as a poet, I was born already crippled."

"Did I say that?"

"Though yours, this is a truth that does not hurt or offend. Disguised as a fantasy, my book is the written testimony of my disillusion with the world. I wagered that no one would understand the secret confession of my disenchantment with history and reality. And I was not wrong because my readers took my novel as a lighthearted and jovial farce, in which they could enjoy, with impunity, their hidden cruelty."

"And aren't you ashamed to think that men will always see in *Don Quixote* a sort of bloodless sacrifice, at which they would laugh and continue mocking as if it were true?"

"I did not make men in my own image, and I am not responsible for their inhumanity."

"Perhaps. But I would not like others to inadvertently make fun

of my hidden pain. Nor would I, perhaps also unintentionally, wish
to reflect their cruelty in a book of mine. I am bewildered and
frightened by your destiny," Lope confesses with a shrug. "I prefer
to rhyme my comedies as quick as a wink, to feel alive without
hurting anyone. There is no greater evil than to offer a mirror to a
blind man. But, let's change the subject. Tell me who is inciting you
with his envy to add another part to your novel."

"Forget it, forget it. Put it away in the dark lost attic of oblivion,
as Góngora would say."

But Lope does not listen to you. He stops to point agitatedly at
the ground with his finger, as if the spot had been made sacred or
at least famous by a most extraordinary event. Say, the beheading
of the Holy Innocents. The birth of the Antichrist. The posthumous
miracle of a saint. The duel of two monarchs. Or the incontinence
of a blushing Empress, urinating behind the wide crinolines of her
ladies-in-waiting.

"Here!" exclaims Lope, The Phoenix, not The Prince, of Wits.
"Here, in front of the Maqueda palace, I met my Flemish love! I
am referring to the wife of that merchant of Valenciennes and tricot.
Old as I am, and besides an Inquisitor of the Holy Office, I should
not think about those breasts that once drove me crazy. But, if we
lived in laxer times, like those of the pagans, I would build a temple
to her naked statue in the middle of the roadway. Each daybreak I
would come to kiss her marble feet, sprinkled with dew."

There is a crack of thunder, and a flock of ringdoves slants across
the sky. Your Grace laughs as if you were in the theater, and Lope
ends his speech by echoing your guffaws. Clouds from the mountains
darken the afternoon, announcing rain. More than a squall, this is
a veritable cascade descending on Madrid. *Honor Lope, donkey, or
watch yourself! / He is the sun, and his anger brings rain.* Soaked
to the bone, you make a dash for the refuge of a porch. Once protected from the downpour, you both start laughing like madmen.
Sparked by the storm, Your Grace will perhaps recall with me a
Sunday of the Easter Octave when you were going with Catalina to
a Mass of the Hieronymites near here. *Suaviter in modo, fortiter in
re, tempus fugit.* Time. Each instant hurts, and the last one kills all
the others. In the middle of El Prado, you met the Royal carriage
as it was returning to the Palace. People would go down on their
knees at the sight of the Monarchs, as if they were the Holy Sacrament of the Altar. Women crossed themselves, and men, bareheaded, hailed their Majesties, waving their berets and plumed
hats.

Sciatica and lumbago were already starting to consume you in spells, followed by hydropsy, all of which would finally remove you from this valley of tears. Certainly each instant hurts, and the last one kills. Blindly, we descend into darkness, not knowing who is who because each person after death is like all the others. Leaning on Catalina, who was kneeling like a suppliant, you barely bent your aching knee. Through the window of the carriage, you caught sight of the prying, aging profile of Mateo Vázquez. You were good friends in Seville as young lads, and in time, that lucky fellow became nothing less than Secretary to the Prudent King. While you were suffering captivity in Algiers, he was court advisor to the father of His Majesty, may he rest in peace. You frowned involuntarily when you saw him beside the King, Don Filipo Hermenegildo. Perhaps, beneath your frown, you were thinking of Azán Bajá, talking to you in your prison. *I will allow you to write as many poems as you want. If they do not please me, they will be burned in the marketplace. If they please me, I will burn you. Ed è di buono ragione because he who lives two dreams is fated to speak with a forked tongue, like a hissing serpent.* But now Azán Bajá belongs to your past. Even though he will also be part of the future of this other book where, in due time, we will cross paths with him once again. In the cell, he said to you that perhaps you were, as a snake, the devil himself. *Addio!* He laughed next to the barred door, but his goshawk eyes refused to meet yours and avoided your dead arm.

Perhaps Don Filipo Hermenegildo, having known Mateo Vázquez in his youth, distinguished him with his august friendship. He would take him hunting in the Casa de Campo, or on outings to the Fuente del Berro, to sip mineral waters with bonbons and soft almonds. Mateo Vázquez did nothing to free Your Grace from your Algerian bondage, even though you wrote him a poetic epistle, whose rhetoric would seem as ridiculous to you today as it was sincere then. *Ten years have I diligently come and gone / in serving the great Filipo, our Master, / sometimes rested, and others weary and wan, / and on the happy day when as sinister / was Fate for the fleet of our enemy / as to ours favorable and friendlier, / athrob with fear, effort, and fidelity, / in person, I was a part of all that occurred, / invested more with hope than with weaponry.* But if, in the past, he did nothing for your liberation, as soon as he saw you that Sunday, Mateo Vázquez rushed to whisper urgent secrets in his Sovereign's ear. Assenting with his head and pulling at the tasseled end of a cord, the King stopped the carriage with the ringing of a bell. Theatrically and impatiently, Mateo Vázquez called to you. As you raised yourself and asked Catalina to get up and follow you, Your Grace understood that fate had ordained that, for the first and perhaps the last time, you would speak with a king of Spain.

Your Grace limping and your wife as reverent as if she were going to confession cross half of El Prado before the eyes of the curious, still on their knees. You try to kneel again, but the Monarchs would not allow it, offering instead through the window their signets to be kissed. While Mateo Vázquez presented you to their Majesties with a solicitous smile, Your Grace remarked that Don Filipo Hermenegildo's hands were as fine and translucent as Catalina's. By contrast, those of the Queen—who was in the habit of a Carmelite—looked as blunt and dark as those of a farm girl. Hands that seemed to have come out of your own book at the end of its first chapter, as those of the peasant girl whom your Knight loved so much: *Her name was Aldonza Lorenzo, and it seemed to him that she was the one upon whom he should bestow the title of mistress of his thoughts. For her he wished a name that should not be incongruous with his own and that would convey the suggestion of a princess or a great lady; and, accordingly, he resolved to call her "Dulcinea del Toboso," she being a native of that place. A musical name to his ears, out of the ordinary and significant, like the others he had chosen for himself and his appurtenances.*

"I had something I was going to ask you about *Don Quixote,* but it has slipped my mind," the King said, blinking and amazed by his own forgetfulness. "I had it on the tip of my tongue."

The crowd was all ears. At that moment, everyone seemed suspended under the spell of an enchanter who may also be embroidered somewhere in the tapestry at Atocha. The whole world stopped in expectation of His Majesty—the Queen, the coachman, Mateo Vázquez, the coursers, the Madrilenians in the Alameda, the birds in the trees, the hunt in the forest, the armies in the midst of battle, the ships at sea, the executioner with his axe raised, the woman about to give birth, the fish in their bowl, the whale at the Pole, the leaf in its fall, the sun at its zenith, Cassiopeia in the firmament, Góngora in the caesura of such verses as *to write my misfortune with my finger* or *black violets, white daffodils,* without omitting Your Grace and Catalina from that immense, immobile tableau. But the universe was about to break free from its spell as Don Filipo Hermenegildo smiled gently.

"I almost forgot what I am forgetting, but now I remember." "Tell us of which king you speak in your book, when you say that he cannot enslave those men in the galleys, because God and nature made them free."

"It was not my purpose to deny the Throne its right to submit the galley slaves to its justice, God forbid!, but to make my Hero say that other vassals could serve the Throne in better conditions," Your Grace was speaking to the Monarch with almost as much ease as if you were chatting with your nephews or with Lope in that gossiping tavern of actors and poets. "I was not referring to any king on this earth in that passage. Fables belong to a world completely different and distant from that of history, even though they pretend to be as true as reality."

"We all know this from the day we see our first puppet show. Whoever your king may be, if man is created twice, which one of his makers, God or nature, conceives and forms him first?"

Don Filipo Hermenegildo's glance became distracted again. Tending to drift into the air, as the bleating of a sheep gets lost in the winter mist. He pulled on the tassel of the bell, and the carriage departed, without waiting for an answer. You would not see him again. *Nothing is wrong here. We can go on a hunting spree to The Pardo. The season is open and I am craving for a nice young rabbit roasted in its own blood with green onions. Give twelve copper coins to that jovial lad to pay for the favor he did me by not going crazy. May God and the Most Gracious Holy Virgin of Gracia be always praised."*

"Tomorrow no one will believe our encounter with their Majesties, if they read about it in the book by another author," Catalina said, as you were leaving the church after Mass. "Did you really write that man was not created only by God but also by nature?"

Your Grace did not answer and continued on your walk in silence. On León Street, beneath the windows of your house, the *Commedia* was being sung by that same blind beggar, Santafiore, whom Góngora often took to the tavern to recite fragments of the Inferno. *Ah quanto a dir qual è cosa dura / Esta selva selvaggia e aspra e forte, / Che nel pensier rinnova la paura!*

"Niccolò," your wife called impulsively, losing her habitual reticence, "do you think that we are created twice, first by God and then by nature?"

"*Certo, certo, bella donna,*" he assented, nodding vigorously. "*La signora* should take me, *per esempio.* God Almighty gave me my eyes, and nature took them away from me after the fevers of Malta which I suffered in Comino. All I have left from my first life is *il ricordo* of La Divina Commedia. Even the faces of my loved ones *infoscan* in my memory."

"*Niccolò, credo propio che non mi sarà possibile di esser soddisfatto con la tua supposta cecità,*" Your Grace said, while Catalina smiled, not understanding a word. "In deceiving us, you deceive yourself, and you ended up as your own metaphor. But I do not admit that you are blind; you see better than I do."

"*Per carità, il signore* should not mock my disgrace! Your Graces will see that I am so stark blind, *ciecco*, that last night I dreamed I had recovered my eyesight, as if the fevers of Malta had never robbed it from me. But suddenly, *nel mio sonno,* I realized that I had forgotten *La Divina Commedia. Tu sei pazzo, Niccolò,* I told myself, and you have lost your mind in your sleep. Immediately, I knew that I was never more sane. I was not then Niccolò Santafiore but Dante Alighieri. I did not remember *La Divina Commedia* because I had not yet written it. *In un subito,* with the beautiful script that Santafiore had when he was a letterer, before he devoted himself to the sale of nutmeg, I concluded the first verse of *mio capolovoro. Nel mezzo del camin di nostra vita.* Then I stopped to think if this was the life of the Santafiore that I had been or that of the Dante that I was beginning to be. *Allora* I woke up."

"Did you also dream of yourself as a blind, old Jew in Algiers?"

"I, *un ciecco* in Algiers, *monsignore? E di sopra un ebreo?* And Hebrew to boot?"

"A Hebrew who read the future with his hands in a bowlful of sand. Old age left him sightless, because he was over a hundred and he had been born in the ghetto before the Indies were ever seen."

"Everything is very strange, *monsignore. Il ricordo* of another dream, that I thought forgotten, comes to me now. *Il mio è un sonno profondo.* Deep in my sleep, Your Excellency is taking me to your house to read aloud from a book. You read in a tone *tanto chiaro* that your words are still imprinted in my memory: *Sliding his finger into the coarse sand, the diviner flattened it with his scrawny palms.* Then Your Grace proceeds: *You are in as much trouble as a mouse in a hole, my lad, he answered in the Ladino of times past. But your name will live longer than you, longer than all of us. Your life might be dark, but your light will brighten all.*

"By the wounds of Christ! How did you know that, Niccolò? How did you know that?" You grabbed the blind man by his arms while Catalina looked at you both in bewilderment. The beggar's words were nothing more to her than the gibbering of a moonstruck man.

"I asked you in my dream if the book that you were reading was yours. You answered: *How could it be, when it will be three centuries before it is written?*" Santafiore lifted his face towards the sky, as if calling heaven as witness to his words. "*Monsignore* must have told me the truth, because in dreams we crossed from one time to another with the swiftness that, wide awake, we flip through the pages of the *Commedia.* Going from the middle to the end or from

the end to the beginning, making the *inferno* follow *il paradiso.*
Forse thinking that, in our dream wanderings, we change names
and faces, *nome e de maschera,* being who we are and many others,
I ask you to tell me who was *quell' altro ciecco,* that other blind
man and why was he using such ancient speech. *Lo so tutto di lei,*
you said. *You and he are variants of the same person in the fable
of the future. Ecco il fatto!"*

"Niccolò, for the last time I beg you. How did you come to dream
that I was reading part of my past in a book that does not exist?"

"There are many things that I know, of which *monsignore* is ignorant," he said with a rather sudden and disparaging indifference.
"*Ma questo, non so,* the question is how I was able to remember
the dream. If *il signore* had not spoken of your *vecchierello* with his
bowlful of sand, I would have forgotten it forever."

"Death and damnation! Did I also refer to the garden of Janus in
your dreams?"

"*Il giardino de Giano? L'antica divinità con due facce?*"

"Yes, the god of two faces!"

"No, *monsignore,* no one ever told me about the garden of Janus."

Suddenly exhausted, you released him and Santafiore left silently,
tapping the walls with his cane. The years have fled by since that
day, and the afternoon light of early spring slowly fades away. Next
to the window, overlooking León Street, you and your wife drink
the glasses of lemonade that Miguel Cortinas brought you on a
woven straw platter. The dusk traces shadows against the walls
while the doves descend to the eaves. In the roadway the children
play at knightly tournaments while their mothers chat. On the corner of San Juan Street, vendors are hawking pastries, rainbow trout,
turnovers from Rute, and river crab. As twilight falls, sadness comes
over Your Grace without altering the timidity that bears upon
your spirit.

"This lemonade is better than that made from the lemons of
Ceuta," Catalina says. "This is just right. The other one is cloyingly
sweet and does not quench your thirst. My mother thought so, too."

"Did you ever deceive me with another man while I was wandering through the world?" Your Grace must surprise yourself, asking
her in a low voice while staring over the rim of your glass.

Smiling, she puts her glass on the tray. Her white hand with its
fine blue veins does not tremble. *If women could consecrate the
Host, I would kneel before yours each morning to receive communion,* Lope told you the year of the expulsion of the Moors. *Her
hands are like alabaster, made for the Eucharist.*

"There was no lack of opportunity," Catalina responds calmly, without losing her smile. "We are husband and wife, but we have lived more apart than together since the day of our wedding."

"More. Much more."

"Entire years, if you include all your trips." There is a tinge of sadness in her voice, as if the memories of so much neglect brought with them the remembrance of her lost youth and her ruined patrimony.

"I know it. Thus the dice fell."

"Thus they rolled. At times we were happy, I suppose, before our wedding and shortly afterwards. And also when you returned from your trips. But, if I could bring back a single instant of those years, I would refuse to live it again. I am afraid to retrace my happiness. Do you know what I mean?"

"Perhaps. I am not sure."

As a string of beads, visions of your past are threaded throughout your life. From Catalina kneeling by the roadway and later by the Royal carriage, the images flash to your wife offering herself to you on your return from your trips. *I never missed him in all the years that he was gone. Now he has returned, and he is only a shadow. Where are my old dreams from Esquivias? Where have they gone?* Unexpectedly, Santafiore returns and bursts into song in the street. He takes up the *Commedia* at the love scene of Paolo and Francesca of Rímini. Together brother- and sister-in-law, as they truly are, read about the guilty passion which brought Queen Guinevere into the arms of Lancelot. Burning with love, their eyes meet, and then they kiss in the midst of the story. Thus Giovanni di Malatesta, Lord of Rímini and Francesca's husband, surprises them. Maddened by jealousy, he pierces them with just one thrust of his spear. *Nessun maggior dolore / Che ricordarsi del tempo felice / Ne la miseria; e ciò sa 'l tuo dottore,* sobs Francesca in the inferno.

"What are you thinking now?" Catalina asks.

"Someone unknown to me is writing the second part of my novel," you confess on the spur of the moment. "Do not ask me how I found out. I could not explain it to you any better than I can avoid it."

Quiescent, your wife stares at you. *Noi leggiavamo un giorno per diletto / Di Lancialotto, come amor lo strinse; / Soli erevamo e senza alcun sospetto. Blind fool! Crazy blind fool!* A gang of children chases and taunts Santafiore. Perhaps you think you were even blinder when you could not anticipate that sooner or later someone else would resolve to continue your book, the second part of that novel you held off for so long. You only came to realize it amidst hallucinations and spurts of madness, when summoned by your own characters in the orchard of Janus. In contrast to your own lack of suspicion, the thief and plagiarist would be a vulture-like man of lax morals, if he was not Catalina's lover as well.

"How could someone else continue your book, when Góngora says that only you, among all men, could have conceived it?" Perhaps novels of chivalry are twice-told tales, as Santafiore states, he has lived two times—once with his sight and once as a blind beggar?" Catalina replies abruptly, as if she wanted to distract you from your jealousy and secret suspicions.

"In truth, I do not know, but I have the feeling that soon we will see the apocryphal second part in print."

"Finish your own continuation of *Don Quixote*. You have been working on it so long. What do you do all alone, when you are behind closed doors, supposedly writing?"

"Perhaps I think about what you say in your sleep."

She seeks your eyes, disconcerted. Then she dismisses your words with a sad, fastidious gesture. Through the window, the afternoon fades, and the lemonade yellows in the glasses. Gradually the sun sets, while another light—half apprehensive and half inquisitive—glitters in your wife's eyes.

"What does Santafiore sing about? You always speak to each other in Italian. Translate it for me now."

"He recites *La Divina Commedia* in his own way."

"That's all he has ever done. Tell me in Spanish what he drones on about, if you can make anything out of that racket."

"He's gone crazy!" They make fun of his madness, yet the children tell the truth.

"Madmen also tell the truth. Tell me of his lunacy?"

"It is not his but Dante's. He is talking about you in verse."

"About me?" Startled, Catalina raises her hands to her chest. "What is that supposed to mean? I did not hear my name."

"Because you do not understand his language. In Tuscan, your name is Francesca. Four centuries ago, Dante foresaw your destiny in a canto of the Inferno."

"What part of my life did he foresee?" laughs Catalina, but she seems tense and her eyes glint greener in her disquiet. She must feel like she is stepping on thorns.

"A wind, which I imagine is that of passions, whirls your soul like a feather in the abyss. Dante asks you what guilt delivered you to that tempest. You tell him that a book brought your perdition, your fall, and your damnation."

"The blind man has fallen quiet," she murmurs, glancing out the window. "He is going towards El Prado, tapping the walls with his cane."

"He finished what he wanted to tell us," withdrawn and shrugging your shoulders, Your Grace continues. "Dead, you confess to Dante that you were murdered by your own husband."

"By my husband before God and the Church?"

"The poet assumes that you had no other."

"It is true."

"One day you and your lover were reading from the book that he had written. Dante does not say if you were incited by the text or by the sort of boredom that so often leads to lust. What is certain is that suddenly you were fused together in a kiss, heedless of the world and original sin. Thus embraced, your husband came upon you, creeping on his toes and with a javelin in his hand. Before you even heard his steps, one swift stroke from his lance pinned you in death like a pair of butterflies. There is no greater sorrow than the memory of lost bliss, you reflect in the Inferno. But then you blame the book for your punishment."

"And for what do I blame my husband? For my murder or the theft of my joy?"

"You do not even mention him. In the Inferno, you must have forgotten him forever."

Catalina laughs openly and without restraint, reminding you of Lope when he was mocking his own lost loves. Miguel Cortinas enters with a candelabrum to give you light and places it on the writing desk. Silently, he retires. *Whoever your King is, if man is created two times, which one of his makers, God or nature, conceives and forms him first?* His Majesty must be revisiting Your Grace in your remembrance.

"You are aging," Catalina murmurs, dashing away a tear.

"I know. If I dream, I forget what I dream."

"I was thinking of fables, not dreams. You used to tell them with more credibility. I remember you many years ago, when you had just gotten out of the Sevillan jail. You appeared in Esquivias again, hungry and barefoot. But you smiled, enjoying your thoughts. You described the Hidalgo that you had imagined as vividly as if you had come from his house and not from a dungeon. You made me see him with more lucidity than I could see you, as you talked next to the apple tree planted by my grandfather. How you painted his pointed-nosed hound, his nag, his lance in its rack, his fluffy slippers, his stockings, his Saturday suppers of eggs and fried bacon, his lentils on Fridays, and even the pots, the ladles, and the skimmer of his kitchen! *What are you going to do with that Knight?*, I asked you. *What will his story be?* You looked at me as if I were speaking in Greek. *I have no idea,* you answered. *The life will come out of the man, as heat comes from fire.*"

"That's the way it was."

"So it was, even though you have forgotten that day and that afternoon."

"I remember very well what we said then. It is as if I were reading it in a book that is being written before my eyes."

Perhaps Your Grace thinks that much later the Hidalgo would appear to you in Atocha more clearly than Catalina had seen Don Quixote, when you were describing him near the apple tree. Now he appears to you as a shadow from limbo to ask you not to abandon the true narrative of his life.

"That night I gave myself to you, under the bedspread scented with the yellow acacia flowers of our chest. Then I had the fancy that it was not you taking me but your pathetic Knight. Even though you called him old, I imagined him as virginal as a monk. Blindly and amidst moans of lust, he would lose his virtue and his soul with me. When it was over, I heard the song of the fountain under the poplars. You were asleep, and for a moment I thought that I was still young and in love with you again."

"No one lives twice, Catalina."

Perchance this evening Your Grace thinks that at some point in the past your wife started to despise you with the worst of rancor— the one that a woman holds for someone she has loved more than herself. Then, with the slowness of rain wearing a rock, she drifted apart from you, until she was as indifferent as if you had never met each other.

"It might be better like this."

"Have I changed that much since then?"

"More than you think. Only someone very different from the man you were then would think me incapable of seeing through your parable of the blind man's song. If a plagiarist is truly writing a new account for your book, I would be his only when the sun rose at midnight."

"In the hyperborean lands, it dawns at midnight in midsummer," you reply gently.

"Stars could also shine at midday like my grandfather used to say happened in Esquivias the year of Saint Quentin. The impossible thing would be that I would give myself to someone who resembles you so much. That would be the same as being yours, turning time inside out like a stocking." Staring at you, she asks slowly, "Do you know for certain that you have not gone mad and are not the one unwittingly continuing the story of your novel?"

"Yes," replies Your Grace immediately, quoting your Hidalgo with a phrase that you ascribed to him almost at the beginning of your novel of chivalry. "I know who I am, or at least I imagine I know it."

* * * * *

Many years later, when you would ask Lope to hear your confession, death would be lying in wait around the corner, and you would never go back to Atocha. Sitting on a sidesaddle, your thin legs covered with a laprug, you know that if you were to return you would not find the Hidalgo or the Squire among the myrtles in the orchard. Perhaps you would not even find the house whose existence Lope questioned before you visited it with him, with Góngora and with Micaela Luján. Like buttons falling off a suit at each snip of the scissors, memories drop onto paper or into fleeting time. Let us remember together, Prince of Wits, another day in God knows what spring of yesteryear. I speak of that amber and hyacinth afternoon, when Catalina and you talked by this same window, sipping lemonade, and Niccolò Santafiore was singing on León Street. *Soli eravamo e senza alcun sospetto.* Let us remember His Majesty the King asking how many times man was created according to your book. Let us remember your Knight and his Peasant. Or their shadows, that you would not see again even if you were to live a century because they no longer belong to your madness. Let us remember the jet black eyes of the specter of your Rustic and the proverbs of that brainy ghost. *When you least expect it, you stumble onto the truth. And, as my old Granny used to say, there are only two kinds of people, those with knowledge and the ignoramuses.* Let us remember the tapestry, where they embroidered your entire life and anticipated Magdalena on her deathbed, yelling that the two faces of the stone man were staring at her. But above all, let us remember Góngora next to the bust on its granite pedestal, wondering if he— Don Luis de Góngora y Argote, sired by a judge of the Holy Inquisition, a true son of Córdoba, ordained in *sacris,* and future Court chaplain—was seeing what he saw or what you had imagined and then made him see.

Your ghosts discreetly absented themselves that afternoon, and, as you were walking with Góngora through the garden of Janus, night fell and a chill in the air began to torment the clergyman's lame leg. At the same time, you both realized you had lost and forgotten Lope and Micaela somewhere while you discussed sonnets and mirages. Looking for them, once you had returned to the house in the twilight, you found them naked on the sofa. In the gray dusk, they embraced without uttering a sigh or a word. Sated, they lay between the canopy and the mirror, like two reflections collapsed or asleep. Immobile, you and Góngora contemplated them. Her eyes closed and her blond hair dishevelled, Micaela's pure profile could have been taken for a newly minted coin. Then you noticed that she was crying without complaint, and slow tears trickled down her face and whitened her cheeks.

"Are they real now or do they also come from my fantasies?" you ask Góngora.

"I would not know. I never dreamed that a man and a woman could make love so quietly."

You stole away—let us say, we stole away—from the house and headed to Atocha by way of the Alameda. With Góngora limping, you passed the hermitages of the Angel and the Holy Christ of Oliva. Behind the friars' orchard, the lights came on in the hostel of the Hieronymites. Next to the fountain of Caño Dorado, Góngora unexpectedly stopped and grasped your arm.

"If you are truly tempted to confess someday, choose Lope instead of me to absolve you of your sins," he said, forcing his thin smile. "I could neither pardon nor condemn you, since I do not know how to judge myself. All I know is that we are both destined to be transformed into our own words."

You promised to keep it in mind. Nor do you forget it as you wait for Lope on your mule chair, palms open on your blanket. Yesterday you asked him to confess you when he appeared without warning and wearing the red cloak of a chaplain of the Holy Office. He said he came *to visit an imaginary infirmed man, and to perform a false act of charity*. Absorbed, he listened to your request and delayed his answer as he played with the brazier shovel.

"If you want to confess and put your soul at ease, I will oblige. Though at heart we loathe each other, death makes us all brothers: you of me and I of Barabbas. But if you mean to tell me your dreams, I refuse to hear them. Not even an Inquisitor should invade the nightmares of another man. Even less if he puts them in writing and publishes them, as you used to do."

You replied that you wanted confession to find who you were before you parted from this world where shadows share the same boundaries with disillusionment. You told Lope how, upon your return from captivity, after twelve years' absence, your parents would look at you, so disconcerted, as if you had changed into another man without ceasing to be yourself. You cited your father, that bloodletting and penniless surgeon, admitting that after so long they were not sure whether you were their child or they had ceased to be your parents. Lope listened to it all as he weighed the shovel in his hand, shaking his well-chiselled, graying head.

"Your father must have been a very sensible man. I will confess you because I imagine that would have been his wish, although deep inside perhaps you envy me as much as I do you. Yet I would prefer you to outlive me, because I would hate myself for mourning your loss. It is as clear as daylight, my friend. And now forget about the soul and try to heal your body. You are down in the dumps. Renew your will to live, at once and with vigor. Let's go have a hot stew and a turnover tomorrow, and then make a platter with that smoked ham which tastes like heaven that my housekeeper bought in the plaza of Trujillo. Afterwards, I will let you borrow a mount, and we will go to Monte del Pardo. That scent of marjoram and the good air are all you need to bring some color to your paper-like cheeks."

You never went to Monte del Pardo with Lope, just as you will never see again the wild myrtles of the garden of Atocha. But many will be the recollections that you shuffle now, before leaving the very last card face up on the table. Slow and merciless, memory will bring you back to the first encounter with your ghosts in the orchard of Janus, such a long time after you had imagined them as characters in your story. Remembering the welcome the first part had and the many times it had been printed, you were still tempted then to proceed with your book. But you never stopped fearing that so much success ought to be mere witchcraft, in a world that was real enough although also enchanted like that of fables. Accustomed to misfortune and abandonment, you withdrew from the flattering of the people into a more secluded life. As if, in your solitude, you could try to read destiny in the water or in the lines of your palm. From time to time you also seemed compelled to flee and repeat those long trips of your past. On such occasions you would ask Lope for a horse and ramble off the beaten path through the pines and oaks of the Casa de Campo. You would like to lose yourself among the pastures and fields of Las Rozas, near the banks of the Aulencia and the Guadarrama. There were days when you stopped by any nameless fountain for a snack of bread, goat cheese, and sweet onions. Now and then you would be absent for almost entire weeks, sleeping wrapped in a cotton blanket under the Bears of the sky in the summer, stopping in the winter at any of those inns in La Mancha of shaded grape vines and white-walled cobblestoned patios around a well. You would get away for hours or days, and Catalina never demanded an explanation upon your return. As she never did when you wandered for entire years throughout the high and low Andalusia.

Having spent the night at one of those inns, you were on your way to Madrid one early morning, when, in the middle of an oak forest full of raspberries and wild strawberries, someone shouted your name. You halted your mount and, upon turning, saw a blond youngster in a purple overcoat spurring his gray, one-eyed donkey after you. As he reached you, he sprang from his saddle, and excitedly, as if he were declaiming on stage, said:

"How many times I watched Your Grace in the poets' tavern and then last night in that lodging-house, yet I did not dare speak to you! You are so well-known and I am a nobody! This morning at least, with no one to witness but the goldfinches and the orioles, permit me to fall on my knees and kiss the hand that wrote *Don Quixote!*"

The lad was already prostrating himself in the leaves, taking your right hand between his palms, when you brushed him aside as if he were a leper. You would vaguely remember that youth, seated at a dining table of the inn, beneath the smoked hams and strings of onions and garlic, hanging from the crossbeams of the stone roof.

"Gently, gently, my boy! Do not ridicule a toothless harquebusier. My novel is only a parody of other fables, a solace for melancholy spirits."

The youngster burst into spontaneous and vigorous laughter, which Your Grace must have found exasperating. Your face must have changed and your soul simmered with bitterness, filling it with a blind and ill-repressed wrath. You would not be offended by the mockery of the lad in the purple coat, hardened as you were to all sorts of affronts. You were angered, instead, by his insolent and scandalous laughter, when you had spent all your life meekly smiling at fleeting happiness and repeated misfortune.

"Your Grace may lie through your teeth, deceiving the world, if that is your pleasure. But allow me to say this, with all due respect. I, Gregorio Nacianceno Patriarca, at your service, see in your novel one of the greatest conquests of the human spirit in this valley of tears. This truth is so evident that it is petty and ludicrous to ignore it."

"And by what right do you fathom and unearth other peoples' lies?" you asked, calm now and almost smiling.

Praises should not affect you more than offenses. But suddenly Gregorio Nacianceno kindled your curiosity, as if he were a vivid image of your own youth: your own double from that past, when your old, soul-stirring dreams of glory were reduced to ashes and restless attempts.

"Though still a youth, I was an actor in the companies of Romero

Retama and Angulo el Malo, whom we should not confuse with the other Angulo, who is the funniest of comedians. I learned to read the truth in the lies of the authors, as if their farces and mystery plays were my ABCs. That is why I see through your lies before Your Grace can even realize it."

You smile, shaking your head in silence. If this encounter by the wild strawberry patch had taken place on stage you could have presented it as a comedy of intrigue and fortuitous circumstances. A farce in which fickle fortune makes incredible things happen to the least deserving, after a tangled web in which the innocent pay for other people's errors. Following the thread of that fantasy, you will think that in the hypothetical play Gregorio Nacianceno would turn out to be your Promontorio: the son you would never meet again in real life. Yet I imagine it would please you to see your lost first-born in that youngster—Patriarca—with his looks and wits, since that beardless Gregorio Nacianceno reminded you of yourself when you were his age. Still shaking your head, Your Grace dismounted with his prompt assistance, and the two of you started to stroll together into the trees. He held your elbow as you walked through the forest, as if he were a solicitous guide to a pilgriming blind man. At that moment, and in passing, you would have heard the singing of the orioles and goldfinches in the oak trees.

"And what do you want of me, besides to kiss my hand which I am not about to allow?"

"Sir, nearly a year ago, the money from an inheritance came to me. In the same bequest I also received some large fields between Quijorna and Villanueva, suitable for good crops, which I have just sold at an excellent price. The demands of the sale forced me to leave Angulo el Malo. He must be performing throughout La Mancha right now, with *The Courts of Death* by the great Lope de Vega Carpio. For my part, I am out of work though not poor and not without dreams."

"And what have you decided to do with your life?"

"Help me, Your Grace, to write a play which we would present everywhere with the greatest of success." The youngster grew excited with more fire and enthusiasm. "We could perform it in this Kingdom of ours and Don Filipo the Third, and in the Barbary of the infidels and even in the Kingdom of Prester John, if he or his domains exist."

Losing nerve and determination, the hand that was pretending to guide you was shaking. Gregorio Nacianceno's stammering voice deepened as if he were lying, although he was telling incredible truths. Even the birds in the branches fell silent to listen to him. In the quietness that absorbed his pauses, you seemed to hear the murmur of a hidden stream. Then, after half a century, you probably remembered your first real master—that Cardinal Acquaviva, whose page you were in Italy at age sixteen—quoting Leonardo when he wrote that the present flows faster than any river through your fingers. You had never heard of Leonardo before, and you were surprised at the way the Cardinal almost crossed himself when he spoke his name in vain. *Never forget this, my child, even though you may not understand it yet. The disillusionment of the world begins here, at the very apex of the Renaissance, the instant when man believes man to be the center of the universe.*

"But what play do you mean, Gregorio Nacianceno?"

"A piece which we would compose together, taking the Hidalgo and the Squire from your book to the stage. In the same manner that you exposed the story of these two characters in your novel, they would tell the life of their creator on stage, while we would be acting it out. I would assume the role of Your Grace in your youth, since I was born an actor in order to be somebody else. Your Grace could pretend to be yourself in the present. It remains to be seen who will be the Knight and his Servant at the playhouse. Perhaps we could give the part of the Rustic to the other Angulo, if he does not demand too high a fee. These are mere trivialities that we will resolve later. With a past like yours, full of battles, shipwrecks, journeys, imprisonments, and books, not to mention the women they talk so much about, Aeschylus himself would envy this presentation. No play could have better characters than your Knight Errant and his Squire, as messengers of so much agony and glory. I will take care of the expenses for this venture. Theater is chance, and chance is sometimes more expensive than life itself. "

"I am pleased and flattered by your idea. In other times, I would have already agreed to the deal. But we will have to delay it until I finish the last part of my novel."

"You will never complete it, Your Grace!" Patriarca protested, his voice edged with anger.

"Why not?"

"I just have the foreboding that you are not going to write it! But on stage, the Hidalgo and the Squire could debate your doubts and reasons for not proceeding with the book while expounding your most recent life."

"How could those characters, without any other reason for being than the one I granted them in my writings, discover and unravel my intentions? Who would accept such nonsense? Where would you place those who never were, to let them show not only who I am but also what I thought and even what I omitted?"

"In the tavern, I heard you talking about an abandoned house with a bust of Janus among the myrtles of Atocha. In vain, I looked for it in those sites. But the orchard, the house, and the statue would look beautiful on the backdrop of the play."

For a long time you had forgotten the garden of Janus, until Gregorio Nacianceno came to remind you of it. At once you saw Magdalena and Luisa again as children, catching sight of the two-faced statue through the brambles. *In spite of being identical, the two faces of this man, each one resembles you more than it resembles the other,* the late Rodrigo had said. And suddenly the presence of Gregorio Nacianceno ceased to annoy you, because you sensed in that moment that your fates had been interwoven since that morning, even though you would never write the piece he proposed and perhaps you would never see each other again. You headed back through the tall fennel to your horse; Patriarca himself was very restless, ready to leave. He shook your hand and mounted his donkey, saying farewell with the same haste as when he was calling and chasing after you.

"I live in a new house, with windows overlooking León Street. It has a hall and a dovecote. You will see it very near Franco Street, and it was built a year ago by a public scribe from Cuenca. Come and we will talk about the play. And now, tell me: what is your sudden urgency to be gone?"

"Is Your Grace oblivious to the fact that today the Holy Office celebrates an auto-da-fe in the Plaza Mayor, and Their Majesties themselves promise to be there? Do you live so secluded that you did not hear the town criers announcing blessings and indulgences for those who attend such a sacred ceremony?"

"I did not know anything about it," you admitted, somewhat chagrined. "I do not leave the house for entire days. I did not even go to the poets' tavern, which is a stone's throw away from my place."

"The judgement promises and will pass into history as one of the best. Beneath the balconies, ornate with canopies and tapestries, they built a theater for the auto-da-fe. A theater with pulpits, altars, rostrums, stages, scaffolds, tiers for the commoners, and even a golden box for our Monarchs, may God save them. Two hundred fifty soldiers of the faith with harquebuses, halberds, muskets, pikes, battle-axes, and good, two-edged sticks will keep order, piety, and justice. Every one of them has already carried fagots of firewood to the Palace, and in the name of the troop the captain offered an armful to Don Filipo Hermenegildo. The major-domo of the Castle has already announced, as he should in such cases: "His Majesty orders that this wood be burned in his name at the stake of the impenitents when the time to punish them arrives." They say that one hundred and ten were sentenced, but twenty died in jail, without confessing their guilt. They will hang them in effigy, and, if they find their bones, they will exhibit them in baskets at the foot of those figures."

"And who is making you witness and enjoy such a spectacle?" you exclaimed indignantly. "Or are you a chaplain of the Holy Office like Lope?"

"I am an actor who inherited a fortune. But above all I am a Christian to whom the Pope has promised Heaven with indulgences if I attend the execution of these heretics. Obviously, after the public sentencing I do not want to miss the conflagration at Fuencarral. They say that even a twelve-year-old boy will be roasted this afternoon. As a man of the theater, I am drawn by a show where death is real and faith is as true as death. God be with you, Your Grace."

Sweeping off his beret, he said farewell with a deep reverence and spurred his donkey away. He never appeared at your house, nor did you see each other again. At least not on earth nor in this book, where he has the singular name of Gregorio Nacianceno Patriarca. If he returned as another person, it would be a different story and one tires of calculating all his possible avatars. You realized today that you had unwittingly remembered him in the second part of your book. There you made your Hidalgo and his Squire cross the path of el Malo and his company, in costume, on their way to stage *il trionfo della morte,* by the great Lope de Vega Carpio, as Patriarca would say. *The demands of the sale forced me to leave Angulo el Malo. He must be performing throughout La Mancha right now with The Courts of Death.* In your novel it was the octave of Corpus Christi, and Angulo and his people were traveling by cart. As in real life, in your book, *Don Quixote,* men and fables seemed to separate and come together, just as spikes of wheat would pass from one sheaf to another. Seeing the actors dressed as Angels, Devils, Emperors, Soldiers, and even Authors, the Squire said that the stage of those histrionics would be like a chessboard, where knights, bishops, pawns, kings and queens each have their own purpose in the game. But they are jumbled up in a bag like entombed men, mixed in death, when the match is done. The Knight praised such a sensible remark and refrained from transforming a reality— that of the theater—which was already disguised in itself. *It is necessary to touch appearances with one's own hand to become disillusioned.*

Many years later, while Lope delays his visit to confess you, you also realize that you had written all of that thinking inadvertently of Acquaviva. The appearances touched by the Knight were nothing but time in the river of da Vinci. The disillusionment that the Cardinal attributed to Leonardo, when man was believed to be the center of the universe, culminated with you in *Don Quixote*. Or, perhaps it was still necessary that someone painted the disenchantment of the world in a picture. You count the chimes of the bells in the street of Cantarranas and shrug. Soon they will bury you there, in the new convent of the Trinitarians, although Lope postpones his arrival as if you were never going to die.

The smoke from some stoves comes in through the half-open window. Grown older and fatter, two women fan the flames with straw mats. They are neighbors of yours, twins that are so identical that people say they were born joined at their shoulders. The physician attending the birth separated them with one stroke of his knife. They are talking about you in the street without realizing that you can hear them. They comment on how much thinner and older you have become in only a few months. You forget about their chattering, as soon as the smoke brings the perfume of burning mimosas and roots of heather. That aroma takes you back to the night that awaited you in Madrid after the auto-da-fe. Sunset reddened the capital, and there was in the air a smell of ashes, like a forest after a fire. With all the shutters and doors closed, Madrid seemed deserted, suddenly abandoned, where you meandered like a lost phantom, before the ivy covered the walls and all the roofs fell in. You touched an herb-scented handkerchief to your lips, because the stagnant smoke was choking your breath and blackening your soul. *God be with you, Your Grace,* Gregorio Nacianceno Patriarca had said to you.

God might be with you. But you refused to go home. Perhaps the same destiny leading you on so many fruitless journeys was then taking you to the Plaza Mayor where they had judged the condemned. You left El Prado by Huertas Street and crossed Cabeza, Olmo, Calvario, Colegiata, and Lechuga Streets. Left behind you now was the small square of Leña and its customhouse. On the hill of Majaderitos, you passed the closed shops of booksellers, guitar merchants, goldsmiths, and shield-makers without turning your head. You left behind the channels and olive groves of Alcalá and the hospital of Buen Suceso. Through the empty open-air theaters of Soledad and Pasión, a gang of cats made a racket with their caterwauling. You did not see or hear any other sign of life before reaching the Plaza Mayor. Yet, a prickling made you feel as if you were being watched. Hidden eyes at the edge of your shadow were following your steps. Empty of words, Madrid remained. But in its muteness, invisible gazes preyed on your conscience. They would force you to repent two sins, one as absurd as the other: that of having been born and that of obstinately getting lost wide-awake in that labyrinth sleeping beneath the smoke.

You entered the Plaza Mayor through the butcher shops. As soon as you stopped, the solitary sound of your steps died away. Even with the canopies taken away, the theater that Patriarca described and that had been built for the auto-da-fe overwhelmed you. Standing bare, the contraption pointed towards the sky through the shadows. Lope, Góngora, and Figueroa would describe it to you later as partly protected by a flower-patterned tent to shield their Majesties from the glare of the sun. Emblazoned tapestries and rich cloths embroidered with hunting scenes decorated the royal throne, the pulpits, the altars, and the grandstand. The green and purple banners of the Inquisition covered the tiers for the commoners and women, the gallery, and the stage for the accused.

"Those who could not fit in the theater crowded in the plaza, in the balconies, and even on the roofs. They were there for twelve whole hours, defecating and urinating where they stood so that they would not miss an instant of the auto-da-fe," said Lope the following day. "Wondrous is the faith of our nation, when it is put to the test. Although we did not see it because it happened behind our balcony, a mother dropped her baby girl from the roof of a house, when the Mass celebrating this heated ritual had reached the *Kyrie Eleison*. The child was not hurt because a soldier caught her in his arms as if in a circus. In a more pious era, they would have called it a miracle. By now the infant would have been beatified, at least."

"Her mother, an ironing woman from Canillas they say, started blaspheming as if possessed. She must have gone crazy with fright," Góngora added in the tavern. "They had to gag her with a wimple, to end her curses. The crowd was so crammed that it took half a day for the officers of the law to make their way through the plaza to arrest her. People supported their efforts, and those having bread and cold omelettes, as well as wine from Rioja, shared them with the constables in their many forced stops. The stairway of the house was also like an anthill of the faithful, waiting for news of the sentencing, carried mouth-to-mouth from the balconies. Lacking a place to enjoy the punishment first-hand, they had to satisfy themselves with the descriptions provided by their neighbors. In order to encourage the bailiffs in their task, some girls on a landing gave themselves to them, their backs to the wall, applauded by those

present. Their carnal hunger satisfied, they arrested the blas-
phemer. If she survives, they will scorch her in the next auto-da-fe.
She will be old then, for we have already had the solemn, general
burning for this reign. We lost track of the little girl after she had
fallen into the soldier's arms."

As a minister of the Holy Office, Lope occupied a balcony in the
plaza. At dawn, Góngora and Figueroa appeared at his house to go
together to the judgement as they had planned. A servant was
brushing the purple cloak of the Phoenix of Wits, when they were
startled by Catalina's arrival, with Miguel Cortinas as her escort.
She said that her husband was on a trip, and that he was probably
lodging in some inn by Fresnadilla or La Herrería. Wishing to attend
the auto-da-fe, she begged them to take her to such a pious and
exemplary ceremony. Surprised, Lope agreed and Góngora kept
quiet, perhaps thinking that he would have expected a less plebeian
faith from such a prudent woman. As a chaplain of the King, Góngora was supposed to earn indulgences by not only witnessing the
sentencing but also the burning of the impenitents. But, perhaps,
he would rather have remained in bed asleep or awake rhyming
some passionate hendecasyllables, where the crystal of a divine
hand was drinking the sweet poison of love, while the sky blos-
somed red.

The morning was already touched with gold when they arrived
at the Plaza Mayor. Miguel Cortinas bade them farewell at Lope's
house and proceeded to the butcher shop of San Ginés to buy lamb
testicles and tripe. As white and mute as if she were in a trance,
Catalina went with them. Looking at her immobile profile and her
wide blue eyes, Góngora must have thought that she seemed to be
out of touch with the world. As morning broke, the Grandees of
Spain arrived in a procession from the Calle Mayor, singing together
the *Angelus domini* and bearing the white and green crosses of the
Holy Office. With measured step they climbed to their seats of
honor: the Prince of Astillano, the Dukes of Abrantes, Albur-
querque, and Béjar, the Counts of Aguilar, Alba de Liste, and Bena-
vente. The Count of Altamira, a gouty homosexual, was carried by
two servants in a chair. When the Monarchs appeared, everyone
got up and knelt for an instant in their presence. Don Filipo Hermenegildo was almost as pale as Catalina as he watched the square
with terrified eyes. Vested in his pontifical robe, the Grand Inquisitor went up to the royal throne to witness his oath, for the greater
glory of the faith and the honor of history. *Does your Majesty swear
and promise on your piety and royal word that, as a true Catholic
King, chosen by the hand of God, you will defend our religion with*

all your power, will persecute and order the persecution of heretics and infidels contrary to our faith, and will support with your favor and assistance the Holy Office of the Inquisition and its ministers, so that the heretics and agitators will be apprehended and punished without any omission on the part of your Majesty and without the exception of any person, no matter how exalted he may be? The King Our Lord so swore and promised. But Lope was dumbfounded at the way the ecclesiastic syntax and style had degenerated since the days of St. John Chrysostom and other fathers of the Mother Church. On his balcony, other ministers of the Holy Office were laughing at his horror and Figueroa assented with an absent-minded nod.

The mass was sung, and Friar Tomás de Sampelayo, Censor of the Supreme Office, delivered a moving sermon. *Exurge, exurge, Domine, judica causam tuam.* Manacled and carrying lit candles in their trembling hands, up to ninety offenders climbed the scaffold. Some had knotted ropes around their necks, with each knot meaning a lash from the executioner. The blasphemous appeared gagged, and many were stripped almost nude, with only a loincloth to cover their private parts. To satisfy the Inquisitorial modesty, the women were dressed in holed sackcloth. As Góngora told you later in the tavern, he observed that, unlike the men, none of them were crying under their louse-filled mops of hair. They saw even fifteen-year-old girls among the penitents and also that twelve-year-old boy of whom Gregorio Nacianceno Patriarca had spoken to you. Wearing sanbenitos with scapulars of St. Dominic, their cone-shaped hats and short capes painted with demons and gallows, the reconciliated passed *de levi* or *de vehementi*. Those were the ones to be burned in the afternoon or to be mercifully strangled at the edge of the bonfire in return for showing signs of remorse after their conviction. Lope and his fellow Inquisitors looked somber when they saw that even the children would be burnt. Figueroa, pale as a ghost, left at that point without saying anything. Only Catalina kept her silent and impassive composure, her eyes fixed on the void and her lips pressed tight.

It took them ten hours to reveal all the sentences in the sandalwood chest, reading them from the pulpit. Towards five in the afternoon, they concluded the condemnation of the sinners, who knew it since the previous day. *Brother, your cause has been considered and discussed with many men learned in letters and sciences. Your crimes are so grave and so dreadful that, to serve as punishment and example, judgment has been passed. Prepare your soul.* They were about to take the doomed to the stake when Lope tried to shout over the cheers of the people. He was trying to tell Catalina that he would have one of his servants—the one flirting with a neighbor's maid—escort her to her home. Obstinately, Catalina shook her head and insisted on going with them to Fuencarral, where, in the name of God, the sentences would be carried out.

"The hole for the stakes was about sixty feet square and seven or eight deep," Góngora continued in the poets' tavern. "Such a crowd followed the criminals that we had to make a way through with our elbows to reach our preferential seats. The wood must have been damp, because it took a long time to burn. The executioners revived it with bellows and stirred it with long pokers until it started burning, scorching those unfortunate souls. That is why the smoke still blackens the air of Madrid. That is also why the screams of the penitents, slowly burning over a low fire, will sound in my nightmares for as long as I live. The child was one of the last to die. When his cries ceased, they had already strangled those who had their sentences mitigated. They were hanging from their poles like puppets, their hats jammed down on their heads. I assume crows and blackbirds have pecked out their eyes by now. Lope covered his head with his cloak and only from time to time would he glance out, coughing and choking from the thick smoke. But your wife remained there impassively, without uttering a complaint or a word."

But that would be tomorrow when Góngora describes the auto-da-fe and the burning. In the Plaza Mayor, the silence and the heavy smoke overwhelmed you. Night fell, and at the top of the bare theater a bluish light from a lantern blinked on. Looking at it, you seemed uneasy and your heart began beating loudly. You tied Lope's roan to a post and climbed up the steps to the scaffold. Your feet must have been guided by unknown deities as you quietly made your way up. At the top of the contraption, you came out on a platform crowned by two flagpoles, where the pennants of the Holy Inquisition and Castile had fluttered that afternoon. Around the lantern, three old women awaited you, seated on wooden blocks. Huddled together, heads bowed, they were wrapped in great cloaks that hid their eyes from you. Thin and chilling, their voices were identical, as if they were a triple echo of themselves.

"Welcome, he who comes in the name of Janus," intoned the nearest.

"Welcome, he who knows who he is. Or at least believes that he knows it."

"Welcome, he whose identity comes out of his own book."

Each drew a sealed envelope from the pleats of her veil and

handed it to you. Their hands were bony and brittle with long fingernails turned bluish by the light.

"Open this when the time comes, and you will find what you have written," said the first one.

"Open this when the time comes and you will see what was said by he who tried to be you."

"Open this when the time comes and you will enter the mirror of the one true deity: the god of departures and arrivals, of birth and death."

They fell silent and then gathered together to begin the humming of a strange, incomprehensible song. Whatever the destiny that brought you to them, you assumed that the encounter was over. Tucking the envelopes in your bosom, under your crippled arm, you descended the stairs, followed by the wails of the witches' chant. In the plaza, you put the letters in a saddlebag. Squinting against the smoke and leading the horse, you returned to the stables: the ones guarded by a one-eyed man who lived in the dovecote. The smoke filtered through the cracks in the stable door and hung in the air. It blackened the straw in the mangers, making it smell like hay burnt by lightning after a rain. That odor would take you back to the haystack of Mesina, where you lay in exhaustion, fearing you would die in your sleep at any time, bleeding to death from the wounds of Lepanto.

You found the door of your house ajar, as if it was waiting for you. Perhaps you had forgotten the three letters crackling against your chest as you pushed it open. Catalina was about to sit down at the diningroom table, her hand extended and forgotten next to a fruit bowl full of nuts and apples. Miguel Cortinas remained standing in front of her, by the candlelight. For an instant—the time it takes to sigh or blink an eye—you thought that your wife and the servant were speaking to each other in Ladino or in another form of Romance Hebrew. Perhaps, in an unforeseen switch, you also thought of what that girl in the inn where you and Gregorio Nacianceno Patriarca spent the night had said to you: *My godfather insisted that you were insane when you were not writing and ignorant of who you were. I think that you will never truly live again until you decide to end your book. Very wise was my godfather, the canon, although he died of an illness in his brain last fall. Then I took to the street.*

"I forgive you for everything," Catalina was suddenly yelling at you. "The lack of love, the separations and that bastard daughter of yours, who does not speak to you now because you promised her a dowry you could not give. I forgive you for everything, because you did not make me a mother. I would not like a son or a daughter, to whom, having arrived at the age of reason, and on a day like today, I would be compelled to say: Everything that you see and call the world and life is only a hell without any other salvation than death."

You left silently, shrugging your shoulders. When such bursts of rage possessed Catalina from time to time, you thought it better to keep quiet than to reply to her. Seated alone at the threshold of the house, you would remember the envelopes that you still had tucked in your doublet. Perhaps you were grateful for the darkness that kept you from opening and reading them. That same night you buried them in a drawer underneath your writing materials, blotting sand, and inkwell. In a most unbelievable way, you must have forgotten the three messages, and only decided to open them that afternoon when you were waiting for Lope to make your confession, so many years after the mysterious Fates had handed the envelopes to you.

When you returned home after an hour, that other night, you dined with Catalina on parsley-flavored sausage omelettes and thimblefuls of red wine from La Mancha. As if nothing had happened, you spoke of trivialities while Miguel Cortinas served you. In bed, you fell asleep immediately, only to dream that you had returned to the garden of Janus and had found unexpected visions of the Hidalgo and his Squire. You were conscious of being in a dream. But you also knew that the next morning your dream would become a reality, without omitting the pair of ghosts emerging from the first part of your novel. As soon as dawn broke, while Catalina and your servant were still asleep, you dressed in order to slip away towards Atocha. The breeze from the Sierra was thinning the smoke and swaying the tree-branches in El Prado. Through the skies, swifts flew in curvy flocks, and in the orchard of the Hieronymites a lark twittered.

The Golden Age

About poets, I do not say that this is a good century. Many are in the making for the next year, but none so bad as Cervantes, nor so dumb as would praise Don Quixote.
                    —Letter from Lope de Vega to an unknown person

It is not difficult, in the Spain of Cervantes, to find a character called Quijada, whom it would be very risky to mock. Emperor Charles the Fifth's private secretary was named *Luis Quijada*. Hardly any man was a more intimate friend of the Emperor than he. We have his portrait by Titian. The data on his life would fill entire books, and does not belong in a literary article. But what interests us, in this order of ideas, are his relations with Cervantes and Don Quixote. Their lives were intertwined to the point that Quijada often determined the fate of Cervantes and Don Quixote. The Emperor had entrusted Quijada with the education of his son, the future Don Juan of Austria, his child by Barbara Blomberg from Flanders. The boy knew nothing of his origins and thought his name was Juan Quijada. A noble and courageous man was Don Luis, just as was Don Quixote. As well as a hardened and strong one (after serving the Emperor more than thirty years, he would exhaust horse after horse running the messenger stables). He ate sparingly (the Emperor's morbid gluttony disgusted him) and had a heart of gold. However, he was a bit of a clown. When he accompanied the Emperor to the Monastery of Yuste, he walked through the mountains before the chair of the Emperor, raising in his right hand something as out-dated as a lance.
                    —Svend Borberg, "Don Juan y Don Quijote," *El Español*, August, 1943. Cited by Angel Valbuena Prat, *Historia de la Literatura Española*, V.I.

> Brother Lope, erase the sonnet
> Of Ariosto and Garcilaso,
> And do not take the Bible in your hands,
> Since you say that you never read it.
> You should also erase your *Dragontea*
> And that little book you call *Arcadia*,
> With all its ludicrous Epitaphs.
> You will burn Angela because she is a Moor,

God and St. Isidore know my intentions;
Since I have him in my devotion,
Erase instead the Pilgrim,
And do not write in four languages,
Your nonsense does not need
To be understood in four countries;
Don't finish writing the *Jerusalem,*
The city has enough problems on its own.

—Anonymous sonnet from Góngora to Lope de Vega, *Poetry of
Don Luis de Góngora,* Fifth Edition of Foulché-Delbosc, V. III.

Since I do not read the Bible, I do not know,
If you are Cervantes, but it makes no difference;
I say only that Lope is Apollo, and you
A pig underneath his chariot.
So that you would not write,
Heaven ordered that you lose your arm;
You spoke, ox, but you made only a moo,
Oh, see your folly as you read this!
Honor Lope, donkey, or watch yourself!
He is the sun, and his anger brings rain;
Your trivial *Don Quixote* makes its way
From ass to ass in the world,
Selling tea and spices and saffron,
And landing, in the end, in the dung heap.

—Anonymous sonnet from Lope to Cervantes, erroneously as-
suming that the above poem by Góngora was his, *Ensayo de una
Biblioteca de Traductores Españoles,* Edition of Juan Antonio
Pellicer.

Before Easter, a certain man of prayer and good faith by the
name of Escobar who was going about dressed in the honest habit
of a clergyman, enjoying the benefits of the Church, but the greatest
chess player known, because many people from many places have
come to play with him and he has beaten them every time, started
to proclaim that within two years their Majesties and their children
would be dead, and no one from the house of Austria would be left,
either here or in Germany, and from the house of Judah, would
come one, age thirty-three, to succeed in these kingdoms, and that
there would be a portent or a prodigy in Heaven at the beginning
of this month. Which we have not seen yet, even though they say
that a comet has been appearing over the Palace in these days; but
very little has been said about it, as a story without basis; and

because the rumor and scandal of this prophecy would not pass, after his other prediction of the return of the Court had been fulfilled, they took him to the Inquisition of Toledo, so that, there, he would await the coming of the events that he announces.

—Luis Cabrera de Córdoba, *Relation of Events in the Spanish Court from 1599 until 1614,* Tuesday, January 19, 1618. Cited by Federico Sánchez Escribano, *Affairs and Events at the Dawn of the Spanish XVII Century*

The Marquis of Hinojosa, who was General of the land and sea, started a reform, when I was returning to Madrid with my troops to receive orders for our galleys. He was already losing his popularity, for they say there was a war in Lombardy, and the Genovese are very powerful. And even though the Duke of Tursis was helping him, as he had his galleys manned with Spaniards, he could not carry forward his projected change-over. Consequently, we had to remain inactive in Madrid, although I did not have it that bad, because Lope de Vega, without my ever having spoken to him in my life, took me to his house, saying, "My Captain, with men like Your Grace, one should share one's cloak," and he sheltered me as his friend for over eight months, providing me with meals and even clothing. God bless him.

—Alonso de Contreras, *Life, Birth, Parents and Education of Captain Alonso de Contreras*.

> Four names with r
> Have my robes:
> Raggedy, raveled,
> Rotten and ratty.
> Ah, robes of mine,
> Raggedy, raveled,
> Rotten and ratty!

—Andalusian song (*Seguidilla*) of the XVII century

This might have been the way in which Cervantes and Doña Catalina met. After a few months of courting, they married on the twelfth of December, 1584, he being thirty-two years of age and she only nineteen, though, with regard to their souls, he was always young and she was always old. What I think, with all due respect, is that not everyone has the privilege to be born with a brand-new soul, but, on the contrary, it seems that by chance some come into this world with a worn-out soul, like an intimate garment from an old-clothes shop. Thus, after only a brief honeymoon, and even during it, both spouses were convinced that they had not been made for each other, and their marriage was like one of those innumerable matches in which husband and wife continually felt that "the solitude of two is company."

—Francisco Rodríguez Marín, "Cervantes and Doña Catalina his Wife," *A Hodge-Podge of Light and Entertaining Erudition.*

Things happen in the world that, if imagination could make these things thus happen before they happen, it would not be able to do so.

—Miguel de Cervantes, *The Trials of Persiles and Segismunda,* Book III, Chapter XVI.

The Academies are furious: in the last session, two scholars were bickering; I read some verses with some *specgs* of Cervantes, which looked like fried *eggs* not well done. Your Excellency will know the result of the suit of the Count of Alba: Don Enrique (Enrique Enríquez, new Count of Alba of Liste) won; congratulations are in order; Your Excellency should send him a pair of good noses. May God keep Your Excellency; Doña Juana and Carlos kiss Your Excellency's hands. From Madrid, March 2, 1612.

—Letter from Lope de Vega to the Duke of Sessa.

> The Queen gave birth and the Lutheran came,
> With all his heretics and heresies;
> In two weeks, we blew a million with ease,
> Giving him jewels, wine, and acclaim.
> We made an ostentatious display,
> Our frolics were frenzies to dazzle eyes,
> For the Anglican who showed with his spies,
> To swear the peace over Calvin, they say.
> Dominic we christened the enfant at Mass,
> Born to the empire of glorious Spain.
> Our extravaganzas were unsurpassed.
> We were left poor, but Luther rich, alas.
> These deeds they ordered written for their reign.
> To Don Quixote, Sancho and his ass.

—Sonnet by Góngora at the festivals for the birth of Prince Don Felipe Dominico Víctor and the gifts made to the English Ambassador. Juan Antonio Pellicer, *Life of Miguel de Cervantes.*

A book of poems with uneven verses and erratic rhymes has appeared in this City under the name of *Solitudes,* composed by Your

Grace, and Andrés de Mendoza has dedicated himself to spreading copies of it. And whether because he pretends to write with wit or because he claims to be spellbound by the heavens, I do not know, but he calls himself Your Grace's son, making himself so much the master of your correspondence and of the declaration and publication of this poetry, that—especially considering the quality of the verses—some of your admirers are doubtful that it is actually yours. And I, who am your extremely obliging servant, wanted to ask you for the truth, both to uproot this error spreading among ignorant rivals (and Your Grace does have them), and because it is necessary for those knowledgeable ones accustomed to the serene style in which Your Grace normally writes superior thoughts and clever witticisms, excelling the most celebrated heroic poems, all of which is enough cause for the well-intentioned to be hurt by Mendoza and his accomplices when they attribute such *Solitudes* to Your Grace.

—Anonymous letter from Lope de Vega to Góngora, on the appearance of the *Solitudes*. Lope de Vega, *Letters*. Edited by Nicolás Marín.

> For your life, dear Lope, do not strike out,
> The nineteen towers of your coat of arms,
> Because, they may all be wind, but I doubt
> That you quite have enough wind for such charms.
> With Arcadia's you should be content!
> To give regalia to a pastor rude,
> You should blush—do not leave a battlement
> On your shield. Oh Nabal bearded and shrewd!
> Arms from Leganes, torso of Micol!
> Take it back to its place, and remove from
> The winged horse in the theater its ticks.
> Build no more towers on sand, for your soul,
> If not that, from a second marriage come,
> He might want to make towers out of sticks.

—Satirical sonnet by Góngora to Lope de Vega, upon the publication of his *Arcadia,* where Lope accompanies his picture with the coat of arms of the Carpios, with nineteen towers and the legend: "Bernardo's is the emblem, the miseries are mine." Lope de Vega, *Complete Sonnets.* Edited by Biruté Ciplijauskaité. Cited by Emilio Orozco Díaz, *Lope and Góngora Face to Face.*

We were in Tunis one year, and the Turkish armada overcame us with three hundred galleys and twenty galleasses. And at the end of fifty-three days of poor leadership we lost *La Goleta* and

Tunis. I became a slave on *La Goleta* with a harquebus shot in the neck that went all the way through the left shoulder and with other injuries. That wound saved my life, because other friends and I, determined not to be slaves, would have killed ourselves. And, I had no sooner arrived at the church, hiding myself against the wall as best I could, when the enemies of the faith entered and conquered the place. With the other wounded, I was bought as a dead man for fifteen ducats, and almost without medical aid, we went seven hundred miles up to Turkey, and I, screaming like a madman, could not die. In Navarino I began to heal, and in the four months of that winter I more or less became well.

Ah, Pasamonte! You tried to be a soldier without realizing that the Apostle Paul, as well as Saint Sebastian and other Saints, had also been soldiers. And, those illustrious Maccabees defended and fought with much bloodshed. Well, happily, a great spirit goes along with a great work! I was in captivity for eighteen years, first under a captain of a galley who, as I have just said, as a venture bought me as a dead man. With some care and no little danger he kept me at his house, digging a garden. The Turkish women of his house harassed me, and flesh and blood you cannot trust; but God watches over all. When spring came, since I was a new slave, my master would allow me to walk alone, and I went to the dockyard there in Constantinople and entered a flagship galley in search of captive friends. The master of that ship was Rechesi Bajá, who was on his way to being Viceroy of Tunis. As I entered, I found a Spaniard and asked him: "Are these slaves Turks?" He told me they were all Christians. I was amazed and said: "Why don't you escape to a Christian land?" And he told me to be quiet. I left, with a great desire to go back to sea and sail on one of those galleys. My master wanted to sell two Christians he had left out of all the wounded he had bought—the others had died—and I, seeing this, begged him to sell me. He was surprised, but, seeing my determination, sold me and I returned with that Viceroy to Tunis, where I had been a soldier before. The wall of the city that I had helped to destroy through so many changes of fortune, I now helped to rebuild under many beatings, and because I was known, the local Moors from there beat me more than anyone else.

—Jerónimo de Pasamonte, *Life and Works of Jerónimo de Pasamonte*. According to José María de Cossío, the only manuscript of this autobiography, the one in the National Library in Naples, has no title and is not written by Pasamonte. It was transcribed by a friend of the former galley slave, the scholar Domingo Machado, whom Pasamonte had met in Naples in 1604.

This one that you see here with aquiline face, brown hair, a smooth, clear forehead, smiling eyes, hooked although well-proportioned nose, a silver beard that twenty years ago was gold, a long moustache, small mouth, teeth not so big, not so small, the six that there are, and those are in bad condition and poorly placed, because they do not fit together, a medium-sized body, neither large nor small, a fresh complexion, more white than tanned, somewhat broad-shouldered, and not very quick on his feet, this, I say, is the figure of the author of *Galatea* and *Don Quixote de La Mancha,* and also of *Journey to Parnassus,* an imitation of César Caporal Perusino, and other works that have gone astray, perhaps without the name of their author. He is commonly known as Miguel de Cervantes Saavedra. He was a soldier for many years, in captivity for five and a half, where he learned to exercise patience in adversity. He lost his left hand in the naval battle of Lepanto from a harquebus shot, a wound that, though it must seem ugly, he holds as beautiful, for he earned it on the most memorable and highest occasion that has been seen in past centuries and the like of which the future cannot expect to see, serving under the conquering banners of the son of the thunder of the war, Charles the Fifth, of happy memory.

—Miguel de Cervantes, Prologue to *The Exemplary Novels.*

INSIDE OUT

Because you, Your Grace, knew your true identity, or at least knew who you wanted to be, one of the faceless witches on top of the scaffold greeted you. You also assured Catalina that you knew yourself for certain, and perhaps you could not be confused with anyone else while you were alive. But the world does not know now where you lie in death. All wrapped up in Franciscan sackcloth, but your face uncovered according to the rules of the Venerable Third Order, you were buried on a Saturday in the church of the Discalced Trinitarian nuns. They closed your grave with red earthen tiles, and it is alleged that you were not even given a name on your tombstone. A few changes and repairs made to the convent in the course of time swept away the tiles and maybe even your ashes.

A quarter of a century ago, I went to the Trinitarians' to see the nave where you were interred. I called at the porter's lodge and no one answered. Across the street and through the open door of his shop, a butcher—a cleaver as he would be called in Your Grace's times—must have seen me while he was carving a leg of lamb. He dried the blood off his hands, rubbing them on his apron, and came over solicitously. He told me the doorkeeper's name at the convent was Pedro, just like the porter of Paradise. A good man, greatly appreciated for his diligence, although deaf as a post. In the middle of the street, the butcher started yelling at the top of his lungs: "Pedro! Pedro! Someone here wants to see your church!" The man did not answer, nor did he appear.

"He must have gone on an errand for the nuns without letting me know. Sometimes he disappears and then appears just as fast. Come back in an hour."

I then resolved to kill that hour at the bar of Palace Hotel. There I unexpectedly ran across the playwright José María Rodríguez Méndez. Or perhaps I did not, and it might only be now, in the spring of 1990, that I come upon him, face to face, under the glass dome of the bar. Twenty-five years ago, Rodríguez Méndez resided in Barcelona and not in Madrid. By now he must have been living for eight or nine years on Huertas Street, right behind the Palace. There is almost no doubt that our unforeseen encounter is rather recent. But memory obeys its own laws—as, in Pascal's words, does the heart—and obstinately persists in placing it a quarter of a century ago. As Your Grace had stated, it is necessary to touch appearances with one's own hand to become disillusioned. But who could feel time with his fingers as if it were water? Pascal or Your Grace? The river of time does not slow down, and memory vainly and stubbornly strains to go back to its mysterious origins. Your Grace did not meet Pascal. He was born seven years after your demise. But these, of course, are irrelevant dates.

"You now live on Huertas Street," I say to Rodríguez Méndez. "Three centuries ago, Cervantes would have been your neighbor."

"I only knew that he lived on León Street and had moved there from Matute Square."

"In 1614, while residing on Huertas Street, he participated in the Poetic Tournament to celebrate the beatification of Saint Theresa. He won third prize, a pair of silk stockings."

After an hour I returned to the Trinitarians'. The convent door was open to the street, and a man leaning against the door awaited me. He could have been of any age between youth and senility. He was of medium height and of harsh appearance. Bold and one-eyed. Staring at me with his good eye, as if he recognized me, though he had never seen me before, he said:

"You want to visit the Prince's tomb. No one knows where his remains are. But never mind, come in."

He did not call Your Grace "Prince of Wits." Just "The Prince," as though you were sole heir to a vanished kingdom or to an empire of deception. He spoke loudly, as if he were trying to hear himself. I never uttered a word. But once in a while the doorkeeper would yell at me: "Do not roar like that! Look, I am not retarded, and I am not deaf! This is a very pious and devout community. The nuns deserve the respect of their visitors."

"The Prince was buried here," screamed the porter before the main altar. "In those days they used to bury people in the churches. They kept throwing dead relatives on top of him. His wife, his daughter, his son-in-law. You know how it is. After the Civil War, Franco tried to move The Prince to the Puerta del Sol, because that is the exact geographic center of Spain. They opened the tomb and took out some bones. They belonged to a nun who had also been dead for centuries. May she rest in peace. There was such a jumble of remains in that grave that no one could tell whose was whose. Franco had to take charge to bring order. 'Enough. We will leave it as it was, because this is too confusing. Let's not bury some nun at the Puerta del Sol, mistaking her for The Prince.'"

Inadvertently, that very morning I started this book. Nevertheless, before I decided to put it on paper, it took me a long time to realize that I had been working on it for a quarter of a century. Also, the hour spent with Rodríguez Méndez at the Palace goes back and forth through time like the shuttle in a loom. An unconscious order of things, remembered or forgotten, shifts it to the morning of another life. Then it comes back here—to this fable of mine, as a virtual image of eternity like all fables. Here, page after page and paragraph after paragraph, I try in vain to conjure you. But my incantation fails, because Your Grace never responds.

Your Grace must be invisible and perhaps also blind. Maybe dumb, even deafer than the doorkeeper at the Discalceds'. Mute, deaf and blind, like that true but always hidden God in whom a dirty and lascivious poet, named Antonio Machado, tried to believe, to his own misfortune and metaphysical hopelessness. The same God about whom he dreamed at times, realizing in his dream that he was only dreaming. I do not know if Your Grace is God or not. To affirm it would be as superfluous as to deny it. It would then be better to return to the old syllogisms about the possible sex of archangels, or find out how many open-winged or broken-winged seraphim could stand tip-toe on the head of a pin. Nevertheless, I know that Your Grace still exists, even though they take you for dead in Madrid that April Friday of 1616. Your death also seemed doubtful to the porter of the Trinitarians, since Franco could not find your remains to inhume them in the Puerta del Sol.

No, I do not know if you are God, even though it is said that your only masterpiece has been printed almost as many times as the Bible. To be precise, I feel tempted to admit that Your Grace did not truly exist as author of Don Quixote, because when you wrote it you were a madman, possessed by the strangest folly. You might have been as insane as your Knight, fancying yourself the creator of a book, composed in your insanity, after writing an endless number of sensible mediocrities. Everything would turn out to be the opposite of what the Canon of Toledo, the deceased lover of María Mercedes del Calvario, had imagined. The madman who believed himself to be the Hidalgo's chronicler only existed as long as he narrated the Knight's deeds and misfortunes. However, your alter ego convinced the world that both parts of the novel belonged to Your Grace. Perhaps you succeeded in persuading everyone because the world is but the oblique reflection of your madness, as, conversely, every fable pretends to treasure eternity.

There must have been a point in your life, upon the success of the first part of Don Quixote, when you realized that you had ceased to be the lunatic who took himself for the author of that novel and who wrote it fully aware of his madness. Your sanity recovered, you

likely decided to abandon the book without proceeding with its second part, of which you had just begun the rough draft. In other
words, unlike Don Quixote, mimicking his own madness before Sancho in the Sierra Morena, Your Grace found it impossible to feign
yours. Having regained your true, sane identity, you cooked up a
tattered, interminable, posthumous story which appeared the very
year of your death: *The Trials of Persiles and Sigismunda.*

More than a maze, the *Persiles* is a Byzantine tangle where
wolves speak, men fly, and women are demonized by love. Many
of the intricate wanderings of the protagonist occur in the distant
and always enigmatic Nordic countries. *In the hyperborean lands,
dawn breaks at midnight in the summer,* Your Grace said to Catalina
while you were having lemonade together. In the *Persiles,* Perian-
dro, who is Persiles in actuality, affirms that all his possessions are
only a dream. Your own case seems even sadder, because you also
confessed to Catalina that you had aged from the moment that,
after dreaming, you forgot your dreams.

Likewise, you might have forgotten *Don Quixote*—was it not a
fruit of your daydreaming insanity?—whilst the world awaited that
ever delayed second part of the novel, had it not been for an unforeseen absurdity. Such was the meddling of another madman, an image or a plagiarism of your own insanity. I am referring to that
Avellaneda, whose true identity will always be unknown—the one
who stole and copied your characters in the apocryphal next part
of your novel. Exasperated by his imitation and by the personal
affronts he poured into his prologue, Your Grace went mad again.
Now, with more reason than ever, you thought of yourself as the
sole authentic creator of *Don Quixote,* chosen by God himself to
write it and obliged by His Providence to give it a climax, a conclusion, and a final epilogue.

Whoever he was, we are in debt to Avellaneda for the second
part of Your Grace's book, not for his poor fake, but rather for the
madman who assumed your last name and person in order to continue it. After delivering the second part of your novel, even more
successful than the first, Your Grace regained your right mind.
While in full possession of your faculties, you concluded your "Nordic Adventure," as you would call the *Persiles,* and then, saner, more
mediocre and defeated than ever, you let yourself die of hydropsy.
Exactly as the Knight in your book passes away after awakening
from a long dream of which we know nothing.

Ten years, from 1605 to 1615, separate the publication of both
parts of *Don Quixote.* Such an entr'acte is, I daresay, the most
prodigious of the entire human comedy. It is also the most fasci-

nating interim of Spanish literature. Not because of what Your Grace wrote, but because of what you omitted or continued delaying for ever and ever. Thinking about the two parts of the novel and the lapse between them, without forgetting the intrusion of Avellaneda with his plagiarism, I encountered some doubts that I would like to express to Your Grace. Is it possible that the real universe may not exist and this ambit, where we believe we are, is just the delirious absurdity of an eternal madman who takes himself for the only God and creator of another true and not yet conceived universe, in the same manner that Avellaneda believed he was Cervantes and thought he was writing that book which Miguel de Cervantes had not yet written?

May it be that Your Grace, *Don Quixote*, Avellaneda, his apocrypha, Machado's God, Machado, the porter at the Trinitarians', I myself, and my book—*The Garden of Janus*—are nothing but rough drafts of another novel, another self of mine, another porter, another poet, another God, another imposture, another impostor, another *Don Quixote,* and another Miguel de Cervantes, not yet created? Are we not perhaps scribbled sketches on a dreamt firmament, still waiting to be fulfilled in the reality of a different book and in a universe, which would be the only true one, after the one we take for certain today is blotted and scratched out, as Your Grace's mortal vestiges vanished into your supposed immortality?

The Tapestry

Morning had already dawned, after the auto-da-fe and the burning, when Your Grace saw the Knight and his Servant for the first time in the garden of Janus. Sitting on their mounts—the skinny nag and the jet-black donkey that you gave them in the novel— they were an outline of shadows within the pebbles and gravel between the bust of Janus and the boarded-up house. Slowly, you opened the iron gate and made your way through the myrtle and bushes, realizing that you were now continuing, awake, the dream of the night before: the same dream that you would try to describe to Lope in your confession, as the years were winding down. You were probably not afraid to meet your characters, and no more surprised to find them in the orchard than, let us say, carved in wood in the attic of a sacristy. But stopping on the grass sprinkled with dewdrops, you hesitated to talk to them.

"By the beard of this man! How disconcerting he is when he stands looking at us this way, without saying a word!" the Squire exclaimed to no one in particular. "Perhaps he waits for our welcome before he greets us?"

"He does not even know what he awaits; if he knew it, he would continue our chronicle," replied the Hidalgo. "I believe that he only wants to assure himself that he exists, as we do. Have pity on him, because he who looks for himself in his characters and wishes to measure himself against them, as equal to equal, he has lost his mind.

I never imagined the author of our history like that. Or shall I say the author of our lives, which may not be saintly, but neither are they unworthy, and they will be envied in the future," reflected the Peasant. "I am not so sure that he is who he is."

Always in profile on his donkey, the apparition of the Peasant looked at Your Grace. For the first time, you would notice that eye of his, so deep and brilliant that it appeared out of place in a ghost. A farmer's eye, darkened by the years as he grew used to contemplating the horizon and examining the skies, fearful of a killing frost over his seeded fields. A farmer's eye, made to measure the droughts and the wet spells, until one of your whims made his Mas-

92

ter go to look for him and tell him something similar to *raise up and follow me*, though such a phrase does not appear in the novel.

"By my soul!" the Knight retorted. "How did you imagine him?"

"I don't know, I don't know. If he is the wizard who composed the first part of our story, I thought he would be wiser and more lordly," he scratched his rough head in perplexity.

"The habit does not make the friar," replied the Hidalgo. "But this man looks like an old dried-up broken soldier. I did not imagine him as a deaf-mute, as he appears to be, standing there watching us without saying a word. Besides, either I am making a terrible mistake or he is crippled in one arm. His left hand is still and white against his chest."

"Confound it! Your Grace knows so much and with such certainty! How did you happen to notice it?"

"He has the glazed look of someone who has survived a war and has buried all hope in his soul. I have only to look at myself in the mirror to understand it. After all, in spite of the poetic licenses which he took, he created me in his own image. I am my father's son."

Under the gaze of the specters, Your Grace would feel naked and helpless. You must have turned red, in face and in soul, as on the beach of Algiers, when they set your price as a prisoner and as a slave. Heavy as lead, the quicklime sun beat down on a curious swirl of sea gulls gathered to see your scars and exposed flesh. *Ti è mai venuto in mente che il braccio non sia che una parola scritta in un libro? Pensi a volta che il tuo braccio non sia soltanto dipinto?*

"His bedroom mirror was from the town of Alcázar de San Juan, according to what his niece told me. Alcázar is a land of gold and silversmiths, although they also make good drums and cart wheels. But, if this mute magician resembles you, it may be inside, because outside you are a head taller and a few years older," the Squire chatters. "By the same token, I think that I may have inherited something from him, because, also in me, he would want to portray a part of himself in his book."

Your Grace would have been tempted to scream that you were who you were and you could not pass for someone else: living, dead, or imaginary. Also, you wanted to wave them away with your good arm, making them disappear as if they were smoke, so that they would not take away your identity with your reason. Grief and fear would tear your memory as you recall that nightmare of Santafiore, where he saw your encounter with the old Jew in Algiers. *I asked you in my dream if the book that you were reading was yours? You answered: How could it be, if it will be three centuries before it is written?* But you would not say anything about the blind man's dream, nor would you refer to the miraculous nature of Atocha, between El Prado and the pastures. That morning, you choked on your words and only managed to exclaim:

"I was a soldier and then a slave! A skiff's harquebusier and an infidel's captive in the dungeons of Algiers! I have had my left arm crippled ever since those trials! Through so many tribulations, I thought I had preserved my reason. It was my only guarantee in life. But I must have lost it, seeing and speaking to you both as if you truly lived!"

Shaking his black head, the Peasant laughed soundlessly. His reaction was predictable and could not be avoided, but with a somber gesture of reproof the Knight stopped him. Then he addressed Your Grace slowly, in a very different tone, as if he were talking to a dull-witted foreigner, barely versed in Castilian. Let's say a farmer from the *langue d'Oc* or a fisherman from the Tyrrhenian Sea.

"The reason we have been waiting here for Your Grace for several days is because we want you to conclude the second part of your book. Recount our wanderings as you once did. Give us new adventures to pursue. As soon as you write them, we will live them for the glory of all three of us. But we cannot continue with any of our deeds, or even exist outside of this garden, if you do not trace our path to the future."

"This is like the stage," the Squire insisted. "My Master and I want to continue in our roles. But first you must confirm what will happen to us. And confirm it in your own hand."

"If Your Grace abandons the book, you condemn us to an imprisonment in this orchard, as if in limbo, even if you leave the rusty gate open. We are consuming ourselves waiting here for you from dawn to dusk, to then sleep and disappear each night until morn."

Your Grace decided then to speak to them very gently and very slowly. As you would much later confide to Lope in your final confession, you would actually become so absorbed in thought that you almost forgot about the ghosts, stopped still in their saddles by the double profile of Janus. On the eaves of the house, a string of blackbirds would listen attentively.

"Having sketched the last part, I abandoned the novel. I was afraid that, instead of writing it, I would bring you to life out of nothingness, as the devil probably does when he mocks creation. Another character had occurred to me—a conceited and loquacious bachelor from the University of Salamanca. He would visit you and tell you that the first edition of your valiant deeds was already on sale. But, at that point, I hesitated. If the book read by the bachelor was the same one that I had written, when he commented on it from outside the printed pages, the three of you would become as real as I was myself. Without burning what I wrote, but also without reading it again, I had to put it away. I was afraid of losing my mind."

"If I clearly understand what you are saying, I believe you had other motives for setting aside what you were writing," the Peasant cut in, skeptical and disdainful. "It seems to me that, although an old soldier, you, Señor, are fainthearted. Since the first part of your book was so well received, you feared that the same luck would not favor you again. Don't you know that, when throwing the dice, good fortune is offended if you hesitate when she befriends you and you do not believe in tempting ventures?"

"I do not understand the tortuous paths of Providence," you replied nervously. "But I know that it would have been a mistake to proceed with my tale, since second parts are never good. You are not eunuchs singing a libretto, nor actors presenting a comedy. Your only life is the one that I have granted to you as my characters. I am your creator and chronicler. Our lives, however, were anticipated in the embroidery of a tapestry. All that we are and will be becomes visible there, in a most unusual disarrangement."

"Our life is predicted in a tapestry?" the Hidalgo asked in perplexity. "Where is it and when did you see it?"

"Did you ever open the door of this house, after awakening in the orchard?"

The Rustic and his Master looked at each other disconcertedly. Raising his pale hand, crisscrossed with labyrinthine lines, the Knight inquired:

"Did you take from the embroidery the events of the novel, to tell them as if they were ours?"

"I did not copy them, though I must have seen them when I was a child, and then I must have forgotten them. My time for writing had not yet arrived. But come with me, and I will show you how the weave mingles and confuses the narration of your story with the contradictions of my life."

You ran to the door and in vain try to lift the crossbar with your good arm. The Squire got off his donkey, tied it to an acacia, and went to give you a hand. With surprising strength and without any visible effort, the ghost raised the bar as if it were made of straw. Together you opened wide the great door, pushing on both of the squeaking panels. Followed by the Hidalgo, already on foot, you entered the empty house. The specters marvelled as you showed them several of their deeds from the first part of the book embroidered in that wall hanging. Or they discovered them on their own, as their eyes grew used to searching for them. There, wrought in raised work, was the duel of the good man of La Mancha and the Biscayan, captured at the point of jostling one another. There was the Knight during the sad days of his supposed enchantment, tied and imprisoned in a madman's cage, going home on an ox-herd cart at the slow pace of the castrated beasts. There was the adventure of the dead body, when the Knight took the priests for devils, as they traveled from Baeza to Segovia to bury the corpse. There was the hero's charge against those clergymen with their torches. The frightened priests fled from his attack, believing that he was a devil loosened in the night. There was the Peasant, drinking from a creek in the midst of a blooming meadow, while his Master heeded the call to resurrect the Twelve Peers of France, the Nine of Fame, the *Platinires, Tablantes, Olivantes, Tirantes, Febos,* and *Belianises.*

But also there, in such an intricate tapestry, appeared scenes of Your Grace's life. You saw yourself again in the kitchen at Imagen Street, while your mother toasted the bread slices. Searching the cloth for another moment of your tired existence, you put on your glasses. Diminished, but accurately portrayed, you found yourself back in Italy at the age of twenty-six on the day that you had your audience with Don Juan of Austria, the King's bastard brother and conqueror of the Turks in Lepanto. The wall hanging showed the embrace of young Don Juan, young as Your Grace, as he raised you from your knees and gracefully prevented you from kissing his hand. *They tell me that you crippled your arm in the battle,* said Don Juan looking obliquely at your frozen arm. *I should have died in Lepanto because since then my life has not been my own. I will never be the same, at least not on this earth.* Without any order or logic, the design transported you from Don Juan to Catalina upon your return from Esquivias, having just been released from prison. Tracing the threads and skipping from Catalina to Ana Franca, you went back to a time when you did not yet know the woman you would marry. Brocaded in a prairie, between Fuencarral to the east and Las Rozas to the west, you were playing chess with Ana Franca. Tumbled on your elbows face to face on a yellow quilt beside the picnic basket, both of you were absorbed in a castle or a gambit. You were never to meet your mistress' cuckold husband, for he was a judge in New Granada, in the same Indies where several times Your Grace wanted to flee. Meanwhile, in the tapestry, she was winning in the chess match over you. Although she stuttered when reading and hardly knew how to write, your lover was unbeatable on the chess board. *Take care, watch out, you seem blind! Your moves are so simple that I guess them before you think about them,* smiled Ana Franca with her face in her hands and her elbows on the coverlet.

"Señor, would you kindly let me borrow your glasses?" the Hidalgo distracted you suddenly, patting your shoulder with his ghostly palm. "I must have lost some of my sight with age. Or perhaps I lost it in the pages of all the books, as you said that I had read before you began yours. My Squire insists that we give our attention to a unique, although very small detail, hidden in this drapery."

Perplexed, you gave him your glasses. The ghost put them on the edge of his hawk nose that years had turned to mere skin and bone. Urged by the Rustic, you both bent over to take note of that minute account on the tapis to which the Farmer, visibly excited, was pointing with his broad-knuckled and thick-nailed finger.

"Do you see what I see? Or is this a delusion of my addled mind?"

Your Grace was on the verge of screaming. But stupefied, you concealed your surprise. Your crippled arm cramped and a chilling sensation ran down your spine. Almost reduced to the size of your thumb, Your Grace and the ghost appeared crammed together in the tapestry. Your heads, side by side, had been embroidered with such perfection that they had even foreseen that instant in which the Hidalgo wore your recently borrowed glasses. We would never know for certain how long the three of you remained staring at your images on the quilted cloth. Finally, the Squire broke the stillness, turning and glancing at the vast mirror which reflected the entire tapestry.

"We see ourselves as we truly are in that gigantic looking glass. But they stitched us as tiny little ants in the cloth facing the mirror. God knows when and who embroidered us before we existed. From my vineyards I come, and I know nothing. But I call this something between a dream and a miracle. Señores, I wonder who is working all these marvels.

"It is the Church's doctrine that dreams are granted by God. He must also give us our nightmares in order to sanction our gluttony and our excesses in drinking," Lope will tell you in your confession when Your Grace relates that first encounter with your characters. "On the contrary, Satan brings the apparitions if they are not the simple result of a fever such as that of the three day flu, or of chicken pox. I will pretend that your hallucination in Atocha came with the croup fever in order to avoid casuistic and deontological conflicts. And now let us put in order the general retelling of your sins. Return to the chess game encompassed in the tapestry of that house. I dare say that it was very appropriate that not having any other company but the picnic basket, you opted to use the grass for a table. By my faith, it would be the perfect scene for a still life with two figures! How did your game with Ana Franca end?"

"I lost", Your Grace answered softly. "I lost, as always."

Like a jovial ringing of bells, Ana Franca's guffaws reverberate in your memory. Reclined on the blanket, she was laughing without contempt, but also without remorse. Although she was almost as old as you when you met her at the home of Figueroa, her distant relative from Alcalá, Your Grace was attracted by her youthful features of a perpetual adolescent. When she laughed her almond face seemed even younger with her Chinese-like eyes and cheeks, and her alabastrine complexion rendered a bluish tone to the darkness of her hair, cut and styled in the fashion of a page.

In your memory, the singing of some birds would transform into the singing of others. Remembrances of the lark greeting dawn at the Hieronymites' would cross with the concert of the canaries in the vine at the inn where you had stayed two days earlier. In another fragment of your past, the twitting of those caged would become as one with the chirping in the poplar tree in the meadow where you engaged in your chess match. Skipping semi-tones, the birds singing would be fused at the end with Ana's laughter following the checkmate. Exasperated by her outbursts, and enraged as you very seldom were, you knocked over the pieces with a single blow.

"It is time to play a different game," you yelled.

Still laughing, and with a double kick into the air, she removed her slippers. Immediately, she started running, holding her skirt in her fingertips. Eager, you chased her up the hill and towards the stream which snaked through the grove. At the edge of the water, among the first poplars you caught her, or she surrendered to your embrace. Clasping your neck, she would kiss you with a passion as ardent as that of Catalina's a few years later when you returned from your Andalusian wanderings. Although you would make love to her almost every day, for Ana Franca, that moment had the frenzy of a first love encounter after Lent.

"And I love you so! And I love you so!"

Your memory would not make it clear which one of the two—Ana Franca or that Catalina, who would later be your wife and whom you had not met yet—repeated it to you in the pauses of kisses. Instead you must have relived your awkwardness, when you insisted on unbuttoning Ana's garments with your good arm, with the same clarity as if that afternoon in the countryside was the very eve of your confession with Lope. She would laugh again seeing you excited and confused. But she laughed now as though feeling pity for the clumsiness of an old man or a child, without repressing her well-disposed hilarity before such ineptitude. In the end, with both of you standing by the creek Ana Franca would be the one to undress you after disrobing herself. Tumbled on the grass, and while you possessed her amid groans, you must have thought of *La Zeffirina* and of *tutte le puttane* whom you enjoyed in Italy. None of them ever had a body as strong as hers. Under the April sun and the sky of Las Rozas, she seemed carved of crystal sugar. You would not think of Ana Franca as coming from a mortal mother, but from a naked statue in her image. It was fitting to think that her moaning in the midst of ecstasy had silenced the sparrows. Then you would lose yourself in the excitement of your own frenzy and almost felt your kidneys severed—as they talked in Mesina about serrating your arm for fear of the gangrene—such was the bliss that plunged you into your rapture. Afterwards, exhausted and embracing Ana Franca on the grass, you heard again the chirping of the birds and shooed away a bluish bumblebee buzzing around your bodies.

"And I love you so!"

The creek must have carried iron in its current because it reddened the sharp rocks and the gravel of its bed as if painting them with blood recently shed. Blood. You always felt certain that you had conceived Isabel in that meadow. The same Isabel whom you recognized as yours after Ana Franca's death, and took to be raised with your sister Magdalena and then with you and Catalina. If alive, Promontorio, the infant child you left so young in Naples, would be in his forties. You thought at the time that you would sail for Spain and return to Italy on a day not too far distant. But you were inadvertently heading into captivity, and unaware that you would never return to the house of *la pendice Santa Barbara,* where your son was born. Confessing to Lope, you would blame yourself for having lost your two offspring. One abandoned unintentionally with *la Zeffirina* and the other angered over a dispute of money, that, to make things worse, you did not even have. In time, you would be deserted by the two main characters created by your imagination: the bony Hidalgo and the bearded, brown-eyed Squire. They disappeared forever from the garden of Janus, when you finally published the second part of *Don Quixote,* as if they had definitely assumed their own identity in the novel.

You must have enjoyed your lucidity in the face of death. You must have been comforted by the certainty of your unworthiness when they praised you as the author of your book. *I had something I was going to ask you about Don Quixote but it has slipped my mind*, the King had said. *I had it on the tip of my tongue.* The memory of the canaries in the vine at the inn would come to dissipate your quietness. Their singing was so vibrant that afternoon when you dismounted in front of the inn that the lark at the Hieronymites', the chirping in the meadow, and the passionate moans of Ana Franca, now dead, were silenced into oblivion. Next to the vine the innkeeper sharpened the sickle with a grinding stone and his wife cleaned the peas for supper. Your Grace knew that man somewhat. He was a brother of the parish priest of San Focas and Ciro, on Niño Street right behind your house. An avid reader and a talker, he had been introduced to you by the priest himself in front of the Confraternity of the Unworthy Slaves. You had to struggle to keep the man from embracing your boots when he found out that you were the author of *Don Quixote*.

"I came to Madrid to buy ginger, cloves, and peppersalt. On the way to the store, I meet the greatest of geniuses. How do I praise God and my brother, His minister, for such an honor?"

Since then Your Grace had stopped twice at the hostel without spending the night. That afternoon the innkeeper did not want to let you go so quickly. As soon as he saw you at the garden, he rushed to grab and hold you against his brown leather apron. He was as corpulent as Polyphemus, and his resounding voice seemed to magnify his size.

"Today you will eat and sleep free of charge. I will furnish you a bedroom with a washstand and an iron bed. Come, woman, and you will meet the wittiest genius in the kingdom. The man who makes us laugh as he romances our sorrows, as my brother, the curate, describes him."

Supper consisted of split pea soup, mutton in green sauce, and baked potatoes. The inn was full of merchants, carriers, traders, and guards of the Holy Office who would go to Madrid and to the auto-da-fe the next day. Beneath the hams, onions, and garlic hanging hooked from the stone roof, Gregorio Nacianceno, wrapped in his purple coat, observed you attentively. There were also a couple of whores who did not appear to be so. No one would have guessed their trade, had they not been alone and loose in the countryside. They were young, discreet, and beautiful, as prudent and falsely modest as fairy tale maidens. Loquacious, the hosteler introduced them to you, as though they came with the room, the iron bed, and the washstand from Cáceres.

"Here I bring you María Isabel del Amor Hermoso and María Mercedes del Calvario. One is from Ribadavia, in Orense and the other from Oviedo. They are well versed in Latin, pastoral novels, and the lives of saints. They are chatterboxes talking about Dianas,

Leahs, Leonisas, and Felicias. And here you have, girls, the most illustrious of all writers. He who is read with equal contentment by the common people, like us, and the scholars of Salamanca."

The dinner ended with a raisin cobbler dessert and curds with spices, the host then requested more lights and his copy of *The Ingenious Gentleman Don Quixote de La Mancha*. Although it secretly displeased Your Grace, he announced your presence to the guests and offered to read them some excerpts from your book. Seated at the head of the bench, deepening his already strong voice, he proceeded with the chapter of *the terrifying and never-before-imagined adventure of the windmills*. Each time he turned the page, the flame of the oil lamp trembled and all turned to look at you on the sly. Occasionally, they would burst out laughing long and heartily at passages which never made you smile when you wrote them. *Such are fortunes of war, which more than any other are subject to constant change. What is more, when I come to think of it, I am sure that this must be the work of the magician Frestón, the one who robbed me of my study and my books and who has thus changed the giants into windmills in order to deprive me of the glory of overcoming them.* While guards and muleteers would split their sides laughing, you were taken aback by the pensive gesture of María Mercedes del Calvario. She was contemplating you as if, instead of acknowledging your presence, she were dreaming about you in the distance. She was as tall as Catalina, and both shared the same steel gaze. But the bar girl did not yet show any gray hair, being as she was in the fullness of her youth. She was wearing a golden bracelet with turquoise from the Indies, a present from her godfather, the canon, as she later informed Your Grace.

I tell you this because I too intend to provide myself with just such a bough as the one he wielded, and with it I propose to do such exploits that you shall deem yourself fortunate to have been found worthy to come with me and behold and witness things that are almost beyond belief. Listening to that passage, you almost felt that you had abandoned reality to enter one of the inns of your own novel. There, an innkeeper as fabulous as the one in this inn would entertain his guests reading from your book. Possibly, the door would open and the Hidalgo and his Servant would come in looking for food and lodging. It could be that they would accommodate themselves next to Your Grace not realizing who you were. Glimpsing still into the imaginary, the host would greet your heroes: *Allow me to welcome you and in no time I will serve you what I have left of the soup and mutton. But before I must conclude reading this chapter of your story.* Over the flames of the candles, Master and

Squire would look at each other and agree with a grimace. With a different expression María Mercedes del Calvario continued spying on you. She would no longer disregard your stare to prove your absence, but, on the contrary, she would fix her eyes on yours as though reading your mind.

They mentioned this chapter to Your Grace more often than any other of your novel. The adventure, however, was roughly about forty lines. On the road to Puerto Lapice, some distant windmills took the appearance of giants for the Hidalgo. Although his Servant denied the vision, the Knight, giving spurs, charged against the imaginary Titans. The wind turned one of the mill blades, as he was spearing. It lifted both horse and Knight, breaking the lance into pieces. Defeated, the pathetic Paladin would say that a magician enemy of his had changed the giants into windmills to rob him of his glory as a conqueror.

While María Mercedes del Calvario was looking at you, you remembered having read this passage to Góngora soon after writing it. Frowning and half-closing his eyes, Góngora then said slowly: *We will never know why certain images, created by a man, remain indelibly in the memory of mankind. Thus Ulysses, blinding the drunken Cyclops with a burning spear. Or Oedipus, eyeless, wandering in Colonus by the hand of Antigone. I wonder if also your Knight in his saddle, taken by the blade whirling in the wind, will not become another immortal memory of something that never existed.* Surprised by the flattering words of that spiteful priest, you told him of having forgotten how you had conceived that nonsensical fable of the windmills. There, you only wanted to ridicule your Hidalgo and also to humanize him by means of derision. Then you added that the incident went along with the disillusionment of the world and your questioning the concept of reality which prevailed throughout the book. In the distance, the windmills could have the appearance of giants. You only had to have the will to see for those machines, newly arrived from Flanders, to transform themselves into giants. Obviously, ambiguity was indispensable—the to be or not to be sort of thing—for such a metamorphosis to occur. That is why it demanded the uncertainty of distance or the twilight of dusk. In the end, stripped of the illusion, the windmills would return to their original condition. *In other words,* Your Grace concluded, shrugging your shoulders, *the disillusionment of the world does not exist. There is only man's inability to understand it and to truly change it. Once the monsters transformed themselves into windmills, the Knight can only attribute the new mutation to an also magical fate. Thus he turns into literature what was once his rational fancy.*

At that point, Góngora interrupted to ask you what you anticipated for your character for the remainder of the novel. *I would let him proceed in the same manner as I conceived him. He will act according to what he is.* Góngora tried to find out whether your Hidalgo would continue transforming inns into palaces, innkeepers into Castilian gentlemen, and whores into maidens. Dazzled by his questions, as before by his backbiting praise, Your Grace assented. *Then, you are mistaken,* sentenced Góngora, picking up his hat. *From what you said, I infer that we are not even what we dream, but we are more limited each time to dream and to be. The power of your Hero to transform reality as he pleases would decrease with time. At the end he will have to see inns as inns and it may be that his Squire is the one who begins to call them castles.*

The reading concluded, several voices joined the innkeeper in demanding to know when Your Grace would publish the other part of the book. Lying through your teeth, you promised to deliver it to the press shortly. Hastily, you said goodnight and went to bed. You struggled to evade the gaze of María Mercedes del Calvario. In the shadows, her eyes seemed to catch your steps as though enchanting their prey. Once in your room, you wanted to sleep with the shutters open. The moon was but a sliver, but the stars cast a glow on the distant Pedriza and on the mirror over the washstand. Naked as you came into the world, you crossed yourself before getting into bed. You scarcely had time to lie down when the door half opened and María Mercedes del Calvario came in. Calm and impassive, she begged your silence with her finger on her lips.

"You are wasting your time, woman. I do not intend to pay you since at my age I cannot take you," you said as soon as she slid the door latch.

As she did not answer, you must have wondered if she was a sleepwalker and a mute emerging from a moonbeam in pursuit of that shepherd, who slept eternally dreaming to be immortal for having loved Selene. The same one whom María Mercedes del Calvario would confuse with an old man like Your Grace, by a mockery of destiny which distorts and falsifies everything. Silently, the little wench sat at the edge of your bed and removed her goatskin leather clogs and stockings. She undressed, garment after garment, hanging her skirt, shawl, cape, and shirt on a chair. Her body was willowy with small breasts and thin hips. Nude, she lifted the bed-clothing and laid down beside you. She was about to slide her hand between your thighs when you stopped her, irritated and impatient.

"I told you that if I cannot take you, I am not going to pay you either. Go and leave me alone."

Unexpectedly, she began to talk to you about her late godfather, the canon of Toledo. Of how such a wise man thought that you, a lunatic, were only completely sane when you wrote the story of your crazy Hidalgo. Little by little, her voice thickened with sleep, and the girl dozed off. More relaxed then, you embraced her shoulders and rested her face on your chest. Her head of hair was scented to its roots with Segovian lavender. Enjoying the aroma, you inhaled deeply, and the fragrance, like a wake in water grew thinner losing itself into a more intense perfume which memory dispersed in the shadows. It was the dewy reminiscence of ferns, mosses, and jasmine in that meadow where you conceived Isabel in Ana Franca. Not knowing for certain whether you were addressing María Mercedes del Calvario or Ana, dead, you asked in a loud voice:

"And you? Do you believe I am crazy?"

The whore's quick reaction was surprising. Suddenly awakened, she leaned on her elbow to stare at you in the darkness. Enlivened, she moved about and her eyes seemed to brighten as if sprinkled with gold in the night. Through the window shutters, dawn was breaking in the sky.

"Crazy? she asked sinking her hand in your trimmed beard, not to caress you but to be assured that you remained by her side. I do not believe that your insanity is like that of the nut of the village nor the madman in a cage.

"What would it be then, María Mercedes?"

"My godfather used to say that you were lacking reason when you did not write because, then, you did not know your own identity. I think that you will never truly live until you decide to finish your book."

Both of you fell silent and after a while the sinner asked you whether you fancied her tongue or her hand, before falling asleep and although you were incapable of enjoying her. You shook your head and María Mercedes del Calvario fell asleep. As years passed, when you concluded the second part of your book, you remembered that woman whom you will never meet again. In the last page of the novel, you wrote that it was for the Knight to act and for Your Grace to write, even though the two of you were one and the same man who was fulfilling your common existence. Immediately, you understood that you had transcended the boundaries between reality and fantasy. From that moment on, the novel would not be an imitation of a chronicle or a fable. Thanks to María Mercedes del Calvario—*I think that you will never truly live until you decide to finish your book*—, and even after your demise, Your Grace would live on in your crazy Hidalgo. Literature and life would become the two inseparable faces of a common destiny. A double destiny, you thought aloud, in the image of that statue of Janus, among the myrtle and brambles in Atocha. Such was the absurd madness that ruled your world.

* * * * *

Letter without a date from Lope de Vega to Fernández de Avellaneda. It belonged to Thornton Wilder, a playwright and a well-known Lope specialist. At present, it is owned by a scholar in emblematic studies, Professor Pedro Campa, from the University of Tennessee at Chattanooga. It was acquired by Doctor Campa at a public auction at Todhunter's in New York, on November 19, 1975, the date of the demise of both the pugilist Georges Carpentier, also known as the Orchid Boy, and of Francisco Franco. The first page is missing.

(. . .) We agreed that I would address you as *Your Grace*, while reserving the less formal *you* for kitchen helpers and servants, or to speak to God Our Father in the *Paternoster*. When Don Luis de Góngora and I entrusted you with the writing of the apocryphal second part of *Don Quixote de la Mancha,* the three of us also decided that in our correspondence I would call you Fernández de Avellaneda, or Avellaneda for short, and to sign the book with this fictitious name. At this moment, I am afraid of my own shadow and I do not want him to find out or even suspect what we are plotting. After all, like all melancholiacs, he is distrustful by nature.

Nor do I want others to discover my contribution to the intrigue. All precautions must be taken to make sure that, at least in appearance, I am not involved in your task now nor will I be at any time in the future. I cannot imagine what the world would say about me if, just making wild conjectures, tomorrow this letter were to fall in the hands of a pedagogue, born three centuries from now in the Havana of the Audience of Santo Domingo. Just suppose that he would permit it to be published in a book in which it is told how Your Grace wrote yours at Góngora's and my request. I am referring to a novel, where my epistle, although authentic, might be considered fictitious. In other words, it would pretend to be a fake with a truthful appearance, when it was a faithful copy of the one I am hereby signing. It is better not to worry about it, although I beg you to shred this after you read it and set fire to the pieces, as you should have done with the others.

I understand the difficulties that you are encountering with the false *Quixote*. But Don Luis de Góngora and I like what you have given us to read, so far. Grotesque as it is, it becomes a fitting mockery of his awkward performance as a novelist, but it is not so ludicrous as to be improbable. Do not hesitate to request with great discretion any small amount you may need to buy ink, pens, blotting powder, or any other supplies needed for your writing. Thus we agreed, although what we sent you should suffice to proceed with your work. You will find Sil blotting powder, which is the best, at the store with the red awning on Lechuga Street. The business is attended by a graceful Galician girl, who does not give herself for money, although she is not at all disdainful towards clergymen when she takes a sacrilegious liking to them.

I close my digression and I rethread the line of my thought. If we give in to divagations, between blotting powder and lasciviousness, life will pass like dust in the wind. Time is pressing for Your Grace to conclude your fable. Two weeks ago, when a full, red, iridescent moon was shining, the strangest of all rumors was spreading at the poets' tavern. They were saying that a mysterious character was compensating him, our armless friend, so that he would once and for all finish his own continuation of *Don Quixote*. Although I did not give credence to that gossip, I casually commented on it myself. Who else but his publisher, Juan de la Cuesta, would pay him beforehand for the last part of the novel? De la Cuesta must not have been very generous to him because he went about with mended clothes and runs in his stockings. Likewise, each time I said amen he asked me for a loan to appease his creditors. I always gave it to him without protesting or demanding interest. Although I may not be prodigal—I was, to my misfortune, only with women—, I agreed to the loan because I knew he was true to his word. He would repay me with the same punctuality as he would return my horse to the stable, after taking it for those solitary rides in which he still indulges on occasion. I assume he was digging a hole to fill another one, and he was satisfying his debt with the advance from the bookseller. Or perhaps with a loan from a friend of his with a high position in the department of Accounting. Someone whose last name was Cetina, if I remember correctly, who ruined the maimed's wife's fortune with a dreadful, although well-intentioned piece of advice. It is a well-known fact that from time to time he still visits with Cetina behind Catalina's back. When he wants to kill one of his many idle hours, he goes to his office and there they either talk about trivialities or about the mystery of the Holy Trinity.

I confess not having suspected anything about his new protector—the one whose identity is still unknown—, until seeing notable transformations in his conduct and spirits. I was rather taken aback for not having paid attention to these changes before and started to remember that he had not solicited a single copper maravedi for entire weeks. We saw that he was wearing new clothes and new stockings, and also some silver-buckled shoes, very proper for the *nouveau rich's* vanity. All of that coincided, more or less, with the time when the rumors started to propagate about a Maecenas, a benefactor ready to finance his time and cover his expenses to help him finish the second part of his novel. To complete the picture, I will add that this material comfort does not affect his disposition. As skeptical as always, he still seems lost between life and a dream or between arms and letters. In this respect, he has not changed although he is impaired from being a man of arms and he procrastinates in proceeding with his great *chef-d'oeuvre*. At least that is how *Don Quixote* is considered by the dim-witted and illiterate, all of them sighing and crossing themselves as if they were writing the title of his novel in the air with broad strokes in red, as in the wild celebrations when a doctoral title is granted to a student. It is really disgusting to have to live among so many fools.

Last week an unknown person appeared at the tavern and immediately everybody suspected that this was his benefactor. Perhaps we thought so because that stranger could have been any man or, at the same time, no one. He was wrapped in a black raincoat and wore a wide-brimmed chambergo hat pulled down to his eyebrows. He was also muffled up to his eyes with his cape, as if to disguise himself as himself. The truth is that of his face we only saw his eyes which seemed to be more like enamel than alive. With the smile of a smug fox, Góngora described him as a very peculiar being, somewhere between magic and comedy. *Someone who would vanish if we were to snatch off his cape and hat because there is nothing underneath and his gaze would be nobody's.* I replied that it sounded too poetic and too much in consonance with his intricate verses. But that the stranger would be someone, if in reality he were assisting our crippled friend with payment to avoid the delay of his renewed efforts. I added that to discover the motives for his generosity would be more important than to find out his name.

A couple of days later the phantom reappeared at the tavern. On a finger of his gloved hand, with which he concealed his face, a gold ring with a sign of Janus glittered. Góngora perceived it, half-opening those slitted, prying eyes which could see the grass grow. In a low voice, he had us looking at it and even I, after much effort, was able to catch a glimpse of it. *Janus Matutinus,* protector of gates and portals, was made by the Romans as the god of the beginning of each calendar year. His celebration would fall on the ninth of January, when the king had a ram slaughtered to honor the deity. Since every beginning implies an end, they used to represent that god with two opposite profiles: one facing forward and the other facing backward. Friezes and minted coins of Janus still exist. But for inscrutable reasons, he is not found among classical statues and there is no testimony of his image ever having been chiseled or cast. I assure you that I know all of this through Góngora, but I do not repeat it to extend myself into pagan matters. The fact is that Janus—father of the entire Olympus, for being the begetter of all beginnings—, has a remarkable relation with what I am expounding to Your Grace.

That ring was the second image of *Janus Matutinus* that I had seen in my life. The other remains in Atocha in the overgrown orchard of an abandoned house, where our one-handed friend took Góngora and me, and a certain lady friend of mine. Although thoroughly acquainted with that quarter, I had never stumbled upon that empty manor before. I give you my word that this is the gospel truth! In the midst of myrtle and wild laurels, he uncovered for us an unbelievable bust of Janus on a granite pedestal which perhaps is the only one on earth. On top of all these wonders, both faces seemed carved using the cripple himself as a common model. I should also tell you about a tapestry and a mirror which hang in the house and are the largest imaginable. But I promised not to cram so many marvels into only one paragraph. I hope I am not being presumptuous. I am not dreaming nor exaggerating. The house, the statue, and its orchard are there. But it is as if everything had come out of the void, the very nothingness from which the world and souls were created. He wants to tell all of this himself, in another book that he has in mind and that he would entitle *Weeks in the Garden.* I doubt he will ever write it.

But I insist on what I told Góngora. If the man of the ring is investing in the continuation of *Don Quixote,* it would be imperative to find out the reasons for his squandering. Although many fools are paying to read the first part of the novel, none of them would recompense the author so that he would hasten to complete the second part. Instead, I see how someone may offer me a fortune so that I would not stop writing plays since his would be a very charitable expense. Just think about the success of my dramas and how many people, from the actors to the stage hands, live off my genius. Your Grace would say that we, too, are making a deal very similar to the one that I denounced as impossible. But, in fact, ours is very different. Profiting from the maimed's condition and the ineptitude of the vulgus, we agreed that you would ridicule him with your clever distortion of *Don Quixote*. Confronted with such a parody, he would feel the same as if a well-liked man discovered that during his absence, in wanderings throughout the world, his deformed image in a mirror had replaced him, and he now faces other people's mockery. In such circumstances, the one of the traveler in the example, and the one of our friend facing the Avellaneda's *Quixote*, neither of them could do anything but to hide the embarrassment at home, sealing the windows and doors.

Everything has gone well and we are pleased with what Your Grace has written, as I told you before. Your beginning is excellent with the invention of a new character, the Grenadine Don Alvaro Tarfe. I also find very fortunate and merciful the passing from madness, in which he left the Hidalgo, to the sanity inspired by the reading of the lives of the Saints. His falling back into madness turns out to be extravagant, yet amusing and believable. I am referring to the rapture of folly that takes the Knight to the joust of Saragossa, upon meeting Don Alvaro and finding that he was heading to that tournament. Notwithstanding, I again urge your haste, and I hope you forgive my obstinacy. If the payment from the mysterious benefactor gives him the incentive to rush the completion of his own book before you finish yours, everything will have been in vain. All of our industry will have gone to the devil along with your work and the money that I have already forwarded to you. In such a case, Your Grace could make kindling with what you have written and forget that once, in dreams, you were Avellaneda.

If our one-armed friend were not so old—out of a superstitious resentment I do not even want to write his name—, if he were not, I say again, so gloomy and advanced in years, I would suspect that his deals with that stranger are of an abominable nature. I do not want to sow infamous rumors, but he himself claims to have been bought for five hundred escudos during his Algerian captivity. A certain Azán Bajá, a Venetian renegade who acted as governor or pasha, became his owner. He even boasts about how Bajá, famous for his rages, willingly forgave him for three of his escape attempts, even though he hung and beat his accomplices. He asserts that after failing to escape—the second or third time—the exasperated despot condemned him to two thousand blows with a stick on his stomach and feet. He brags about meeting the news of his death sentence with a flash of wit, thinking perhaps that *una bella morte onora tutta una vita*. He alleges that he said: *With so much beating, my soul will go to heaven cleaner than that rug from The Arabian Nights! I mean the one that unrolls and flies at a prince's will.* He swears that Azán Bajá burst out laughing at such ironic courage. He then willingly forgave him.

If I put on stage such an adventure, not to mention the other escape attempts and their immediate pardons, the most ignorant audience would hiss at my play. Nevertheless, I firmly believe all that he tells me about his captivity. I wish not to believe it because what he does not reveal terrifies and repels me even more. Not long ago, at the dawn of the century, I was in Seville with a lady friend. Fate made me cross paths with a former captive from the Algerian prisons. He was a native of Sanlúcar la Mayor, as lisping and boozy as they come. He had been in those dungeons, shortly after the maimed, when Algerian buccaneers boarded his ship between Sicily and Pantellaria. As he talked about his ordeal, he mentioned Azán Bajá but hastened to tell me that he was never a slave of such a feared pasha. He crossed himself as he swore it thanking Divine Providence for sparing him from such pain and infamy. The said Azán Bajá, he proceeded, was given to write Zejels and Casidas which are poems as appreciated among Muslims as ballads and love sonnets are here. He also played the rebec and the guzla with great skill and grace. But those refinements did not exclude him from a heartless perversity, which made him show his authority by ordering beatings, hangings, and mortal flagellations for any crime committed or suspected. He himself presided over all punishments, which were prolonged by the executioners from sunrise to sunset to distract the pasha from his ill moods with the slaying of his victims.

Some prisoners suffered a fate worse than death. Azán Bajá not only delighted himself with music and poetry but also liked to enjoy the handsomest Christian captives. He was a sodomite besides being cruel. The man from Sanlúcar told me that the pederast forced many young lads to please him with crimes of the flesh that burn your tongue when you mention them. Knowing that they would lose their souls, ever more precious than life, the youngsters submitted themselves to his depravity. But my loquacious Andalusian would not cease to thank God for taking him to Algiers when the monster had already returned to Constantinople. I repeat that it is not my intention to defame anyone but Your Grace can put the pieces together and deduce the Bajá's reasons for tolerating our friend's many attempts at flight. We are forced to think that the beastly faggot was head over heals in love with him as he showed with his repeated mercy. How he came to fall for his looks and his dubious wit, forty years ago, I do not dare imagine.

I entrust your health to Heaven, and wish you well always. I bid
Your Grace farewell cordially and affectionately.

—Félix Lope de Vega Carpio.

When Lope comes to hear your confession, he wants to know nothing about your five years in Algiers. You will leave this world without
confiding in anyone about your life in captivity. If you once wrote
a piece about those misfortunes and hardships, you did it more to
hide them than to reveal them. But, for an endless instant, you will
bring back the memory of that long-buried morning when Azán
Bajá was touching and feeling you like a horse at the beach of Fanal.
*Pensi a volte che il braccio non sia tuo e sia soltanto dipinto? Ti è
mai venuto in mente che il braccio non sia una parola scritta in un
libro?* You did not know, yet, that Azán Bajá, a viceroy recently
sent by the Sublime Gate of Istanbul, was a renegade from Venice.
His trimmed and reddish beard was sparse and he had a bad and
dull color—a deep sallow complexion—which underscored his lean
features. Fits of anger or scorn brightened and darkened his eyes.
The passing years since his apostasy had turned his aquiline profile
even more like one of an Arab.

"But your arm is real and not imagined. It is not a word lost in
a book"—he proceeded in Castillian, as he was versed in several
languages and even in the jargon of an African port, a jumble of
Spanish, Moorish, and Ligurian. "There is no other reality than the
one you live in. Paintings and books are dreams of idolaters or
madmen. This crippled arm is as yours as someday your death
will be."

Although he caressed your chest, your shoulders, and your face,
he dared not touch your frozen arm. With a whip he pointed to your
immobile elbow on your chest. Then he retreated a few steps to
tell you:

"You are my slave, but I am going to give you a piece of advice.
Do not renounce Christianity to become a Muslim because then my
faith will oblige me to free you. I never want to give up what is
mine, even if mandated by the Koran and the Secret Tablets of the
Law, the other sacred book in Heaven."

They imprisoned you in a cell where a beam of light came in from
a very high peephole. You could hear in the distance the murmur of
a sea that remained very calm the whole month of your confinement.
With your fingernail you scratched the earthen jug in which they
brought your water, to keep track of your days. The guard, a one-
eyed, cheerful and stocky Turk, faithfully delivered rye bread and
cured meat to you. He would remove your irons so that you could

eat and let you stroll in your enclosure before he shackled you and cleaned the bile. He spoke slowly in Arabic and combined it with a few Italian words to make himself understood. It was through him that you found out—should I say we found out?—that Azán Bajá had bought you from Alí Mami for five hundred gold escudos, before your former owner embarked for Constantinople. The guard did not know why they kept you in the cell while the other captives were already working for the viceroy. Each morning they would go to their chores chased by the jeers of children. *Errnajil, chufuti, queldi, chupech, manaora, raspeni! Bastard, Jew, cuckold, dog, faggot, heathen!* He encouraged you not to lose heart because Allah would show his mercy upon those who kept hope even if they were infidels. Then he would leave you all alone with the whispering of the soft sea breeze.

One afternoon Azán Bajá himself made his appearance. He had you unchained and sat by your side on a stone set in the wall. Impatiently, he dismissed the guard. He was wearing a caftan made of silk—of Bursan silk, as you would later learn to call it—adorned with cut parchment roses. An emerald hung in the middle of his turban.

"I wonder why Don Juan of Austria gave you the letters that you carried when we captured you. He praises you as Jupiter would flatter his handsome cupbearer. Were you perhaps his lover, *il coqlia del suo cuore?*"

"Don Juan gave me only one audience in Naples"—you blushed as if you were lying, even though you spoke the truth. "He asked me how I was injured in Lepanto and said that he must have died in the battle because he would never be the same after that victory."

"*Di qui da picciol tempo,* you are probably old enough to understand how right your King's bastard was. We all are who we are only once, even though many die without knowing it. Do you also believe that we should have killed you in Lepanto, *caro ragazzo?* Would you like to be withered and cold like your arm?"

"One of the men I wanted to be died in Lepanto. I did not want to fulfill myself through only one ideal but through two."

"This is too much"—laughed the Bajá. "No one splits himself into two different beings in order to realize his dreams. Not even Don Juan of Austria aspired to reach so high, so they say. He only wanted to conquer the Sublime Gate, crown himself emperor of a new Byzantium, and send messages from the palace of Topkapi to his half-brother, the King of Spain, to find out which of the two was to rule the universe."

"My double dream was to be a soldier and a poet. The dream of

arms ended in Lepanto with my maimed arm. I am left with the
dream of words. But it demands that the dreamer believes himself
free, although he might not be. Destiny made me your slave. You
can kill me, but if you do not, I will escape in order to become what
I want to be."

"Do not think of fleeing. *Questo sarebbe diversi d'ogne costume.*
This would be contrary to all morality"—the Bajá laughed again. I
will allow you to write as many poems as you want. If they displease
me, they will be burned at the marketplace. If I like them, I will
burn you. *Ed è di buona ragione,* and with good reason because he
who lives two dreams will speak with a split tongue like a snake
hisses. Yet, it is possible that being a serpent, you may be the
Devil. *Addio!"*

Two days later, in the midmorning, the guard would free you
from your imprisonment. His good eye shone with joy as he smiled
from ear to ear. He led you to the viceroy's palace through the
streets swept by the sea breeze and whitened by the dazzling sun.
He took leave then, not without wishing you Allah's protection. Two
tall janissaries took you to a room with a ledge and latticework
where some women were laughing behind a tapestry. Cheerful and
talkative, six slaves or renegades were waiting for you by a tub full
of steaming water. The Turkish solders gone, the slave women told
you that they were going to bathe, perfume, and dress you, so that
you would be worthy of Azán Bajá. Boiled with kindling wood from
wild orange trees and perfumed with sage and rosemary, the water
was bubbling in the bathtub.

"Come, come. See, if you not well, we know cure you. No talk
and let do, if you sick. We take you to Bajá sane as apple and
handsome like bride."

In his harem, Azán Bajá greeted you with a sad smile. Reclined
on a yellow sofa cushion, he looked at himself in a hand mirror and
touched his beard with a comb. Five women were stretching out on
pillows spread on the floor. They had donned embroidered shirts
and skirts of fine scarlet Valencian cloth. They wore hair nets and
exhibited their red fingers and toenails. Fragrant with orange blossoms and jasmine, they would make themselves up with blushes and
white powders, and bejewel themselves amidst a clinking display of
necklaces, pendants, bracelets, earrings, finger rings, and anklets.

The chirping of sea gulls broke the silence. A tiny eunuch on a
walnut bench readied himself to play the lute on his crossed knees.
Acknowledging your presence with a gesture, the capon burst into
singing in Turkish, his eyes closed on that thin and pointed face.
Stretched out in idleness before—looking at their nails or playing

with their anklets—the dazzled women now listened to him completely absorbed. Some embraced their knees and lifted up their faces. Others, stretched out on their breasts and pensive, held their faces in the palms of their hands.

"He sings of the glory of my assault on the Goleta," sighed the Bajá shrugging his shoulders and inviting you to sit down at the end of the sofa cushion. "Not even three years have passed but it seems to me that my victory was just a dream. Can you understand any Turkish at all?"

"Very little."

"At the foot of the hill of Cartago, the Bajá's brave men land. They are engaged by a grand master with his aides-de-camp and four hundred harquebusiers. The Turks struggle with them and force them to retreat to the fortress. On the slopes, the defenders leave their casualties to the flies beneath the August sun." The Bajá was translating in third person as if, besides supposing it a dream, his past would have been written by someone else. "The cannons of the Islam open fire against the Goleta. Among olive trees the Bajá's soldiers advance through the hillsides. Blood washes the slopes and many faithful fall in the trenches. A thousand times the Bajá risks his life to set an example. But the Prophet himself must be protecting him because he is invulnerable to the lombards and harquebuses."

"Lilailá, lelilí! Lilailá, lelilí!"—sighed the women in chorus—"Lilailá, lelilí!"

Those shouts of war took you back to Lepanto. "Lilailá, lelilí!" Above the turmoil of combat, emerged the double roar of the Turkish galleys. Those were the last screams which you heard before they felled you, torn with harquebuses shots. "Lilailá, lelilí!" In their frenzy, the Bajá's wives accelerated the rhythm of the cadence. On their knees, the five women, embracing shoulders, swayed in a common motion each time more frenetic. "Lilailá, lelilí!" Unmindful of them, the eunuch continued his song. A sharp pain pierced your left shoulder down to your fingers. Immediately you assumed that it was an imaginary pain since your arm was as lifeless as if they had amputated it in Mesina. Through time and from Lepanto, that pain brought you back to Azán Bajá's harem.

"Our cannons have made a breach in the fort. Standing beneath the enemy's fire, the Bajá admonished his men: *Friends, now or never! Siamo i giustizieri, i bruciatori, i disperati, i pugnalatori!* The Turks stormed through the opening like an unchained desert gale which no one stops. They beheaded those who resisted. Don Pedro de Portocarrero surrendered on his knees. Blessed be Allah's victory. May the only true God be forever praised!"

"Lilailá, lelilí! Lilailá, lelilí!"

The viceroy's wives ripped and tore their clothes off their bodies. They removed their shirts, skirts, and hair nets and threw their anklets and jewels against the wall and onto the rug. Feverishly, they scratched their makeup off their faces and wiped the charcoal colored paint off their eyes. Lilailá, lelilí! Lilailá, lelilí! Naked they revealed who they really were: five strong vigorous lads. Their shaved skin was covered with serpentine scars. Stark naked, except for scanty loincloths, they ran to the porch and jumped into the street through the open window. At the corner of the marketplace, tied to posts, their horses awaited them. They mounted them and rode through Cazernas followed by a mob of screaming children. At full gallop they went down the ridge and waded in the shallow sea as if to disappear in the opaline horizon. "Lilailá, lelilí! Lilailá, lelilí!" shouted the children at the beach. By the window, Azán Bajá laughed beneath the sky crossed by sea gulls. Bent over and with his lute between his knees, the eunuch slept, forgotten. "The five of them fought in my army and survived the battle," said the Bajá. "Together we burst into the fortress through the breach. They are my sons and my wives, my guards and my lovers." He kept silent and shook his head. "But sometimes they bore and disgust me. Then, I feel like they are strangers." *Cinque stranieri sconosciuti.*

That morning you became a dweller in the palace. You came and went as you pleased. When alone, you continued your letter to Mateo Vázquez. *This life of mine, Señor, / in which I am dying / among barbaric unbelievers / my ill-fated youth I am losing.* Also in those days you met the blind seer from the Jewish quarters, *You are in as much trouble as a mouse in a hole, my lad.* From time to time, entire weeks passed without your seeing Azán Bajá. You almost forgot about that renegade, who you despised because he loved you and who you feared because he protected you. At times, you cursed Don Juan of Austria's letters and your dead arm because they had kept you from dying while rowing in the Turkish galleys. Unexpectedly, the Bajá would seek you out to talk for long hours, and then go away, ignoring you. Most of the time he conversed with you while walking along the beach escorted by two soldiers of the guard. Barefoot, Azán Bajá waded, dissipating the waves among his steps. His toenails were painted purple. You could not help but wonder if the guards were there to protect him from your good arm or to contain his instincts which attracted you to him. It was also true that he had not touched you since the day he bought you.

"At fifteen, I was already a cabin boy aboard a Venetian ship, the *Santa Maria Assunta*. My name then was Paulo Masini. Uluch Alí captured us. He was taken with me and I become a Turk. He did not force me. I surrendered after a year and a half of captivity. Upon apostatizing, it was *una insignificanza* to renounce my manhood. The eve of my adjuration I was exhibited riding on a mare holding an arrow as is customary in public apostasis. My master also ordered a ram to be beheaded and the blood to be poured into the sea as a symbol of the blood I would shed in my circumcision. I was sliced the following night, after the *sosfia* or banquet of initiation to the Islam, amid a concert with rebecs, tambourines, and hymns to the greatness of the Prophet"—the Bajá seemed to hesitate, before proceeding in a lower voice. "That day I stopped calling myself Paulo Masini to become Azán Agá. Now I am a viceroy in Algiers. *Adesso io so pascià ad Algeri*. But I only began to approximate myself as the true Azán Bajá, whom they suppose I am, when I took La Goleta under the command of Uluch Alí. That morning I started to repay the love he had for me when he was alive. He died of smallpox a few years ago at his home by the sea of Mármara."

Meanwhile in a distant and somber corner of the Bajá's gardens you found a spacious grotto opening in the rock near the beach. If later, once free, you would suffer so much to make a living, in captivity, you went on a spree with more than one thousand reales. You had begged the money from Genoese merchants who constantly disembarked and traded without shame with the Turks. A slave gardener of Azán Bajá's from Navarra had hidden fourteen prisoners in that cave. A renegade servant to the despot ran errands for them and bought provisions with your money. He was a man from Nerja and no one knew why they called him *el Dorador*. Neither of the two wanted to flee, but both faithfully promised to help you with your plans. You had high hopes and the intrigue was going well. But all failed the night of the attempted escape. Arranged by your own brother, Rodrigo, a Mallorcan schooner secretly anchored by the sea wall. Two row boats stealthily approached the beach to pick you up. But it was written that the Devil would get the best of you and rob you of your freedom once more. A large Moorish boat casting its nets for tuna and bass discovered the two small boats. The rowers fled to the ship which immediately escaped into the shadows of the high seas. All of you were apprehended at the mouth of the cave. Frightened, *el Dorador* had denounced you.

Before the Bajá, you assumed the total responsibility. *I planned the escape and I gathered the money to carry it out. No one should be blamed but me, and I alone should be hanged or beaten, if justice*

*deems that I should pay with my life for this ill-fated deed. May
the Virgin Mary assist me.* With his elbow on his chair, Azán Bajá
listened to you smoothing his sparse beard. He kept quiet. He did
not argue or accuse you. Finally, he ordered that you be taken away.
You felt diminished in your worth. Your words appeared as vain as
if you had pronounced them on stage. Back in your prison alone,
they chained you and again it fell to your lot that the one-eyed
corpulent Turk would be your jailer. He served you water, artichokes, and meat baked with eggplant. But this time, he was silent
and answered no questions. You had been in your dungeon for five
months when suddenly he told you that they had killed the gardener
in your place. He was hanged in the marketplace, as an example of
Azán Bajá's justice. You bit your lips and shook your chained hands.
But you did not understand how someone could die for another
fellow being if death is the most inalienable part of every life. You
also realized that the one-eyed jailer delivered the news by the
Bajá's express and wicked will. Right away, you amazed yourself
by swearing in silence to try to escape as many times as it would
be necessary until you breathed the air under a free sky. A few
days later, they bathed and dressed you with new clothes and took
you down to the beach of Fanal where the Bajá awaited you all
perfumed in patchouli and civet. He greeted you cordially as if
nothing had happened and invited you to take a stroll along the edge
of the waves, silvered by the morning sun. He stopped suddenly to
show you his hand mirror, the one with which he was looking at
himself when they took you to the harem. The crystal was mounted
in a carved wooden frame and handle where an entanglement of
brambles, fancies, and gardens as a thick scribble of perplexed images had been engraved.

"The adornment was carved in the *saz* style, which means *bosco
incantato,* enchanted forest. I bought this mirror in Istanbul and it
is one of the masterpieces of Sahkulu, the father of this school of
engravers and painters of illustrated manuscripts. If you look at it
closely, you will see it as a symbol of creation before man's appearance on earth. On one side, it reflects the sea and the sky. On the
other, it shows a *paradiso* where an exuberant forest and fantastic
beasts endlessly mingle. Between the mirror and the garden of delights, humanity is captured in all its history."

"But not dreams. For instance, the two of mine: the one of arms
and the one of letters."

"Or perhaps another of your dreams, the one of your escape?"

"You said it, not I."

"I say it all because at least here I am sovereign master. If you try to escape again and you fail, I will have you hanged and I will grab your feet myself to finish you off."

A short while later, the evasion again seemed feasible and even accessible. By mere chance you discovered that an acquaintance of yours, the Marquis of Córdoba, was the governor of Orán and general of its forces. Escapes to Orán were common, although three had failed in the past months. They captured a Mallorcan slave in Boufarik and the Bajá had him whipped to death. Later, they sentenced a Biscayan and a man from Santander, who were captured in other unfortunate attempts at flight. With three other important gentlemen, slaves like yourself, you bribed a Moorish merchant who traded spices in Orán. By the route to the beach, through Tenès, Mostaganem, Mohammadia, and the oasis of Arcew, he was to take your letters to the Marquis in Córdoba. You requested that, after hiding water and supplies between the sea and Boufarik, a regiment be readied to protect you in case the Turks were to chase you. If arrested, the Moor was supposed to say that he had tied his horse to the drinking trough in the marketplace while he went to say his prayers. Enough time for a daring and unknown Christian to sneak the letters into his saddlebags.

Only a few of you were involved in the intrigue. But one of you— we will never know who—betrayed you, just like *el Dorador* had done. They captured the Moorish merchant, and then they told you that the Bajá had cried out in anger when he saw your signature on the letters. You shrugged your shoulders while they tied your good arm to your crippled one and looped a rope around your neck as if they were going to hang you right then. A feeling of invulnerability gave you the certainty that this time you would not be executed either. But if it was God's will that you be sacrificed, death did not frighten you. More than death pangs, you seemed overwhelmed by a dull resignation and fatigue. A traveler's loss of heart upon facing the splendor of a river and realizing that the river, the sky, and he himself were nothing but a mirage of a fabled world.

Blinded by anger, the Bajá confronted you. He banged on your letters to the Marquis, spread on the table. He shouted that the Moor swore not to know you, and insisted that if you placed the papers in his saddlebags, you must have done it while he was praying in the Mosque. They had already pulled out three of his fingernails and two of his teeth, but he did not change his confession not even under the threat of impaling him alive. *The man is telling the truth. I do not personally know him either except by sight and by rumors, as a merchant with business in Orán. I left the letters in his saddlebags on the mare and alerted my friends in Orán to stop him and get the papers without letting him know that he carried them. The scheme was mine. All mine. Believe me. May the Virgin Mary assist me.* Azán Bajá listened to you in silence. Then he bellowed: *Anche io voglio che tu mi credi! You exhausted my patience with your tricks and deceits! But I am now fed up, you big hypocrite. Your punishment will be two thousand blows to your stomach and to the bottom of your feet!* You shrugged your shoulders again. Although you will later consider your unjudicious reply to the Bajá almost incredible in its extravagance, you then slowly said:

"With so much beating, my soul will go to heaven cleaner than that rug from *The Arabian Nights.* I mean the one which unrolls and flies at the prince's will."

And Azán Bajá burst into laughter. He laughed until he cried. To please and imitate him, everyone in his court began to laugh. The Moorish magistrates laughed, those who along with him pretended to carry out justice, at first discreetly and slavishly and then more feverishly. Those who in Algiers passed for peace officers laughed. The Viceroy's keepers and inspectors of weights laughed. The revenue treasurer laughed and even the janissaries of the guard laughed. Handcuffed and with a rope around your neck, you were the only one inhibited by such an outbreak of hilarity. You wondered if once free, provided that one day they redeemed you, you would dare to describe this madness. It would perhaps be better to let someone else tell it and let his audience disbelieve him. The deafening guffaws were abruptly interrupted by the despot's sudden silence. Everyone copied him at once. In that ominous quietness the Bajá calmly said to you:

"Gladly I absolve you because a mighty man like me who is almost a king should not hang a *quasi buffone* like you. Someone, however, must be punished in your place and must pay for your crime"—he paused for a moment and then proceeded. "Let the Moor be impaled immediately, so that we can hear his screams coming from the courtyard in the orange grove."

The Moor must have been tortured very slowly because he was still yelling at the time of the curfew. The one which is announced with drums and pipes to signal the Christian slaves to retire until dawn. Although Algiers was already accustomed to the shrieking of the tormented, his uproar shook the entire city. In the pauses of his howling, as the unfortunate one fainted and before they revived him to make him aware of his suffering, you begged them at the top of your voice to hang you instead and to stop the Moor's misery. Or at least to put an end to his life because no one deserved such punishment. For many years in the wretched berths of your inns, in the restless nights of your imprisonment or in your own bed with Catalina, the memory of those cries—his and yours—would wake you up in the midst of the most dreadful nightmares.

At the Palace, no one seemed to listen to your pleading. If they heard your voice it must have sounded so remote as to be unreal. When you yelled imploring that they kill you or finish off the Moor, everyone turned slowly towards you. Janissaries, inspectors, peace officers, revenue treasurers, magistrates, and the Bajá himself looked at you with indolence, gazing through you as if you were made out of glass, or as if searching for you at a distance though squinted eyes. At dusk, under a yellow-toned sky and with the sea crossed by shadows, the Moor's moaning ended. A long and calm silence descended upon the city. It was the quiet silence of an intimate night with a clear sky perfumed by the sweet scent of orange blossoms.

Two years later, after your release had been settled, the Bajá took you once more for a stroll on the beach. It must have been three o'clock in a vermilion afternoon, because the murmur of the sea mingled with the murmurs of the prayers of one hundred Mosques. *La iláho ila Alláh! . . . Alahu acbar! . . . Axhad en la iláho ila Alláh! . . . Axahad an Mohámed rasul Alláh! . . . Hai ala es-salá! . . . Hai ala es-salá! . . . Alahu acbar! . . . La iláho ila Alláh!* This was the chanting of the Muslims. *There is no other God but Allah! God is great! Verily I say to you that there is no other God but Allah! Verily I say to you that Mohammed is Allah's prophet! Let us pray! God is great! There is no other God but Allah!* This was the unison prayer that came from all of the minarets. But the Bajá, that renegade who considered as a triviality the loss of his manhood after renouncing his faith, did not pray. Or perhaps he omits his supplications in order not to share them with the masses. Unmindful of the psalms and hymns, he walked barefooted, his arm around a young lad no older than thirteen or fourteen. He was wearing *sualfes* around his temples with dyed curls like a girl's plastered on his head. His face, toned down with make-up, had two painted rosy cheeks.

"We will go with my sweet, little Agi Butaibo to pick up the fishing line. And we will see what the sea has left for us on our hooks," Azán Bajá said to you while he contemplated the bright skies. "Perhaps, once free, you will be saddened by your memories of these beaches and horizons. We always miss what we have lost, including one's own slavery, *anche la stessa schiavitù*. Do you not believe so?"

"Who knows, sir!"

The three of you went inside one of the caves on a reef where they had left a fish basket. The young boy laughed incessantly,

while he unhooked the fish. Azán Bajá sat comfortably on the sand
and made you join him. Absorbed, he lost himself in a lengthy
silence. He kept his thoughts to himself, brusquely ignoring you and
Agi Butaibo. The waves broke on the rocks monotonously. Tongues
of green water penetrated the grotto and licked your feet. Rescued
by Trinitarian friars, you will be free within two days. But your
anguished fatigue should have upset and surprised you. You must
have been trying to remember *la Zeffirina* and the son you had in
Naples. You saw or evoked them on the stage of your soul, although
their faces had already begun to dissipate in your memory. As an
echo of your thoughts, although in a different key, Azán Bajá then
spoke to you.

"It must be Allah's will that we do not see each other again after
you leave for your land. I only hope and wish to forget you"—he
shook his head and started to draw in the sand with his finger.
"When I had assumed that I was unable to love, and love was
reduced to a shadow of itself which is only the pleasure of the senses,
I fell for you on that morning when Alí Mami sold you to me. Now
they rescue you for the same price I paid for you that day. But the
pain you caused me cannot be measured because I loved you as I
never thought I could. Do not ask me why. Perhaps because you
have lived two dreams, while all dreams dwindle and end in disillusionment. Perhaps because you seem to have the aura of someone
who belongs more to eternity than to this painted veil. In my exas-
peration, I would have given you a thousand deaths after each of
your frustrated flights. I could have given you up to your rescuers,
as I am doing now, but I could never have let you escape against
my will. Loving you, I also desired you. I do not remember having
felt like this before in my life glutted with carnal pleasures. It might
have surprised you that I did not force you or even lay my hand
on you. You were spared from this mortal sin, as you would have
called it, because of your crippled arm. It horrified me to touch your
frozen flesh. To have taken you would have been like embracing
someone, who at least in part, was possessed by death.

With his shoulders slumped and his aquiline profile saddened,
Azán Bajá fell silent. Agi Butaibo laughed although he had not
understood a single word his owner had said. In the sand with his
finger the Bajá finished sketching his self-portrait. One wave, larger
than the others, erased his drawing with its foam. Years later, when
you have definitely forgotten the faces of Ana Franca, *la Zeffirina*,
and the son whom you lost or abandoned, you will remember the
Bajá's image—not the Bajá himself—in the sand at the cave. You
partially attributed those features to Cide Hamete Benengeli, sup-

posed author of your novel. Also partially, you gave Cide the features of the seer in the Jewish quarters of Algiers. Then, you
shuffled the faces and both men became one. Someone who would
be a living metaphor of that Janus in the garden of Atocha, although
he was no one, as that wicked, lamed canon, Don Luis de Góngora,
had concluded with his ironic smile.

* * * * *

You may omit it in your confession. But so near eternity, you,
Your Excellency the Prince, as the porter at the Trinitarians' calls
or will call you, are still convinced that Catalina had a lover. An
inamorato who emerged from the shadows as do the characters in
the theater and in books, although at times they transformed themselves into ghosts. *There was no lack of opportunity. We are husband
and wife, but we have lived more apart than together since the day
of our wedding.* On León Street, a few afternoons after that day
when both of you enjoyed your lemonade by the window, Your Excellency crossed paths for the first time with the man in the black
cape and the plumed broad-brimmed soft hat. He was carried by
two helpers on a sedan chair and placed on the street in front of
your door. Impassive and immobile, both servants remained standing while their master contemplated you through the curtains of the
litter. Actually, you did not look at his plumed hat but at his eyes,
since Your Excellency could not distinguish between the brim of his
hat and the cloak covering his face. Looking at his gaze, you must
have believed that it had a dreamlike aura. One moment his eyes
reminded you of the shepherd who witnessed your kiss with Catalina
amidst the swirling wind and the next they brought back the glazed
stare of Rodrigo, dead. In a lifeless tone, he was calling your name
whilst staring at you incessantly.

"Would Your Grace be so kind as to have two words with me? I
came to make you an offer."

His voice was calm. It was distant and different from anxiety
or expectation. Lacking inflection it was also depersonalized. Your
Excellency must have wondered if that importune individual was
Catalina's secret lover. Someone who was ready to beg your pardon,
if you were a true Christian and therefore forebearing, for loving
her behind your back. And if you would forget the offense to your
honor, you would become a willing cuckold, although also a good
follower of Christ. Meanwhile, the man opened the curtains and
motioned for you to sit by him. Your Excellency neither hesitated
nor declined the invitation, and as soon as you were comfortable in
the litter, he asked his servants to take you both to El Prado.

"What were you about to propose to me?"

"A retribution. Five hundred escudos in two installments of two hundred and fifty each"—he slightly opened his cloak and showed you a bag filled with gold and fastened with yarn between his heavily lined riding boots.

"Why five hundred? Why a retribution?" Your good hand began to tremble on your knee. Before he answered you must have anticipated his response.

"It was the price Azán Bajá paid for you to be his slave. Five hundred gold escudos. Mine are gold too and I have half of them in this bag."

You must have seen yourself chained again and facing that Algerian sea, so green and smooth so similar to malachite, while the Bajá opened your eyelids to examine the whites of your eyes; he half-opened your lips to count your teeth or felt your chest with touches close to caresses. *Come hai fatto a perdere quel braccio? Ti fa male nei pomerigi umidi? Ti sentiresti più completo se io te lo facessi tagliare con una scure?* He was speaking Italian without any accent, as if he had always lived in Italy: on the beach of Pesto and between the columns of the temple of Neptune or in those cypress gardens of the Vía Apia perfumed by sage. *How did you lose your arm? Does it hurt you on humid afternoons? Would you feel more comfortable if I had it amputated by the blow of a hatchet?* In your fright, the voices of the Bajá and Góngora would imbricate, when many years later Góngora will advise you to chop your arm off with a carving knife and offer it to the Christ of Lepanto in Barcelona. Then, he would fall silent smiling to himself.

"Yes," you said finally. "That was my price. How did you find out?"

"We all serve the same master," the stranger shrugged his shoulders. "I do not want, however, to enslave you to me, but to your own self. You should chain yourself to your writing table, finish the next part of your book and release it to a publisher. I am now giving you half of the anticipated amount. The rest will be yours as soon as you conclude the second volume of your novel. But beware, days are dwindling and hours are diminishing."

You must have asked yourself in which world you lived. Not only the ghosts from Atocha were pushing you to proceed with the thread of your story without stopping, but also you were pressured by a *sconosciuto,* similar to a masked man during the carnival days before Ash Wednesday. Would the muffled man be the anticipation of a character for the next part of your fable, not yet conceived in the depth of your consciousness? Does every writer carry inside a dark and unknown book, just as they quoted Buonarroti to you in Italy, saying that the statue pre-existed in the stone and the only thing needed to do was to clear away the marble?

"If Your Grace knows me and wants me to finish my tale, it is only fair and appropriate that you tell me why and what your name is."

"In lands not yet discovered, the day after tomorrow they will quote your name," the man replied beneath his muffle. "Mine does not matter, as long as my escudos are sound. Without any lavish descriptions or adornments, I could be called, Nobody."

"Tell me at least the motives of your commission and your eager persistence."

The stranger laughed. His laughter and his gaze above his muffled cape reminded Your Excellency more of your dead father than your brother, Rodrigo. Those were the same guffaws, so absurd in the old man, which overtook him when he surprised you absorbed in thought, sitting in a corner, and recently returned from your captivity. As if you were still in the prison of Algiers striving to get a glimpse of the sky between the iron bars of the window, you crouched between the two walls near the cedar chest. Your father, that surgeon inclined to monosyllables, put more phrases together that day than he had ever said before or will thread again for the rest of his life. A surgeon, Your Excellency always took for an impostor, although you owed him your own life: a deceitful barber turned into an unsuccessful doctor. *Reconsider and do not fool yourself. There is no more life than the one time unravels. You have a woman, you marry her and she bears your children. You raise your offspring and end up tired of one another, wishing that you had never had a wife much less having begotten anybody. If you find wealth, things will be even worse. Fortune will bring along the boredom of opulence thus teaching another lesson more severe still. We are doomed to chase a dream that does not exist without ever forgetting that we are pursuing it.* You did not know how to reply, but perhaps deep inside you scorned yourself for scorning him. Much later, Góngora would define your fate more precisely saying that both of you would end up transforming yourselves into your own books. He assured you that the two of you were but merchants of the written word: skillful traders of fables of smoke and mirrors.

"If Your Grace desires, we could get off and stroll to the fountain of Caño de Oro," offered the muffled man, his laughter silenced and the curtains of the litter half-opened.

You were beneath the poplars at San Jerónimo's. The larks at the convent were not chirping; but black martins continued their flitting about in a sky fragrant with acacias soaked by the early morning showers. Lepers with bells around their necks begged under the trees. Gypsy girls from Cádiz tried to sell you freshly cut hyacinths. Servants were sweeping the entrance to the Lermas's palace and the green ivy spread on the iron railing. The lackeys were left waiting immobile like two caryatides. They not only dressed alike and wore the same shoes but they also had identical features. A small party of soldiers must have been exercising behind the grove of El Buen Retiro. The chirping of swallows crossed the soldiers' bugles and the crying of street vendors selling parsley, artichokes, and curd. The man in the waterproof cape seemed to shrug his shoulders again. Then he proceeded slowly:

"I also questioned my motives before coming to see Your Grace. At the end the answer is simple. I do not want to die before reading the last part of *Don Quixote*. That is why I am paying and asking you to complete it without further delay."

"Are you in pain? Is some malady keeping you from uncovering your face?"

"My face would not say any more to Your Grace than my name does. Again, it could be anybody's and, also, nobody's. No, I am not ill. But perhaps I do not belong to this earth and time. Sometimes I feel I am the shadow of someone who lived in the past, or perhaps the mere sketch of what I will be in the future. Only once did I feel full of joy and life. It was when I read the first part of your fable. And now I refuse to leave this world without having read the continuation.

"And what if I do not accept the proposal? Or if I were not able to proceed with my story?"

"Five hundred escudos redeemed Your Grace from captivity. That same amount would rescue you now from poverty. What you do after you end *Don Quixote*, I do not care to know as it is not my affair."

I would like to know what your future will be. Will you perhaps appear in the next part of my novel, under a phony name, of course, since I do not know your own?"

"I do not belong to your novel under any name." His firm and quick reply must have surprised you. "If there is room for me in a book it will be in a story yet to be written and reserved for the future."

Your Excellency must have thought about your dream when the Hidalgo and his Squire were daring you to confront another man, made to your image, stopped in the middle of the road holding the hilt of his sword. In the mirror of your nightmare, your double shouted that it was not worth it to die nor to kill for a book. Both, he added, were living the dream of a third man who would take the two of you to another story. Through the spiral of your memory, you would go to the scene of a second dream, more absurd yet. The one of the beggar, Santafiore, listening to your reading of a book, which Your Excellency would deny to be yours since it would take at least three hundred years to be written.

"I believe I understand you well," you murmured.

"I would like to say the same about myself. If I were to confess all that I think, you would take me for a madman, more so than Don Quixote himself. But I am not going to conceal my wish to live and to read the end of your novel. I also fear that I will die as soon I read it. Only men of flesh and blood would endure such contradictions. Such absurdities would not even occur to beings almost human, like your Hidalgo and his Squire."

"If you plan to die as soon as I sign and seal the end of my fable, you make me your executioner," smiled Your Excellency. "If I leave it incomplete you may live forever."

"I made my calculations. I am easy to please. I accepted my condition and the risk of dying at a set time, provided that I would read what you have not yet written."

Your Excellency shook your gray head. Perhaps you remembered María Mercedes del Calvario at the inn where you also met Gregorio Nacianceno Patriarca. The girl's godfather, the late Canon, only considered you sane when you were writing *Don Quixote* because only then did you know who you were. This is what the gray-eyed whore used to say. But she also believed that you were not going to truly live until you had decided to finish your book. *And now I lick and caress you with my hand, although you cannot possess me, to make you feel like a man before falling asleep.* Your Excellency rejected her offer and its dubious delights.

"I will be frank with you. Although there were many reasons for abandoning the second part of my book, I inadvertently overlooked the main one. I imagine it must have remained hidden deep within the dark chambers of my unconsciousness, lost in my mind. If then I did not fully realize it, the idea of going crazy as soon as I finished the novel must have horrified me."

"Unaware, Your Grace must have feared losing your mind upon leaving your Knight, his world, and his Servant. Rather than leaving them forever, you seemed to have preferred to deceive yourself and delay the end of the story for years."

"I suppose it was in the cards."

"Those are the risks of our trade. Since we are not going to dodge them it is better to accept them. I am amazed by how much we have talked during our walk. But let us put words into action. If you will allow me I will take Your Grace back to the sedan chair, escort you to your house and deliver the agreed upon amount. In a month I will send you the remainder according to how much progress you make in the next part of your book. I hope you rise with the dawn and that your time is well spent.

Holding you by your arm, as Patriarca did in your stroll through the woods, the faceless man led you back to the litter. For an instant you suspected that perhaps Góngora and Lope had something to do with the stranger's proposition. You dismissed your conjectures immediately. The lascivious Inquisitor and the clerical administrator from Córdoba, now aspiring to be Chaplain of the King, were not getting along very well, although they feigned friendship more out of habit than two-facedness. To Góngora, who conceived the world to be nothing but smoke, dust, and shadows, the vanity of the officer of the Holy Office and his always unsatiated desire for pleasure inspired greater scorn each time. Everyone in Madrid repeated the lame priest's latest verses mocking Lope's arrogance. *For your life, dear Lope, do strike out, / The nineteen towers of your coat of arms, / Because, they may all be wind, but I doubt / That you quite have enough wind for such charms.*

Smiling again deep inside yourself near that dark turn where forgetfulness sleeps, Your Excellency thought that perhaps if your unexpected protector was not one of your characters, he could be from another author. Was not he himself confessing to be the protagonist of a work waiting to be created in a remote future? Why could he not be from another work, written in the present by a dreamer, although his escudos seemed sound and real? You could have asked him then: *Are you one of the Sylvan gods who inebriate the unfortunate sailors as they reach the Sicilian shores and are devoured by those cyclops so admired by Don Luis de Góngora, after falling into a drunken stupor and perhaps being sodomized by such hybrid beings, half man and half goat? Or are you perhaps a jingling buffoon with a cow bladder in his shepherd's staff who appears in "Las Cortes de la Muerte," The Courts of Death, by the great Lope de Vega Carpio?* But you did not say any of this. On the contrary, with a certain uneasiness you surprised yourself by asking him:

"Did you hear the rumors about an impostor who is writing an apocryphal second part to my book and expects the world to accept it for the true one? As though the world had turned upside down and as if he were the author and I his plagiarist?"

First nodding his head and then with words, the flustered caped one assented. As if embarrassed by acknowledging a well-known truth, which implied Your Excellency's shameful ignorance. We could say an ignorance similar to that of a cuckold, mocked behind his back, or the embarrassment of an illiterate peasant lost in the Sanhedrin among the doctors of the law, keepers of all knowledge.

"If you are just now finding that out, I am afraid you are the last to know the talk of the city. Yes, someone is diligently completing your book. They gossip about his persistence in all the taverns and even Their Majesties are well up on it, according to your former friend, Mateo Vázquez."

"Has the rumor reached the Palace then?"

"It is neither rumor nor a cock and bull story. I do not know who the plagiarist is but I do know the pen name that he will use in the book. Either by his own decision or by someone else's advice, he shall sign it under the pseudonym of ALONSO FERNANDEZ DE AVELLANEDA. And there is more. On the back he wants to call himself a college graduate and a native of Tordesillas. Although probably he is neither one."

ALONSO FERNANDEZ DE AVELLANEDA. There was nobody on earth by that name. Even though Nobody was the name chosen by the masked stranger who was taking you by the arm through El Prado past the fountain of Caño de Oro. Both nobodies must surely be different. Behind the foggy mirror of your soul, the writer within Your Excellency must have realized that you were thinking in incomplete phrases, as if an oblique and sharp fear, like a carving knife, would cut off your silent monologue. ALONSO FERNANDEZ DE AVELLANEDA. You must have also noticed that you did not ask the muffled man how he had found out the pseudonym. Or how all of Madrid came to know. In another time, Azán Bajá asked Your Excellency your name after touching your face. The Bajá who adored you with the despair of a pederast who had thought to be free of love and desire in the autumn of his life, as they say that Michelangelo had fallen for the young Tommaso Cavalieri.

You lied in spite of the fact that you knew the Bajá was aware of your identity through the letters from Don Juan of Austria that were confiscated when you were captured. You said that your name was Saavedra, the family name that you gave the daughter that you had, or that you were going to have with Ana Franca. You never gave your reasons why you preferred that name over your mother's. Likewise, in vain you would ask yourself the reasons your plagiarist had to choose Alonso Fernández de Avellaneda as a pen name. Or, the reasons that someone—that other Nobody—had to want your book so avidly as to make the second his own.

Perhaps at that moment you feared to be forgotten by men, although you thought you scorned them so much. Maybe your written words would transform themselves into smoke, dust, shadow, and nothingness—your irreversible fate as a writer, according to Góngora. On the contrary, it was possible that the so called Avellaneda would perpetuate himself in the memory of posterity like a galloping phantom through the mist. All of a sudden with the clarity of an enlightened vision, Your Excellency perceived that you would definitely complete the second part of your novel, before or after Avellaneda finishes his deceit. If that impostor, whose identity you suspected would always be unknown, loved your fable to the point of stealing it, he would also love you, although perhaps he only thought to envy your success and scorn your genius. In such a case, you were going to ruin Avellaneda, without your knowing him. Since your destiny was to destroy all who loved you: *la Zeffirina*, Promontorio, Azán Bajá, Ana Franca, Isabel, and Catalina. In one way or another, you always ruined those who offered their love. Such was your incurable and unavoidable fate.

"Please, take me home with my two-hundred and fifty escudos. You keep the rest in an account to pay me on the due date. Here and at this hour, whatever it might be, I give you my word that I will finish the next part of my book. Thus said, it will be done. A man has to be true to himself. Nothing else matters.

There are days when Your Excellency dictates entire pages to your servant to speed up your work and fulfill the commitment made to yourself and to the muffled stranger with the plumed and broad-brimmed hat. Miguel Cortinas's penmanship is better than Your Excellency's and he writes so fast that he barely blinks an eye as you dictate words or phrases. He leaves wide spaces between the lines so that you can correct, erase, or add as you please. The composition concluded, he dries it with blotting powder and leaves silently, bidding farewell with a very discreet bow.

In a clear spot, the Hero and his Squire encountered two men lunching on ham and bread, with a dessert of curds and wild strawberries, and drinking wine from their leather wine bags. They stopped to look at them, while the two strangers stared openmouthed because the Knight and the Servant were identical to them: in features, beards, and attire. The Knight told the Peasant to notice their doubles, but warned him not to succumb to the illusion. Although pretending to mimic them, they were only imitating them in the same lifeless way that a lake would replicate their reflection.

Likewise the Hidalgo advised him not to be frightened because they were not even phantoms but vain parodies.

It appears to me that they are the fakes of the plagiarist of our true story, replied the Servant. *I am talking about the ill-intended storyteller who hides behind the foolish name of Avellanar or Avellaneda. If he would show his face and we could shake him we would prove that more than an avellano—a nut tree—as his name implies, he is nothing but a blockhead throwing acorns for punches. Only in dreams could we be confused with such grotesque figures. Awake, blast it! Those scoundrels would dissipate like shadows in our fingers if we tried to touch them.*

They were shadows, his Master assented. You could only distinguish them in the same way as, at times, one sees imaginary and distant lands at the Poles or in the Sahara, such as the Kingdom of the Great Khan or Atlantis. Lands and places that would vanish in the sun, as those two old rags would if you moved closer to them. And he would say no more having said enough. *Truth like wine, should not be watered down. As you would put it, my son, being as you are more inclined to proverbs and sayings than I am.*

The Peasant did not understand the reference to the Sahara. Nor did he recall any poles besides some Andalusian peasant songs, thus named, and brought by the merchants of La Mancha through Despeñaperros. *But I do not need my ABCs to deduce that those reflections of ourselves are bastards, although they are nobodies. Bastards they are and they come from a bad father's house, which in this case is Avellaneda's book: a brazen-faced ruffian whose real name is unknown even to them, although he created and portrayed them in our image.* His Master congratulated him on his good sense, praising himself at the same time for how much and how well he was educating his Servant in that second part of their story.

In the dictation, the Hidalgo and his Squire were about to continue their journey, leaving behind their doubles or perhaps passing through them as if they were merely mist, when they were brought to a halt by the screaming of the other Knight, the one who was having his lunch in the clearing when the four of you crossed paths. Echoed by his Footman, he rudely lambasted them. *Confound the Antichrist! That Your Grace and your Muleteer are naught but confirmed knaves, downright long-tongued, strolling comedians! If you call us bastards because the world does not know our father's name, you both should know that soon you will be orphans! Your ill and maimed historian solely vegetates and will give up his soul as soon as he finishes the tale of your wanderings. He will be buried at the convent of the Trinitarians on Cantarranas Street and they will also*

inter there the memory of your lives. Instead, our father, whoever
he may be, will proceed with the telling of our adventures over and
over for as long as it is God's will for him to outlive your chronicler.

Miguel Cortinas writes down religiously what you dictate. But at
the end of that passage, when the spectral Hidalgo says that Your
Excellency's days are numbered, pending upon the completion of
your delayed second part, he leaves the quill pen in the ink bottle.
His arms crossed, he stares at you with the same care and concern
with which he had gazed at you that night so long ago upon your
return from the garden of Janus, after having learned that someone
else was ready to take over the continuation of your novel. Through
the eye of the needle of time, memory threads Miguel Cortinas's
pale image as he waits for you with a lamp in his hand. He re-
proached you then for venturing so late and alone through a Madrid
full of ruffians. For your dinner he had roasted half a pigeon and
prepared a vinaigrette salad.

"Señor, do you really want me to write this?"

"You wrote it already," you replied with a casual gesture. "Leave
it like it is, and this will be enough for today."

"If Your Grace would like, I can continue writing."

"At this hour, I am no longer myself. My will is strong but my
strength is failing fast. Dry what you have written before you go."

He obeys reluctantly. Miguel Cortinas is about to reach the door
when he stops, hesitating. Without turning completely, as if he did
not dare to face you, he says:

"Would you, Señor, allow me a question?"

"Ask what you like."

"Are you certain that this Avellaneda of whom you speak in your
book really exists?"

"Yes, he does exist and he plagiarizes me in his own way. But I
do not know if I will ever know his true name or see his face."

Bowing goodnight, the servant leaves quietly. Stroking your grayish blond beard, Your Excellency reads the dictation. On the bridge
of your nose, each day more curved and pointed, ride your foggy
glasses. *Your ill and maimed historian solely vegetates and will give*
up his soul, as soon as he finishes the tale of your wanderings. Shaking your head, you proceeded with the reading. You are not satisfied
with the encounter of your characters with those replicas coming
from the supposed book written by your plagiarist. If you want to
identify yourself through your characters it would be better to imagine another confrontation with the impostors. To pretend for instance, that your Knight challenges Avellaneda's to a duel. In the
same way that in your dream Your Excellency defied your imitator,

both of you resembling each other as do two drops of water. The same dream where your double yelled at you not to be foolish because it was not worth it to kill each other in someone else's novel, a novel like the one where you were going to do mortal battle.

Your eyes half-closed, you conjure the scene in your dream. You do not know the apocryphal version, and you had not yet decided to take your characters to Barcelona in a sort of dissenting reply, because the plagiarist had moved his fake Knight to Saragossa. Little by little you start imagining the duel of the Hidalgos in front of the palace of the Aljafería. At that crucial moment of a fight to the death the true identity of your Paladin would be decided. Whoever survives, your hero or the unsightly scarecrow, is going to be Don Quixote de La Mancha for ever and ever. There is not a better conclusion to the book than that of the crowds in Saragossa acclaiming the conqueror. There will not be a better way to silence Avellaneda than to finish with him in a *guerre a mort* with Your Excellency's Knight.

Then you smiled sadly remembering perhaps your leave-taking from Azán Bajá at the end of five years of captivity and barely one hour before sailing to Spain. *Maimed and blond, you seem the most defenseless of men,* the Bajá said plucking the petals from a white rose of Alexandria. *But I pity whoever crosses you because your cruelty exceeds mine, although you are too young to understand it. Troppo giovanetto e giovanotto.* He threw the rose at your face and instinctively you caught it in the air with your good hand. *I should have killed you before giving you up to those who ransomed you,* the despot proceeded amid the laughter of the young lads around him, all stretched out on floor rugs and painting their nails crimson. *One must destroy his loved one to feel alive, as one should blind the goldfinches to appreciate their trills. Do you not agree? At any rate, if you accept I will take you to Istanbul with me. To Byzantium, as it is called by all Christians, like you, who have not had the opportunity to renege. I am a converted Muslim but I am also a man of honor and I would give back to the friars the last escudo they paid for you.* Your Excellency bowed, bewildered, and left the harem. You were trembling in fear that another of the Bajá's whims would rob you of your freedom, just recently bought. As soon as the boat sailed away you threw the rose into the sea and spat in the water.

Without forgetting about Azán Bajá, you tear up your dictation of that afternoon and throw the pieces into the wastebasket. You give up the encounter of the Hidalgos. In some turbid although inescapable way you understand that you must not write it, since this is not the time to anticipate the future. In an era still far away,

another man will tell the episode unaware that Your Excellency had
imagined it centuries before. He will set up a duel between the
Knight and Avellaneda's impostor. But he would not let them cross
lances in defense of their identities. He is going to leave them on
the brink of the attack, in the same way that Your Excellency ended
a chapter by suspending your enduring Hero and the gallant Biscayan Knight with their swords raised high and poised for the attack.
Even today Your Excellency anticipates the future paragraph: *How
splendid it would have been if instead of that hasty and vague last
encounter with the disguised Carrasco, who tumbles our knight in
a jiffy, the real Don Quixote had fought his crucial battle with the
false Don Quixote!*

Your Excellency intends for Sansón Carrasco, pretending to be
the Knight of the White Moon, to tumble and defeat your Paladin
in the jousts of Saragossa. Thus, forcing him to renounce knight-
errantry for an entire year and to return to his nameless village as
a humble penitent. When Your Excellency sees that Avellaneda
places the tournament at the Corso in Saragossa, you decide that
the encounter of your Hero and Carrasco would not be in front of
Aljafería but on the beach of Barcelona, deviating the route of the
characters so that they will never stop in the shade of El Pilar. But
you do not know any of this as you tear the dictation this afternoon
of 1614, since you had not read Avellaneda nor had you concluded
the second part of your book. But let us bide our time and let us
not put today's birds in yesterday's nests.

At any rate, the challenge that you now anticipate—*How splendid
it would have been if instead of that hasty and vague last encounter
with the disguised Carrasco, who tumbles our Knight in a jiffy . . .* —
will not be a part of any novel, although it is mentioned or will be
mentioned by a Russian novelist in a public lecture. As a motto or
emblem it will precede and summarize the meaning of another book,
where, in part, the tapestry of Atocha is reflected through a mirror,
which is time. Likewise, Your Excellency re-encounters all of the
beings and shadows around you in your journey through this world.
Here are the faceless Avellaneda, Lope, Góngora, Catalina, Miguel
Cortinas, your muffled protector, Azán Bajá, the one-eyed Turk,
the tortured Moor, your parents, Magdalena, the prioress Luisa
of Bethlehem, Rodrigo, Casilda del Carpio—your brother Juan's
mistress whom we shall find in due time in this true story—, Ana
Franca, Isabel, *la Zeffirina*, Gregorio Nacianceno, the trio of witches
around the street light, Promontorio—the son whom you never
met—, Mateo Vázquez, and even Their Majesties speaking to you
through the window of their carriage. It matters little that Your

Excellency tears the dictation and perhaps pretends, thus, to rip today's day, as the sun sets. The same day on which ironically a novel of another century reaches this point through the mirror where time transforms itself. Bridging all of the human and divine abysses, the hinge between Your Excellency and me would be the words of the Russian writer. Believing the original chimera to be his own, he must have assumed it, without knowing that Your Excellency had already considered that incident in 1614, although you discarded it promptly. That is to say, the incident becomes the quote of a writer unknown to you, who will live or did live three hundred years after your death under the name of Vladimir Nabokov.

Nor this afternoon do you foresee another encounter of your characters with those of Avellaneda's in the third to the last chapter of your novel. You will begin to envision it within a few months after reading the impostor's book. You will then describe an event that will please Góngora a great deal upon reading it after its publication. The defeated Hero and his Squire stop at an inn very near the village where the Hidalgo lived, lost his mind, and now returns to die. As soon as noon strikes a horseman appears with three or four servants. One of them addresses his master with plain and simple words that later will flatter and please Your Excellency almost as much as the entire novel. *Here Your Grace, Señor Don Alvaro Tarfe, may take a siesta: the inn seems clean and fresh.*

Upon hearing it, the Knight whispers to his Servant that such a name, Alvaro Tarfe, sounds identical or at least very similar to another name he ran across in Avellaneda's poorly written plagiarism. The Peasant replies that everything is possible in this mad world. To dispel his doubts, his Master asks the newcomer if he is the Don Alvaro Tarfe from Granada. He whose wanderings have been written about in the second part of the *History of Don Quixote de La Mancha,* a work recently published under a pseudonym. The traveler agrees, very pleased to see how soon he is recognized by strangers. Affable and loquacious, he adds that he had been a very close friend of the protagonist of that tale.

Keeping their composure, the Hidalgo and the Squire seek his opinion as to whether or not they resemble the protagonists of that book. Don Alvaro ponders in hesitation. But at the end he replies that he perceives no likeness by any stretch of the imagination. Nor does that clever Servant remind him of the yokel he met nor does his Master have any resemblance to that wretched Hero who is now locked up at the Nuncio's house in Toledo because of his madness. To Don Alvaro's astonishment, they reveal their identity and denounce the impostor in the false legend of their lives. Since what is

written remains written, they beg him to testify before the mayor
of the town, with an affidavit drawn up and validated by an official
seal, that they are who they are and no one can impersonate them.
Gladly does Alvaro concede and leaves them puffed with pride and
in possession of that document. Don Alvaro, however, will find himself forever confused and puzzled, as Góngora points out. Having
attested to the existence of others, he will have serious doubts about
his own.

"I am not speaking about doubts concerning who he was then,
but about his origin," muses Góngora stroking his pointed and bluish
chin. "If the first part of your novel was a book, as it is called in
the other, by contrast, the second part would be true real life where
books come in and out as easily as the drawers of a chiffonnier. You
abandoned the last part in fear of incurring the same transgression
as the Great Mime, the Devil, when he parodies too closely the
divine creation. A fear which did not exceed a simple casuistic scru-
ple, as I once said to you, if I remember correctly. The truth is
that unfortunately I am more forgetful each day. Please pardon my
complaining and excuse the digression." Your Excellency is about
to reply but Góngora halts you with a gesture," Let me proceed
before I lose my train of thought. You did not mock God, although
Avellaneda did try to mimic you. The first volume of your tale being
a book and the second, life, where that book is commented upon,
the novel of your impostor would then belong to the kingdom of
shadows, in other words, to the inferno and empire of the Great
Mime. Incorporating Don Alvaro de Tarfe into your manuscript,
by your own will and not by Avellaneda's, you rescued him from
the abyss and granted him true existence." Góngora collects his
shovel hat to bid farewell. It is the midseason of a clear and cold
autumn. Prostrate with a chronic illness, Your Excellency was paid
a visit by the illustrious chaplin and poet. Together you snacked on
roasted chestnuts and a glass of rose wine served by your wife. "Just
imagine the tragedy of someone returning from Hades to assert the
identity of others without being able to state whether he had been
resurrected into the world or into a book which parodied his inferno." He tarries on the threshold and kisses Catalina's hand as
the bells chime at the convent of the Discalced Trinitarians. "Good
Heavens, it is getting late! Days streak by like greyhounds. I am
going to say my prayers and may San Ginés, patron saint of the
theater, bless you both."

* * * * *

*Letter from Góngora to the supposed Alonso Fernández de Avella-
neda. The first page is missing. All pages are numbered at the top
of the left hand margin. The cross of Saint Andrew heads the rest.
It was the property of the late Juan Manuel Cieza del Carmen,
Professor of literature at the University of Barcelona, who used to
amuse himself doubting its authenticity, although he had no com-
punctions about showing it. With his eyes half-closed beneath his
long and melancholic eyelashes, he also argued about the existence
of that part of the universe where our planet is located. But, this is
another story that does not belong here. Instead, and in passing, let
us remember the ferocious polemic right after Góngora's death and
upon the publication of his poems written previous to 1620, by Ló-
pez de Vicuña. The latter calls the poet "the Spanish Homer." But
Pellicer accuses him of changing and deliberately damaging the com-
pilation and even of destroying the Gongorian poems composed after
1620 which were in his possession.*

*The penmanship of the letter corresponds to that of the poet's in
others of his handwritten texts. For instance his reply to a reader who
censures his "Soledades" (National Library manuscript M. 3811).
Likewise, the letter contains phrases and idioms that literally repro-
duce well-known Gongorian expressions. His first sentence "The
greater the din of this city, the greater my longing for your Illustrious
Excellency." (Poetic Works of Don Luis de Góngora, edition R.
Foulché-Delbosc. Hispanic Society of America, New York, 1921, v.I,
p. IX).*

*The signature at the end of the page is very clear, although the
date is illegible. Professor Cieza del Carmen donated the document
to the University library where it now appears as manuscript M.
5622. Just as in Lope's letter to Avellaneda, no changes have been
made to the punctuation nor of course to the content. In some in-
stances the spelling has been modernized.*

The greater the din of this city, the greater my longing for you.
That is why I celebrated your coming the other day bringing chapters XXVI and XXVII of the next volume of *Don Quixote* which
you are writing behind the back of him whose name must not be
thought or mentioned, as Lope puts it in a clever circumlocution
that could be mine. Soon afterwards, our maimed friend himself
came to read me another chapter of the second part of his book. I
assume he was proud of what he had written although it is very
difficult to interpret his feelings, being as he is so circumspect and
withdrawn. Speaking aloud to himself, he said something that I
cannot forget: *My novel is destined to transform itself into a poem,*

between silence and eternity. It will reach a point in which almost lacking a plot it will become a mere pretext. The few things I say or present, however, will tend to be as enduring as rocks or statues. Surprised, I argued that this had also been my purpose in the *Soledades.* Immediately, he nodded his head, which years and the cut of his beard render more triangular. *I always think of your Soledades as a novel of rhymed verses. Perhaps that is why I came to read these pages of mine to you.*

In that chapter, the Hidalgo and his Servant ran across a cart where a very peculiar crowd traveled together. They have a demon as a driver and squeezed in the back are a crowned emperor, an empress, a decked out paladin, an angel with wide open wings, a jingling buffoon, and Cupid himself, without a blindfold but with his quiver and arrows, next to other no less strange characters. The Hero stops them and asks the muleteer—devil, Charon, or whoever he might be—to identify the travelers and to say where they are heading. The demon answers that they are only the company of Angulo el Malo, and they are going to represent the drama, *The Courts of Death,* by the great Lope de Vega Carpio, on that morning of the eighth of Corpus Christi.

Although what follows is a hodgepodge of blows and nonsense from which I spare you because its purpose in the book is to make the foolish laugh, the best part of it is the passive reaction of the Knight upon hearing the actor's reply. Actually, nothing happens then either, since the madman accepts reality, plain and unpredictable. He takes leave of the gang of players, biding them to go with God and wishing them success. One of his phrases impressed itself upon my mind, a phrase that would define the essence of our century: *One must touch appearances with one's own hand for deceit to take place.*

I asked him why it was necessary to feel the appearances to experience disillusionment. In my judgement the greatest lesson comes from touching reality. He answered that he had written it thinking about the theater. A stage production is an appearance halfway between life and fantasy, accepted by a tacit agreement between the actors and the public. *If in the middle of a field and all of a sudden we were to meet a theatrical group on stage, we would believe it to be a dream or a delirium. We would be lacking the previous agreement with the actors and with ourselves to indicate that all of it responds to an artifice with a margin of truthfulness. The theater also demands a certain physical distance. If we burst onto the stage in the middle of an allegorical play or a comedy, the drama would disappear to become a hubbub of angry actors, screaming actresses, and falling stage props. Once appearances are put to the test, we are left with the disillusionment of a world which is ultimately reduced to mere and irrevocable reality.*

Imagine my amazement upon reading the passage of your own novel where other actors are rehearsing *Testimony Avenged*—also a play by Lope—in the patio of an inn. Irascible and vindictive, because his mother has denied him a sorrel-colored Cordobian horse, King Sancho's son lies and accuses his mother of committing adultery with a servant. At that point of the *Testimony*, the Hidalgo of your book, Martín Quijada, as you call him, gets up, grabs his sword, and assumes the defense of the infamous lady in terms that I here transcribe for you: *This is a great evil, treachery, and perfidy against God and all his law inflicted upon the most innocent and chaste queen; and that gentleman who slanders is a traitor, a liar, and an evil man, and for that I hereby challenge him to a duel and an extraordinary battle without any other weapons than the ones I am now wearing, which is only my sword.*

Although you were not acquainted with that episode of our illustrious maimed friend, where the people of Angulo el Malo appear, inadvertently, you were literally following his reasoning about the theater. The proximity of the Knight and the actors on the patio of the inn is such that he forgets to accept the illusion without which the theater would not exist. Touching fantasy with one's own hands, as he who you are parodying would say, your Martín Quijada challenges the actor who plays the part of the mendacious prince and son of Don Sancho. If he had been sane, he would have noticed the extent of the deceit of the world which his insanity ignores. Challenging a comedian, as if he were a true prince, he, himself, becomes another puppet among the players. Thus the Hidalgo loses his identity at the moment in which *Testimony Avenged* becomes a chorus of buffoons laughing about a madman. Once the convention with illusion is broken the comedy fades before one's eyes.

But the coincidences in your books in progress do not end there. One holiday afternoon our maimed man came back to read me another of his chapters. By his own admission he was quite satisfied with it. In it he transformed all that he had said about appearance and deceit into a fable, after the encounter with *The Courts of Death*. While tidying his papers on my desk with his good hand, he spoke without looking at me: *At least now you will not be able to repeat what others say about the writing of my first part. They insist that out of carelessness, I never go over what I have written, thus whimsically confusing or forgetting the names and the donkeys of my characters.*

Putting on his glasses, he starts reading. The event takes place in another inn, where the Master and Servant coincidentally meet a puppeteer called Master Pedro. Although he is more courteous and talkative than most, he covers one eye and half of a cheek with a patch of green taffeta like a one-eyed man with half his face corroded. In a jiffy, and assisted by a young boy, the comedian sets up his stage and lights the candles of the proscenium. According to the boy's announcement, they are about to present the Castilian version of the story of the Frenchman, Don Gaiferos, and his tender lover Melisendra, the Emperor Charlemagne's stepdaughter and hostage at the time of the Moorish king of Sansueña or Saragossa. Very quiet and attentive to what is to happen, the Squire and the Hidalgo remain before the improvised stage.

Kettledrums, trumpets, and artillery resound. The puppet on stage is the great Gaiferos who lives indifferent to his wife's captivity, because distance and time cools passions and widens forgetfulness. The Emperor himself reproaches his idleness and carelessness in hopes that passion and desires will sprout again in his heart. Then, Gaiferos mounts his horse in a single bound and swears to rescue his loved one even if the infidels have taken her to the end of the earth.

He sees her waiting for him in a tower of the Aljafería. From such a high lookout, Melisendra cannot recognize him. *Gentleman, if to France thou goest / inquireth for Don Gaiferos.* Desperate for recognition, he shouts her name. I will omit the grotesque part of the episode which is only for the merriment of the populace who read the book or have someone read it. Such as, the Knight's reprimands to the young boy who helps Master Pedro, the puppeteer's growing impatience, and the tearing of the captive's underskirt when she comes down from her tower and mounts astride the horse behind her husband as they spur and flee to Paris.

The beating of kettledrums spreads the alarm. Amid drums, harmonicas, and bugles, the Moorish calvary hurriedly gallops in pursuit of the lovers. At the inn, the Hidalgo loses his mind and forgets that *one must touch appearances with one's own hand for deceit to take place.* As if the Moorish horsemen were real, he yells to the puppets to stop and not to be scalawags if they do not want to be engaged in a ferocious battle with him. Then, he attacks the Muslims with his sword destroying the theater and the puppets in the blink of an eye. He even almost cuts Master Pedro's head off with a single stroke, who saves himself miraculously by sidestepping just in time to narrowly escape the two-handed blow of the Hidalgo's sword.

Only when the Knight calms down, does he realize that he did not destroy real people but puppets. Yesterday, claims and cries Master Pedro, he was Master of Kings and Emperors. Coffers and stables overflowed with treasures and horses. Now he is left poor and desolate because of the senselessness of an intemperate man. The Hidalgo himself regrets his mistaking the puppets for the people they represented such as the Moors, Melisendra, Charlemagne, and Don Gaiferos, without excluding that puppet stage transformed into Sansueña. All of this was by the working grace and disgrace of invisible enemies. Both Master Pedro and the Hidalgo make a great fuss for having blindly transposed the mirage of appearances. The puppeteer's misfortunes are partially overcome when the Squire compensates him with a good amount of Castilian money. The Knight's sorrows, however, have no repair.

I am overwhelmed by the similarity of your episodes. Weaving on different looms, both of you made the Knight enter into the illusion of the theater, as if it were life and as if he had the power to change it by his own hand. It amazes me how closely your versions coincide, as different as you are. It appears as though the books that you are creating, each one on your own, are mere fragments of another book where all of us will fit: you, he, and I myself, along with both novels and the letter I am writing. I also have the feeling that he anticipated that book, although it is not his own. I wonder if its title will be *Weeks in the Garden,* like another that our maimed friend says he wants to write one day about that orchard of Atocha with the bust of Janus in the middle of which I spoke to you once, or perhaps it will be simply called, *The Garden of Janus.*

I am haunted, though, by the idea of the disappearance of theater. If by any chance one crosses the proscenium where a performance of *Oedipus Rex* or *The Fall of Man* is taking place, everything will become a gibberish of effeminate actors and whores with smeared curtains as a backdrop. My blood drains from me, fearing that something like that may be happening to me regarding my vision of the world. Lately, I am afraid I have been losing my memory. In the wee hours of the morning, I could not sleep trying to remember your face and the name we decided to call you. And then I suddenly remembered, either by the Devil's doings or the grace of the Holy Spirit. Not only do I lose track of things and miss important appointments, but I even forgot the day I was born. Also, for entire hours I am unable to recall the name of the city, Córdoba, where I came into the world. Perhaps, I shall soon forget who I am and all of you will try in vain to make me remember.

I am tormented by the idea of waking up one day to read my

poems and to realize that I do not understand anything of what I have written. Just like the beheaded figures on stage in the inn—broken puppets who stopped being who they pretended to be—I will read my *silvas* and sonnets to witness sadly their transformation into a hurly-burly of unintelligible words. I will wander lost among purple hours, obscure Lethean waters, timorous daylight, wondering artist's strokes, ethereal crystals, black violets, frail pearls, days that double smell the fields, viscous and smooth sea eels, white poplars that comb green hair, and Bengal sparklers that greet the Ganges like a swan. As soon as all of this becomes undecipherable, I will have lost my own self. I will not know who I am, and I will not know those who try to bring my memory back. In such great misery, perhaps unavoidable, do not come to see me because I will not be who I am but another man without a yesterday and without memories. I will be reduced to the reflection of my own self, since the images in a mirror also lack a past and memories. In such misfortune, you should leave me alone, and try to believe that he who here and now greets and embraces you never existed.

—Luis de Góngora y Argote

* * * * *

One week before you found yourself prostrated in the throes of death, you, Señor, decide to quietly say goodbye to your brother. You want to see him without telling him that your suffering and thirst are not signs of old age but announcements of your unavoidable end. That supreme trance that your anxious hope, at times, still denies. In a disquieted and ephemeral fashion, you then intend to write another book—*Weeks in the Garden*—that would begin with the day that you and your brothers and sisters discovered the enchanted orchard. You casually told Góngora of your plans, omitting the encounters with the shadows of the Hidalgo and his Squire beneath the myrtle and among the blackberry bushes.

Juan was the youngest of the family and was his grandfather's namesake since he passed away on the eve of Juan's birthday. He was still a crawling toddler when they found the house with the statue of Janus. He lives now in the neighborhood of Alcalá and you, Señor, along with Catalina went to his home on the occasion of his wedding to a diligent widow, proprietress of her own farm. She had graying hair, was timid in her gestures and smiles, and was taller and older than the bridegroom. Such a betrothal would partially inspire Camacho's wedding in *Don Quixote*. You did not see your sister-in-law again since she died of a heart attack a few years later. Her widower still lives in the same farmhouse near the Henares River. His land borders Meco's inn where Avellaneda placed a chapter of his apocryphal novel. You had forgotten that inn and you have misgivings about seeing it. Sheep from Segovia graze in apple orchards. In Alcalá the arrival of some traveling actors is being announced.

Haltingly, you get off the coach by the portico on Calle Mayor. You pause and lean against the wall because your hip had gone to sleep during the trip. First of all you go to the convent of the Discalced because you also want to quietly bid farewell to your sister, the prioress. Now somber and limping, you remember the afternoon that you went to tell her about Magdalena's serious condition. *Neither as a child nor as a grown woman was I ever with you in a house that had Janus in its garden. The canopy and mirror you describe never existed. Are you mocking the world, after having suffered so many of its hardships and injustices?* You will not be able to see Luisa since your visit coincides with that of the bishop and the provincial priest. God knows what business is keeping her so busy with them that she cannot be bothered. Upset, you leave on foot, helping yourself with a cane, and proceed to your brother's house. In a vast field as long as hunger, you meet Juan watching over a farmhand who plows with no rest and no rush. He turns the ground with a moldboard, sinking the plowshare, and opening a furrow in a straight line. You two embrace and bowing his head the farmhand responds to your greeting.

"The land is dry and it used to be rocky," Juan says. "This is Pedro del Carpio and he is my foreman. Do not be offended by his reticence. He was born as mute as his sister Casilda, who is my housekeeper. I also have a shepherd, a cow herder, and a stable boy. I inherited all of this from my late wife and I would not change my farm for Croesus' fortune. Come, let us have lunch together since the bells have struck twelve. *Laus Deo.*

You both eat in the kitchen and you meet Casilda del Carpio. Blond and svelte, with braids to her waist, she was more becoming than you had imagined. By the fire, she serves you the steaming hot stew in wooden bowls and freshly roasted pork chops in plates from Guadalajara. Noticing your crippled arm, she carves your meat and returns it to you with a smile. Purposely, or out of carelessness, she wears her tunic loose and very open. When she bends over to stoke the fire, she even shows the aureole of her breasts. Without a doubt, this rural lass must be Juan's lover. But the cohabitation must not have yet cooled the ardor of the first encounters. Looking at them, you must have remembered the years shared with *la Zeffirina* and Santafiore singing Dante in the street. *Nessum maggior dolore / Che ricordarse del tempo felice*, there isn't a greater sorrow *than remembering happy times*. Perhaps it is true; but in the end, it is necessary that a writer change memories and sorrows into words and lines on the blackboards of the past.

"You do not envy Croesus, but I do envy you. Among all of us, only you live off the land and it gives you the peace that none of us ever had."

Juan laughs heartily as if amused by the most extravagant and witty remark. At the end of the bench, Casilda also looks at you smiling. The deaf-mute must understand what you say and you feel undressed and mocked by those eyes, between green and gray, of Toledan jasper.

"It is hard for me to believe that you envy me since I grew up regarding you as a god: a faceless god, imprisoned and forbidden, if I daresay. I was too young to remember you when you left home. My first memories come always attached to your interminable absence. Each Sunday while you were in captivity our mother used to dress my sisters and me in black. As soon as the high mass was over, she would take us, in mourning, to Calle Mayor or to the street of San Jerónimo to mendicate for your rescue."

"Mother never mentioned this to me. Perhaps not to force me to feel obligated to all of you. Or perhaps she later thought I was unworthy of all your efforts."

"It may be that she forgot about it. But those first recollections of mine, pleading for your damned freedom, will stay with me for as long as I live. As I told you I was begging for someone, who was for me both a god and a nobody because I could neither remember nor imagine him. All cleaned up and in mourning, we used to sit at a door, next to a plate and a sign where I learned to read my first words: A CHARITY FOR THE LOVE OF GOD TO REDEEM ONE OF OUR BROTHERS, A CAPTIVE IN BARBARY."

"Is this all true or are you lying to humiliate me?"

You want to believe that this is an imaginary story from someone who is almost a stranger to you. But judging by Juan's tone of voice, you realize that he is telling the truth. Also, Casilda del Carpio's stare and the way her eyes shine in the light of the fire or among the fugitive shadows, underscores the sad and bitter reality of that account.

"The art of deceit in our family ended with you. I am telling you today the honest truth, although you cannot believe the humiliations that we had to endure. Storekeepers and lackeys swept us away, porters of palaces threatened us with their dogs, the real beggars looked at us sarcastically and with the same scorn in which an au-

thentic cripple would look at a fake leper on stage. Constables drove
us away amid thrashes and curses. I do not know how much we
collected in those years that was more out of mockery than out of
human compassion. But our mother delivered the money, up to last
maravedi to the Trinitarians. When you were released, I must have
contributed with something to your freedom. It is said that each
man has his price, even though the majority of them die without
knowing it. Your case is different. Your price was five hundred escudos. You owe me part of that payment. A small part perhaps, but
you owe it to me."

"I will never pay you back."

Perhaps you want to soften the sudden rancor that sharpens his
words. In your eyes you feel Casilda del Carpio's gaze. You smile
and assent as if expecting her reply. If you had met her at a different
time—perhaps in another life—she would have given herself to you
without love and almost without desire, with the same resigned lucidity in which you, Señor, saw many men die, or with which Magdalena entered the darkness of eternity.

"When you came back from Algiers, I saw you in flesh and blood.
You disappointed me so much that for the first time I realized my
inability to understand myself. *Is he really my brother?*, I wondered. *Is this blond scarecrow, skinny as a greyhound and maimed,
besides, truly my brother? Was it for him that I begged in the streets
while other children played with tops or were at bullfights? Will I
be like him when I grow up?*

"If, inadvertently, I hurt you so badly for only having survived,—
you shrug your shoulders—I suppose you have hated me ever
since."

"Actually, I forgot you as soon as you left," replies Juan, perhaps
with pretended indifference. "In Esquivias, the day of your wedding
with Catalina, I would not have recognized you except for your arm.
Then the wind took away the years, and I never stopped to think
of you. Someone, I am not saying who, told me that you had caused
your wife's ruin with your foolishness. At home, she came close to
starving while you hustled and bustled hither and yon. I filled a
basket with apples from the orchard, carried a milk goat on my
shoulders, and went to take them to her on the stagecoach. My wife
was still alive and she wanted to give her sister-in-law a bottle of
water from Alcalá which was good for the menses and even better
for a melancholic spirit.

"Did you think that Catalina had a lover?"

You berate yourself for asking although you know you cannot
help it. With her hands open over the hearth, Casilda smiles and

shakes her head. The fire flushes her face and chest. A pine cone opens like a pomegranate and bursts into sparks in the fire.

"What I thought does not matter. Besides I keep quiet since I am not my brother's keeper. And do not interrupt because we are reaching the time when the first part of your book was published. One must strand one's thoughts. But if you prefer I will keep silent and leave it for another day.

"No, proceed."

"I laughed like a madman with *Don Quixote*. But then I wondered if the book did not hide a motive on which to meditate rather than to laugh. I am speaking of a significance that I do not manage to comprehend and that will be recognized only in the future. Then I wondered if I was wrong, and your novel was nothing but a piece of buffoonery after all. In such a case, tomorrow, they will take you for an extravagant writer, and they will not know whether to consider you a witty genius or a philosopher. I envied you again. But I did not want to be you because our family name was going to be remembered through you, but because they would never truly know who you were nor what the purpose of your book was."

You touch your frozen arm. Casilda del Carpio leans over the fire in such a way that she shows her thick, rugose nipples. Looking at her without seeing her perhaps you now think: *Words will make us immortal, as Góngora says. Juan is a man and I am another. Little would be needed to change and transpose us. If we were characters in another book, they would almost confuse us because more than brothers we seem to be only one being with different names.*

"Juan, are you the one who called himself Avellaneda and wrote the fake continuation of my book before I could finish it?"

"I already told you that I know very little about myself. But I am not my brother's keeper."

"Perhaps you wanted to be his redeemer."

"How was I going to redeem you? That was already done by the friars in Algiers."

"Perhaps you intended to save your brother through more entangled means. To write for fun the false second part to his book in order to release him from his idleness and the doubts that kept him from finishing it. Even the offenses that Avellaneda addresses to him would be nothing but an enticement that would spur him to complete the book."

"You said it," laughs your brother. "Who am I to assent or refute? Besides, what would Avellaneda's book be next to yours? A deformed mirror like the concave mirrors at a fair where villagers look at themselves in a daze. Not long ago I bought and read the second part of your novel. I closed it when the Hidalgo died. Then I thought again: *Now he will remain eternally in the memory of men.* Whoever Avellaneda may be, do you imagine him reasoning like this? Or do you prefer to imagine him full of pride with the futile certainty that the apocryphal work is going to outlive you and *Don Quixote?*"

"I can conceive of him both ways. At least two different men are united in him like in any human being. Let us say for instance one similar to you and the other closer to me."

Both of you keep quiet and Juan absorbs himself staring into the flames. The wind whistles in the chimney. The woman notices her open tunic and covers herself smiling. Perhaps, you, Señor, remember the first encounter with the ghosts in the garden of Janus and see yourself again with them before the tapestry where you contemplated your embroidered images. As clear as a living man's, the voice of the Squire resounds in your memory: *God knows when and who embroidered us before we existed. From my vineyards I come and I know nothing. But I call this something between a dream and a miracle. Señores, I wonder who is working all these marvels.* Your soul changes settings and returns to the *sonno profondo* of Santafiore where you read the blind man pages of a book not yet written. Immediately, Santafiore becomes the muffled man with his wide-brimmed plumed chambergo hat offering you a payment for the completion of your work. He was proposing his protection knowing that he—the nameless man—would disappear as soon you concluded the second part of your story. *As soon as I leave this home, I am going to diffuse into the morning sun with my litter and my two lackeys. I do not have another destiny in this world, although perhaps I will return in that other book of the future to which I believe I belong.*

"Juan . . ."

"I am all ears."

"Imagine a house in Atocha between the rows of tents and Puerta Cerrada. An empty palace with a garden full of briars and weeds around a bust of Janus. All of that seems as old as the world and you do not remember. But you and I were there together when you were just a child. Two ghosts lived in the orchard."

"There are ghosts in every park," nods Juan as if he knew everything about it. "In the Garden of Eden the shadows of our poor parents wander lonely. I saw them one time in my sleep. Very old or looking aged, they were shivering naked among rose bushes. In my dream I asked them if they had read your book in Paradise. But they must have been mute like Casilda, because they looked at me without responding."

The apparitions of Atocha were my Hidalgo and his Servant. They spoke and they listened even though they were always dispelled at dusk like wakes in the water. They only emerged in my presence, but I believe that you, too, could have seen them. When I finished the second part of my novel they disappeared forever as if they were the chimera of an endless delirium."

"If we had gone together to that garden I would have strained my eyes staring at your ghosts. But I would be as nonexistent to them as I am to your readers. Eternities will pass and you will endure in your novel. Avellaneda and his book will be reduced to a vain mockery, if they are even remembered." — Juan contemplates you from head to toe as if he wanted to make sure that you both share the same blood of those parents who he saw shivering in Eden. — "My destiny is to perish and vanish. I have no other fate."

"Perhaps someday someone will give evidence of what we are saying today in this kitchen. In good faith, he will believe that he is creating it. But for reasons that transcend all of us, he will do nothing but quote us. At least, whoever reads what he writes will know that you and I were brothers."

Casilda's eyes are still fixed on yours. You cannot deduce from her stare if she is trying to understand you or if she pities the three of you because your ultimate lot is the dream of a stranger translated into words. Impassively, Juan looks at his open palms. They are as calloused as those of a farmhand. But perhaps those could be Avellaneda's hands.

"Although tomorrow they will relate what we talk about today, how and why will they believe us brothers? In the story of your life, I am no longer anyone."

You, Señor, smile to yourself. You will be the one to die; but it is Juan who speaks about disappearing in time. Outside bells are striking. Through the crack of the partly opened door, the evening shadows fall crosswise.

"It is late. I must go back to Alcalá. I do not want to miss the stagecoach."

Casilda kisses your hairy cheeks goodbye. She must suspect your approaching death and you are moved by her compassion. Juan wants to accompany you to Calle Mayor but you absolutely refuse. It is necessary to cut the goodbyes short before a wave of melancholy breaks over you and tears your soul. Without great protest, your brother accepts while the bells strike the hour. *The great Leonardo believed that each man hears different words in the ringing bells*, Niccolò Santafiore said as he mendicated one Christmas. *When it strikes twelve, I remember Dante and Your Grace. Per vostra dignitate / mia conscienza dritto mi rimorse. Precisely your dignity / brings remorse to my conscience.* You, Señor, burst into laughter. You told the blind man that if by his fancy rhetoric he deserved an award for his flattery, he had now lost it.

You are thinking of Santafiore, the bells and the hours when unexpectedly Juan embraces you and probably surprises himself hugging you tightly against his chest. The two of you clasp as if each one would recognize in his brother the only reason for his existence. All of which you consider extravagant and inexplicable because you have always lived so far apart. You also remember that passage from your own book where the Knight and another madman, The Ragged One of the Sickly Countenance, embrace one another without having ever set eyes on each other before. The same as if each one would reflect and recognize himself in the gaze of the other. Almost as if that pair of crazy men, born out of your imagination, had anticipated this instant between you and your brother.

Deep inside you wonder if in Juan you are accepting Avellaneda and absolving him in your brother. If they really are the same person, Juan and your plagiarist will be united in one man in the same way that, very soon, you will become your eternal shadow in the endless captivity. Then not even your brother could bring you back mendicating, as he did or was forced to do in his childhood. Perhaps, imprisoned in endless death, he will forgive you for the years that he begged for your redemption from your earthly captivity and the envy that you would unwillingly inspire in him.

As soon as Juan opens his arms, you leave hurriedly without turning your head. Still the afternoon paints the horizon, and tall fields of fennel covered with snails perfume the breeze. Sheep from Segovia graze in the meadows and in Calle Mayor the comedians announce their play. It is then, in a disconcerted and unforgettable instant that suddenly and unforeseenly you see that brook suspended in the air crossing the skies from one end to the other. Silvered by the sunset and reddened in its brightness, the river runs shimmering across the cloudless firmament between sunflowers and genista in bloom. A constellation of rock fences, intricate olive groves, ocher mounds and distant hills form the river valley sustained in the light. On sandy ground with blooming gladiolus—just above the church of Santa María la Mayor where you were christened—you see a boat tied to a dead poplar surrounded by a flock of circling gray crows. The river and its landscape are so vivid that, through your glasses, you almost feel your foggy vision become clear and rejuvenated. The voices and apparitions in the garden of Janus could have been a hallucination; but not that brook and its banks in the zenith. It is neither a dream nor a fancy, like others that you imagined about the Indies when in vain you tried to go there to escape your poverty. You invented estuaries and mazes as wide as oceans and full of red fish snaking among palm trees and gigantic eucalyptus. Now you feel certain that the river reflected in the sky flows at some point in time, although it might not be printed on maps. From east to west, the river must be running through these same hills, olive groves, and open fields fenced with small stone walls. But at the blink of your eye, with the same unpredictable haste in which it appeared in the heavens, your vision vanished. The sunset is now as clean and deserted as before, deepening the distance with its warm transparency.

Beneath the gates of Calle Mayor, once again the actors announce their play. They cry *The Courts of Death* by Lope. The same piece that you included in the second part of your novel when Angulo el Malo and his troop, already dressed for their performance, ran into the Hidalgo and his Squire. That play that you incorporated into your book thinking about Gregorio Nacianceno Patriarca. *Now I say that one must touch appearances with one's hand to experience deceit.* Also with plenty of jingling bells on the horses, your stage coach comes down Calle Mayor. You cannot help but wonder if those comedians are not the same ones of your novel. The same actors emerging from your story who come to represent in the real world the play by the Monster of Nature or Phoenix of Wits, as Lope is called. You are tempted to miss your ride to Madrid and ask the performers if by any chance they are spending the night at the inn of El Meco, as once Avellaneda's comedians did, and if they know that the Hidalgo who stopped them to request their identity has died in a book that all of them shared and whose shadow disappeared in the garden of Janus.

THE GOLDEN AGE

Before unfolding the congruities, I want to explain my belief in an Avellaneda as the motivator of Cervantes in the Second Part, rather than the opposite. Examining Cervantes' passages of the First Part which the apocryphal author copies closely, one is impressed by his manner of imitating, intensifying, solemnizing, and extending (to the grotesque, if possible) that which he considers to be the essence of the original. It is an exaggeration and an imitation that proves to be typical. The imitated episodes then usually adjust—in conformity with the apocryphal's narrative preferences—to a more urban stage; they are determined more in space and time.

—Ramón Díaz-Solís, *Avellaneda in His Quixote*

Another time, my mother and my grandmother being dead, I do not know what malady befell me, which was considered terminal by the doctors, and I saw the casket and the lighted torches in the chamber to carry me to a monastery in San Bernardo, a league away, which was our burial site. And my father entered the chamber to give me his blessing, with his spurs on since he was going to Saragossa on business for the kingdom, and spoke to me. Crying, I asked him for whom were the torches and the casket. He consoled me and gave me his blessing and left. From thence, to I do not know how many days, I got well.

After the death of my parents, there were three sisters and two brothers left. I was ten years old or thereabouts. My father had appointed Pedro Luján and his wife, Doña María de Pasamonte, as our guardians. This couple, because of certain edicts, moved to the land of Count Aranda. I was sent to Soria to serve the bishop, and because I was late he entrusted me to a friend of his, a medical doctor. This man lived in a house that had a goblin, and many nights this bad ghost would throw himself on top of me. I was on the brink of death and no one would take care of me. My master died and with him deceased, I left that house; and Lent came, and confessing and taking communion, I was cured.

—Jerónimo de Pasamonte, *Life and Works of Jerónimo de Pasamonte*

"Señor Commissary," spoke up the prisoner at this point, "go easy there and let us not be so free with names and surnames. My just

name is Ginés and not Ginesillo, and Pasamonte is my family name
and not Parapilla, as you make it out to be. Let each one mind his
own affairs, and he will have his hands full."

"Speak with less airs, you big thief," replied the Commissary,
"unless you want me to make you shut up in a way you won't like."

"Man goes as God pleases, that is plain to be seen," replied the
galley slave, "but someday someone will know whether my name is
Ginesillo de Parapilla or not."

"But, you liar, isn't that what they call you?" said the guard.

"Yes," said Ginés, they do call me that; but I'll put a stop to it,
or else I'll skin their you-know-what. And you, sir, if you have anything to give us, give it and may God go with you, for I am tired of
all this prying into other people's lives. If you want to know anything
about my life, know that I am Ginés de Pasamonte whose life story
has been written down by these fingers that you see here."

—Miguel Cervantes, *Don Quixote de La Mancha*, (I, XXII)

The conclusions that follow enter the realm of hypothesis. Gerónimo
de Passamonte, in Naples, where he resided, read the first part of
Don Quixote in which his old military comrade (Cervantes) deni-
grated and even slandered him by transforming his sad but dignified
condition as a captive rower in the Turkish galleys to that of a galley
slave who atoned for his crimes in the Spanish galleys, and even
called him by his own last name, Passamonte, preceded by a first
name with the same initial as his, Ginés instead of Gerónimo; and
the only literary work to which he had been engaged thus far, *Life
of Gerónimo de Passamonte,* Cervantes' sarcasm converted into *Life
of Ginés de Passamonte,* autobiography of a malefactor. The Aragonese soldier, who we know was a vengeful and bitter man and
suffered from a persecution complex, decided to respond by writing
a continuation of *Don Quixote* preceded by a prologue in which he
insults Cervantes.

—Martín de Riquer, *Cervantes, Passamonte, and Avellaneda*

However grand his sense of sarcasm may have been, Cervantes
could have hardly changed *Life of Jerónimo de Pasamonte*—actually *Life and Works of Jerónimo de Pasamonte*—to the parodical
name of the supposed autobiography of a criminal *Life of Ginés de
Pasamonte* since the manuscript of that work in the National Library
of Naples lacks a title. The title *Life and Works of Jerónimo de
Pasamonte* was given by its first editor R. Foulché-Delbosc in 1922
based upon a brief introduction by Pasamonte: "I here write my life

and works since childhood." To assume that Cervantes anticipates
Foulché-Delbosc's title in 1605 seems a little risky.

In *Cervantes, Passamonte, and Avellaneda,* Martín de Riquer
declares it not to be "in some way impossible" that Cervantes read
Pasamonte's unedited autobiography because Father Jerónimo Xavierre, generalissimo of the Sacred Religion of Santo Domingo, must
have owned a copy of the work that Pasamonte had dedicated to
him. The Dominican priest, who is in Rome when they offer him
the original in 1605, shortly thereafter moves to Valladolid. Until
his death in 1608, he will be the confessor of Felipe III in the Court.
Cervantes also resided in Valladolid from 1603 to 1608, but there
is no evidence that he knew Xavierre. Also it would be hazardous
to assume that they frequented the same circles.

From August of 1571 to April 1572, Cervantes and Pasamonte
serve in Miguel de Moncada's infantry regiment in Naples. Riquer
believes that they struck up an acquaintance. And he believes it
"with all evidence." Incidentally, he asks himself if they would not
have engaged in bitter disputes, so natural, at times, among soldiers.
But the possibility that they crossed paths in a regiment of thousands of men is quite remote. Even if their time of service did
coincide in Naples, as different as they were, they would have had
very little in common outside of military life.

Riquer contradicts himself without realizing it, when he affirms
that the author of *Life and Works of Jerónimo de Pasamonte* is very
capable of writing a novel (p. 38), although the lexicon of the *Quixote*
of Avellaneda is very different from the prose of the Aragonese
soldier (p. 138).

On the fourteenth of January in 1605 Domingo Machado concludes the copy of the autobiography and Pasamonte disappears
without us ever hearing from him again. There is no proof, therefore, that he reads the first part of Cervantes' novel. We know that
in 1605 he has already lost the vision of one eye and his other is
deteriorating rapidly. One-eyed and myopic, it is possible that his
penmanship is so poor that he entrusts Domingo Machado with the
copying of his book. The work is ready to be printed when a denun-
ciation to the Holy Office subjects it to an episcopal investigation
that takes four months. Finally, it is approved since nothing is found
"against our faith or against our morality."

In spite of certain partial coincidences to which Riquer concedes
excessive importance, nothing indicates that Pasamonte is capable
of writing a satirical novel of chivalry like Avellaneda's almost ten
years after composing the story of his life. If he has survived he
must be blind or bleary-eyed by then. Nor does he seem to be fond

of reading. On the contrary, as Riquer himself points out in other places, Cervantes has an extensive knowledge of the knight-errantry books which he satirizes. Very different identities, in their personality and education, distinguish and definitely separate Pasamonte from the supposed Avellaneda.

—Excerpts from "Cervantes, Passamonte, and Avellaneda by Martín de Riquer," Whitney Matthews, *Baroque and Renaissance Notes,* Winter 1989.

INSIDE OUT

In 1617, a year after Your Grace's demise, Góngora finally settles down in Madrid. Even though for all practical purposes he has resided there since 1612, he only goes to the Court for official errands and dispositions of his various ecclesiastic sinecures. Ironically, although he prolongs his trips and escapades as much as he can, in Madrid he is overwhelmingly homesick for Córdoba, and in Córdoba he longs to return to Madrid.

By a royal decree of October 15, 1617, Luis de Góngora y Argote—in reality Luis de Argote y Góngora since he inverts his parents' last names—becomes the chaplain for his Catholic Majesty. In Córdoba he had been Prebendary, Deputy Head of Rents, Deputy and Secretary of the Capitular public funds, accountant for the Chapter, and key bearer for the Treasury. He passes through those offices without making a remarkable impression and, yet, indulges in love affairs and pleasures not well concealed from the zealous guard of his ecclesiastic superiors. Since his youth, and even more so than Your Grace, he has been engulfed with playing cards and throwing dice. This will be his ruin in Madrid, and he will die consumed with debts up to his neck.

As early as 1588, officers under the bishop of Córdoba press serious charges against the young Prebendary of only twenty-seven years. The Inquisitors say that he very seldom attends the choir and, if he goes, he does not sing nor occupy his chair. That he talks and gets distracted during his prayers, as much as he gossips with those who gather by the Arco de Bendiciones. That he does not deprive himself of bullfights and festivities, thus doing away with the regulations given by the Pope per *motu propio* to the clergy. And, that day and night he behaves like a layman by mingling with female comedians and writing profane verses to them.

Góngora must have great favor with the bishop himself, Don Francisco Pacheco, because he replies with the sardonic mockery of an irreverent humorist. At the same time that he defends himself he also attacks and denounces. If he attended bullfights at the Corredera, tonsured clergymen, older and of a higher rank "with greater obligation to keep and understand his Holiness *motu propio*," are also known to enjoy those fiestas. He does not chat during prayers, but keeps quiet because of a plain and simple physical impossibility.

On one side of the choir he has a priest who, like a lark, sings without stopping, and on the other he has a cleric as deaf as a door. In other words, there is no one there with whom to engage in conversation. Most of the verses attributed to him, he says, belong to someone else. If his poetry is not as spiritual as it should be, it is due to his scant knowledge of theology; only his ignorance is to blame. After all, it is better to be condemned for frivolity than for heresy. Góngora must have had a number of protectors, because the Inquisitors shelved the investigation.

In Madrid, he witnesses the ill-fated end of his supporters. On the twenty-first of October of 1621, Don Rodrigo Calderón, Marquis of Siete Iglesias and Count of Oliva, goes to the scaffold. Don Rodrigo who had tried in vain to obtain the Preceptorship of Córdoba for Góngora at the time that Góngora was overtaken by nostalgia for his city. On the gallows, Don Rodrigo kisses his confessor's feet and asks him if a disregard for death, as great as the one he is feeling, might not be the sin of pride. Twice he embraces his executioner and then raises his head, without closing his eyes, so that the executioner can comfortably behead him. A few months later, Don Juan de Tassis y Peralta, first Count of Villamediana, Góngora's protector, poetic disciple, and gambling partner is stabbed to death in Calle Mayor. In his infuriated grief, Góngora writes that "they buried him that evening in a box for hanged men brought from San Ginés because of the royal haste which did not allow a coffin to be made for the Count." An anonymous poem which the whole city recognizes to be Góngora's accuses the King of the crime. "Lowly foolishness! / the truth of the case is clear / that the killer was Bellido / and the guilt falls in the king's sphere."

In January of 1625, Góngora sells his most precious pieces of furniture to cover his gambling debts. The gaps in his memory are more frequent and prolonged than those that he suffered during Your Grace's lifetime. The Count Duke of Olivares, favorite of the new Monarch, encourages him to publish his complete works and promises him a pension of four thousand ducados to be paid in Córdoba, where he wanted to retire. As he himself says to Olivares: "Even to die, one needs more peace than that which one finds in Madrid. Here, not even death comes quietly." As soon as spring arrives the Count Duke and the Monarch take a trip together to Aragón. Olivares had promised Góngora to resolve the problem of his retirement upon his return. The two prominent men are still in Aragón when Góngora suffers a serious stroke. The Queen, who had remained in Madrid, immediately sends the Palace surgeons. Miraculously, they save him. They restore his speech as well as the use of the half of his body damaged by the attack. But now his amnesia is more acute. In his delirium, he pleads for the love of God: "Tell me, Your Graces, who was that Avellaneda whom I invented with someone else, whose name I do not want to remember."

He writes his will in March of 1626 in a respite of his failing memory. "Let my body lie in the monastery of the Holy Trinity of the Discalced Order, so that from there my bones and body may be taken to the sepulcher that I have in the chapel of Saint Bartolomé in the Holy Church of the said city of Córdoba and where my parents are buried." He also disposes that his debts be paid to his fellow bishop in Madrid, to the Count of Paredes, to the first sexton of the Monastery of the Trinity, to his servants Bernal, Martín González, and María Rodríguez, to the moneylenders Pedro Cebrián and Josep Franqueza, to his tailor Alonso Hermosilla, to the baker woman, Inés de Moral, to the linen maker, Antonio Sánchez, to his coachman, Domingo González, and to the oil man, Pedro, without omitting Ana de Retes, who rents to him the bed where he now sleeps.

In Córdoba, his moments of coherence are even more scarce. Lucid, he always remembers his childhood games with his sister, now departed. "And in the sweet sunny afternoon, / in our cozy town square, / I'll pretend to be a bullfighter / while you tend to your dolls with care/ with the two of our sisters, / Sweet Juana and fair Magdalena, / and both of our naughty cousins, / Marica and the cross-eyed girl, there." On the eve of his death, they offer to take him the relics of San Alonso for him to kiss and perhaps be cured. Góngora smiles sardonically and says, "Gentlemen, the saint would say in Heaven: This dog won't hunt." On the day of his death, he wakes up and surprises everyone with what will be his last words: "Now that I was beginning to know something about the first letter of the ABCs, God calls me? May his will be done." He passes away on Monday the twenty-fourth of May, 1627, the second day of Pentecost.

I wonder if during the last months of his agony in Córdoba, all that he had feared many years before and shared with Avellaneda in his unpublished letter had become true. I wonder, for instance, if Góngora saw his poems transformed into an incomprehensible jargon of dubious daybreaks, rivers like swans, swift-footed seas, tongues of tempered fire, lascivious vineyards, pastures of stars, lugubrious ostriches, oceans like centaurs, purifying knives, reborn or tawny blood, purple libation, and blind gods. Then, not remembering that he had been the author, perhaps he ended up by wondering what strange madman, so distant from his sanity, put together such an obstreperous medley of hallucinations.

During his last nights, each time dwindling more, I imagine him dreaming about himself and his evenings in the tavern with Lope and Your Grace. Or perhaps he sees himself in other dreams, as when you and he contemplated Lope and Micaela Luján, naked and languid in the house of Janus. Or again, perchance he dreams of the two of you standing by the fountain of Caño Dorado while Góngora says to Your Grace: "I could not absolve nor condemn you as I could not judge myself either. I only know for sure that we were born destined to transform ourselves into words." Then, the poet may wonder in his dream who can that thin and pale man be with those squinted eyes and sharp features and who keeps appearing in his nightmares. He lives in such oblivion of who he is that not even in dreams can he succeed in recognizing himself. Soon, he will not be able to distinguish Your Grace or Lope when you appear in his lethargy. Just as he once forgot Avellaneda, the name of God, and even his own name.

Anticipating such misfortune, in another time, he had asked Your Grace's plagiarist not to look for him in his agony, out of respect for his sorrow. Although I do not know why, I suppose that Góngora is begging the same from me now, through the always mysterious Avellaneda and after the three long centuries that have passed since his death. This conviction started to persuade me one evening of 1948 or 1949 while professor Cieza del Carmen was showing me the letter from the author of the "Polyphemus," which he treasured in spite of his doubts about its authenticity. For reasons that I never knew, that well-to-do bachelor lived in a dark and gloomy pension behind the university. While we dined on a plate of vermicelli in the saffroned broth of the house, he left the letter in its cellophane envelope on the tablecloth with printed pagodas and finches. I am also abandoning Góngora here, in the oblivion of his last dream, between that Córdoba where he was born and the lasting immortality of death. A Góngora who definitely does not know who he is and forever ignores those of us who try to remind him.

The River

ALTHOUGH mornings in April are golden and the mountains look blue, by sunset the afternoons turn cold. Shivering in your chair, you tuck the blanket around your legs. You dwell on the irony that the cold weather bothers your knees when you should be preparing yourself to entrust your soul to God in your confession. Looking at your hands on the blanket, Lope must realize how old age has spotted them. Then, he pokes in the coals with a shovel and wraps himself in his red cloak. There is silence. You break it while contemplating the red pleats of his cape.

"The cloak you are wearing must be new. Unfolded and spread on the stage it would seem to be a premonition of a river of blood across the theater. Who made it for you?"

"Did I not tell you?" Lope asks, surprised. "I purchased the fabric with the lining at a very good price from the tailor who is the son of your servant. Nowadays, he is the most reputable tailor in Madrid. In his shop, I met your friend Mateo Vázquez, the former secretary of the Prudent King, may he rest in peace."

"We stopped being friends quite some time ago," you explain, although Lope does not listen. "What are you thinking about? Did you not come to hear my confession?"

As accustomed as you are to his sharp changes of mood, his sudden turn of humor startles you. Fixed on yours, his eyes brighten. His face pales, his features sharpen and then his cheeks flush.

"If in Algiers you committed a nefarious crime with a Turkish viceroy, please do not tell me. I do not want to know and I do not want to absolve you."

"I did not commit it."

"I also refuse to find out, or to condemn you. If your life was at stake, you should have surrendered yourself. As the Squire says to his Master at the end of your novel, there is no greater madness than to let yourself perish."

Although always reserved with his compliments, Lope brings back the memory of your book. *There is something so poetic in the agony of your Hero that by the force of its truthfulness it transcends human boundaries. Its shadow grows so that it breaks through the book*

158

covers to obliquely cross the world. You never resented his envy or his rancor when he so cynically admitted them. But, the memory of what he said about your book suddenly upsets you. Crisply, you demand:

"And you, my confessor, in this crucial hour, do not have anything to confess to me?"

Startled, Lope frowns and shakes his head. When he pulls himself together, without even looking at you, he shrugs his shoulders beneath his bright red cape.

"Nothing, absolutely nothing."

Lope keeps quiet. This April, bright and cold, brings back memories of your first snowfall in Esquivias shortly after your wedding. It snowed for a couple of hours in the evening, and the cold northerly wind from Illescas beat on the snow at Calle Real. The storm calmed down and the wind swept away the clouds to make way for a full luminous moon. Catalina ordered two young field hands to set up leather ropes at the vineyards. A sudden fever excited the gaze of that ordinarily calm woman.

"This light entices the rabbits to come out of their dens and makes them playful. They look for the vineyards and dig in the snow where they smell the violets. They chase their mates or run madly in circles in the fields. Unaware, they fall in the ropes and choke. My father used to say that such whiteness blinds them and makes them crazy. They are never as tender and tasty as when you strangle them in the snow beneath the moon."

Crippled by age, the old greyhound rarely moved from his moth eaten blanket by the fire in the kitchen. With his nose between his paws, he looked up with his sad, brown eyes, as if he were listening and understanding. That night, laughing, Catalina gave herself to you. You did not understand how she could laugh amidst her passionate moaning. Giggles intermixed with her frenzy while she wrapped her frozen legs around you. She screamed with convulsions as she reached her pleasure. Afterwards, you remained awake for long hours thinking about the wheat fields under the snow. Once in a while the greyhound howled in his sleep. He was probably dreaming about other snowfalls when Catalina's father used to go hunting in the oak grove at Santa Barbara and the wind from the Gredos mountains would freeze the partridges on the branches. The dog's name was Perro, or perro Perro because they never saw the need to give him a real name. It was the same greyhound that you ascribed to the Knight in the first page of your novel in that quick inventory of his belongings, but which you forgot in the rest of your

book and for the rest of your life. You fell asleep to the imaginary
sounds of guns and the murmur of a faraway storm mingled with
the rocking of the Algerian tide. At dawn you awoke nervously to
find that Catalina was shaking you by the shoulders.

"Get up, lazybones, let us go find the rabbits in the snow. If we
do not catch them at this early hour, they will be tough and tasteless.
If it does not freeze, the wine will be good this year. Snow perfumes
the grapes."

Even after the storm, Esquivias was restless. Up Calle Real, the
muleteers were going to Borox for bread or to Aranjuez and La
Alhóndiga to grind wheat. Women came out to clean the streets with
shovels and brooms. *May the skies be clear and may we prosper.
May God and our patron saint, Roque, grant your graces a good
day. Señor. Señora.* The housewives smiled and the neighbors tipped
their hats before Catalina. Like the Quijadas, Vozmedianos, Villa-
fuertes, Cárdenas, and the Chinchillas, the Salazars had a coat of
arms with two crosses. In the town hall square, children chased one
another with handfuls of snow. Suddenly rejuvenated, the dog ran
and howled among them. In the end, he was rolling in the snow
much to the delight of the children who almost died laughing.

On the lawn of la Poza you met the priest, the constable, and the
mayor. They were bundled up and headed to the church of Asunción, where the priest would say mass. Although the weather was
cold enough to freeze your lips they stopped to chat. The mayor
reminded you of the chess game scheduled for next Sunday and
asked you not to forget it. The priest was saying that he had to go
to Puñoenrostro to baptize an infant. Even though Puñoenrostro
was three times larger than Esquivias, its permanent vicar was sick
in bed with a fever, aches, and pains. The priest could not persuade
himself to travel through that snow on a stiff old mule. The child
could wait to be christened until the other minister recovered or
until the snow melted. Two Franciscan nuns walked up the hill of
San Bernabé arm in arm. Upon seeing them, the three men said
goodbye and left hurriedly. The nuns always begged for money for
the hospital. Irritated, the priest excused himself, alleging that he
was as poor as the mice in his church. Heavens!

"May God be praised and may He protect you, Doña Catalina.
Would you give us a donation to buy kindling for the sick? They
are going to freeze to death if the Lord does not show his mercy.
We still owe for the last load of brushwood and they will not give
us any more credit, not even for a limb."

"There are people more unmerciful than a ravenous wolf. Cruel
people who call themselves Christians and even ministers of God

but who in reality are not. We will pray for you, Doña Catalina, so that you may conceive and give birth to a baby more beautiful than the lilies in the valley."

Their breath smoked in the cold air while they talked and smiled. The greyhound did not cease running around the four of you. At the church, the bells were ringing. Catalina asked the sisters to come to her house that afternoon. They left blessing her, beneath a shining blue sky that was turning red on the horizon. With Esquivias to your back and through the paths to the vineyards, the whiteness of the snow extended over all. It covered abandoned towns that lay in ruins and were only names in the snow: Hontova, Moratalaz, Palomero, Pozuela. The same white blanket extended through pastures and apple orchards. Between la Perla and Torrejón de Velasco, the Guadatén meandered through the white fields. The Bobadilla, which had jumped its bed last winter, continued overflowing with the storm, flooding the rocks on the hillside. You had sat on those rocks to fish many a time before. While waiting, you used to count syllables for a sonnet, half-cooked in your imagination. The dog went down to drink and to see his reflection in the water. He was lapping the water and from time to time he turned to look at you. Slowly, silence descended over the snow.

In the vineyards you found half-a-dozen young rabbits caught in the ropes. The dogs spotted them and barked, calling you to come and get them. Catalina noticed your repulsion and smiling she kneeled in the snow. She released the ropes with nimble fingers and held the dead animals by their feet or their stiff ears. They all kept their pinkish eyes half-opened and they seemed to be staring at you. Ashamed, you avoided looking while she beat each rabbit against a stone fence before putting them one by one in the game bag.

"You were a soldier and must have killed Turks before they almost finished with you in Lepanto," she said laughing, "and here you are now afraid of some skins. Let us go now that the other ropes are empty."

"Human corpses, I saw many. I never turned my face or avoided their sight. But dead animals frighten me. I do not know why. Perhaps because they make me think that only by a caprice of destiny was I conceived different from them."

"And is it nothing to be Avellaneda?" Who else but you could have been the one? Does it not say in his book that in Saragossa they built an arch covered with white damask with one of your poems in Latin praising the late King: *Philippo Regi, Caesari invic-*

tissimo . . . ? Did you not compose that apocryphal novel, your
novel, to parody and mock me?"

"No, but I know who did it." Now you had to control yourself in
view of his prompt answer. Then, urged to make his words believable, Lope added emphatically: "And do not ask anymore about this
matter because I will not answer. I gave my word of honor."

You knew Lope too well to expect him to change his mind. He
wanted to know nothing about your years in Algiers, and he would
say nothing about Avellaneda. You would leave this world without
sharing your life in captivity with him. And also without his revealing the identity of your plagiarist. When his book was published
the ferocious rancor with which your plagiarist attacked you in the
prologue hurt and stunned you. He called you maimed, old, and
jealous with more tongue than hands. He added that the many errors of the first part of your novel were due to your having written
it in jail. He proceeded, saying that each imprisonment made you
more desperate, angry, and foulmouthed. Without mentioning his
name, almost immediately, he praised Lope as the father of many
successful comedies, as well as a pious member of the Inquisition.
You were infuriated by so many insults, but you concluded that the
reference to Lope made his authorship very doubtful. You suspected, however, that for tangled motives he protected the person
responsible for that monstrosity, as the Phoenix himself had just
admitted.

Without doubt, what the false Avellaneda wrote was a counterfeit.
In the beginning, you impatiently exhausted your eyes reading, to
see up to what point the impostor had mimicked you. But you had
to force yourself to keep awake because the rough mockery of your
novel only inspired the most interminable tedium. Had it not been
for the personal insults of the prologue, perhaps you would not have
proceeded with your own book and thus replied to the ill-fated challenge by Avellaneda. Only when you concluded—snatching the impostor's Alvaro de Tarfe to incorporate him in your story and
mocking him you fear having stepped in a trap set by others. It
would have been better not to have published that chapter and the
second part of your novel, if you did not want to submit yourself to
another man's will. But it was too late for anything and the only
thing to do was to face it and let it be, as the Squire would say, thus
forgetting the snare in which you were caught.

After so many years, you no longer paid attention to what had
happened. But there was that last paragraph of your story with the
ink still fresh waiting for the blotting powder. *For me alone Don
Quixote was born and I for him; it was for him to act, for me to*

*write, and we two are one in spite of that Tordesillesque pretender
who had, and may have had, the audacity to write with a coarse and
ill-trimmed ostrich quill of the deeds of my valiant Knight.* The so-
called Avellaneda said that he was a native of Tordesillas. But the
place was as false as his name. Even then, when the task that you
had thought endless reached an end, you reiterated the insults to
your impostor one by one. You must have felt, however, almost as
untruthful in your attacks as in your outburst of criticism against
novels of chivalry with which you close you story, as if this was its
finishing flourish and its raison d'etre . . . *since I have had no other
purpose than to arouse the abhorrence of mankind toward those
false and nonsensical stories to be met within books of chivalry,
which thanks to this tale of the genuine Don Quixote, are already
tottering and without doubt are doomed to fall. Adieu.*

It was not your will to take the book to the publisher that morning
and to have it printed as soon as possible. First you wanted to give
the good news to the ghosts. Whether they were real—with the
ambiguous veracity of the souls of the Blessed Host—, or the fake
chimeras of your insanity, you were going to tell them that they
were now free to sleep and vanish forever, although their freedom
was as spectral as they themselves. You had rescued them from
their own parodies: from the mockery of the impostor's unrefined
version, irrevocably condemned to the forgetfulness of men. You
took your hat and your worn-out cape, and yelled goodbye to Miguel
Cortinas telling him you would return for lunch. The servant said
that Catalina was in church. A cynical flash made you wonder if
your wife would be praying for your death so that she could go back
to Esquivias with the little money you had left. *I could not live far
from here without our vineyards, pastures, fallow land, and copses.
At least, not for too long.* If those were her prayers, you should not
interrupt her, least of all reproach her for praying.

Slowly you went back to Esquivias. Here and there smoke came
out of chimneys and the old olive trees bent, whitened by early
light. Many years later, when you concluded the last part of the
novel, you revived your many memories of Catalina returning from
the vineyards. In the novel you transfigured them, as sooner or later
all that you had lived would be imbricated in those pages. You
wondered if you had not begun to sketch then the Duchess of your
story with Catalina as a model. Although ironically you did not know
yet that you would conceive it in its entirety in a jail of the future.
Contemplating Catalina, standing in the field with the game bag full
of rabbits you called her *the beautiful huntress* and you both
laughed again. Also in a chapter of the second part of your book,

your characters ran across an elegant and gracious duchess, whom all called *the beautiful huntress*. That unidentified Duchess of your story was supposed to be a reflection of Doña María de Aragón whom Lope met with her husband—Don Carlos de Borja—in the palace of Pedrola. Until then you had thought to have narrated the misadventures of the Hidalgo and his Servant in the palace of the dukes, embellishing Lope's idle gossip. Only now you realize that both huntresses were one and the same. Catalina and the Duchess in the prairie. One and the same, although you would recall your wife wrapped in shawls and carrying a game bag slung over her shoulders, while you presented the Duchess riding on the back of a mare as white as the snow of Esquivias, on a silver saddle and dressed in green with a goshawk on her arm. It was worth seeing, you thought, how the imagined and true intermixed in a man's writing, as memories and forgetfulness crossed in the cavernous galleries of his soul.

At home, Catalina and the housekeeper skinned and washed the rabbits. Then, they cut them with a carving knife and scissors. They put oil to heat on the hearth. When it was almost boiling they added the rabbits dressed with diced cloves of garlic, rosemary, a few tablespoons of tavern wine, salt, black pepper, chicken broth, six or seven tomatoes well washed, peeled and mashed, and some black olives from the olive grove. They covered the pot and simmered it over a slow fire, adding broth from time to time to tenderize the meat. They were following a recipe that you had brought from Italy and that *la Zeffirina* taught you in Naples. You will eat that *conigliotto con le olive,* a plate which originated in Liguria and came down to Campania through Latium and Toscany. Mixing the rabbit, Catalina recited an old ballad from La Mancha. "Young and beautiful Rose / so beautiful and in love / and now that I may serve you / I cannot have your love / no!" The whole house smelled like sweet basil and pine wood. The windows were fogging up. Once in a while the crackling of the kindling would break the silence.

Scarcely had you tasted your lunch when the Franciscan nuns arrived. They were shivering because at the Orchard of Perales they had slipped and sank up to their knees in a puddle of melted snow. Catalina made them take their sandals off and sit by the fire which the housekeeper revived with the bellows. She also invited them to eat and placed two more plates on the table. At first, for the sake of good manners, they declined the invitation.

"Señora, you are too kind. We, poor souls, would be satisfied with a slice of brown bread and a glass of water. Let our sick people enjoy the scrumptious food that you are offering to us."

"We only came to collect the donation Your Grace promised. We are not asking anything for ourselves."

They ate heartily and tasted the wine with apparent resignation. After lunch, Catalina gave them some money and a portion of the *conigliotto con le olive* for the sick. They insisted on kissing her hand and left blessing her again. For a good while you remained quietly together by the fire. You were overtaken by a serene calmness and a joyful fatigue. Like the flames in the hearth your memories were sparked as you recalled Catalina and your first visit to Esquivias. You saw her again, next to her mother when you went to ask for her hand in marriage. You remembered your amazement at the sight of their two identical gazes—gray, blue, and cold—, while the woman who would become your mother-in-law perfumed the room with camphor when she took an embroidered handkerchief to her red and teary eyes. By Easter that year, Catalina's mother had died. She was buried at the church of Asunción beside her husband, the perpetual treasurer of the Fraternity of the Holy Rosary. His widow was in mourning for him that afternoon when you asked for her daughter's hand.

The nuns said they would pray that Catalina would give birth to a child more beautiful than the lilies. But you had often desperately tried to make her a mother. Then you thought about your Promontorio who would now have sprouted in Naples. You ruminated on the irony that both of you, father and son, would never see each other and would not even recognize each other if an absurd act of fate would have you cross paths. Slowly Catalina fell asleep on the bench while the housekeeper did the dishes. Looking at her profile as she was napping, perhaps you remembered her excitement when you loved her on your wedding night. It did not hurt you to find her deflowered. Beyond your honor and deep inside your soul, you kept her secret with zeal. You would respect Catalina's privacy because you were convinced that you loved her as you had never loved anyone else before. Thus you had the certainty that your wanderings had come to an end and that you would never leave Esquivias. You were going to stay in town, taking care of the vineyards and the apple orchards as you had promised your wife so many times.

While Catalina slept, you tiptoed to the garden. The pearly iridescent sky was covered with wispy clouds. At sunset you were expected to go and play cards at the Rectory with the priest and the barber from Calle Real. You would play chess with the mayor on Sunday. Catalina's sleepiness must have been inviting because the cold and the fatigue made you want to close your eyes. Among the snow covered apple trees you eased into calmness. Like lightening, memories came zigzagging into your consciousness. As a child with your brothers and sisters you went in and out of the empty house. On the pedestal of Peguerinos, the double faces of Janus turned to look at you. The deity was erased by the memory of the Algerian sea as you left its shores. Redeemed from your slavery, you were heading towards your freedom, the greatest marvel on earth.

Broken by the snow, a branch suddenly fell. The unexpected noise seized you. Suddenly awake, your heart beat with anguish. At once you realized that you could not settle down in Esquivias. In vain you had tried to convince yourself, but you had not been born to watch Catalina's vineyards and to keep her accounts forever. The same uncertain destiny that made you wander over half the country and took you to Italy in your youth was now impelling you to go to Andalusia. Without any further delay, you would leave the following morning in search of that fleeting fortune. You needed only to tell your wife as soon as she awoke that afternoon. Or perhaps tomorrow morning, before departing quickly and ashamed.

"*Ego te absolvo*. I absolve you of any fault because I am not the one to cast the first stone," says Lope. "If I were, I would stone you to death like Saint Stephen, in revenge for what I suffered because I envied you so."

You both laugh and he gets up, wrapping himself in his scarlet robe. In a sudden impulse, he bends over to embrace you and you almost tremble. You think perhaps that it is the embrace of Judas. Then you probably say to yourself that Lope recognizes how near you are to death and he pities himself. He foresees how, in spite of his will and desire, he will miss you. You must feel angry knowing that the end is imminent and that you will definitely lose what you have already lost: that past of yours which, in spite of disillusions, was ample enough to have fulfilled the lives of several men.

"Góngora said that if I wanted to confess for the last time, I should call you, not him. He feels unable to condemn me or to absolve me, as he does not know how to judge himself. He only feels certain that our destiny is to transform ourselves into words. The same words that we write."

"Perhaps he is right," assents Lope pensively. "But I prefer to live as the unhappiest of all men than to find immortality in my comedies. If I had the choice, I would trade places with Santafiore, even if my destiny were to beg, singing what you wrote."

"A blind man singing that there are no birds today in the nests of yesteryear."

"Those are words from your book."

"Into which words, it seems, I am beginning to transform myself."

The officer of the Holy Office does not reply. Catalina comes to see him off. Ceremoniously, he takes her hands to kiss them. You remember what Lope had said the year of the expulsion of the Moriscos. *If women consecrated the Host, I would kneel down before Catalina to receive communion each morning. She has hands of alabaster made purposely for the Eucharist.* You did not pay much attention to the sacrilegious compliment. Now it seems to reveal a more intimate and naked truth emerging from the shadows and twilights. From your window you see Lope reach León Street. He walks rapidly fanning the pleats of his cape as if to escape from your memory. The bells at the Discalced call for the rosary. Catalina comes and puts her hand on your shoulder. Then she asks you if you need her help or that of Miguel Cortinas. Closing your eyes you shake your head but you ask her to sit by you.

"The first time I left you in Esquivias, I told you that I was going in search of my fortune. It was not true. Without knowing it then, I was going in search of my novel: the fable that lived inside of me even before I wrote it. I had to find it far from you and your home because the idea of that book was awaiting me in a jail. I do not know if I make myself clear or if you understand me."

You did not go without trust in fate, although you did take the risk to leave. Speechless in her astonishment, Catalina listened to the news of your sudden departure. In her silence you thought you were reading the disturbing question that was consuming her. Had you gone insane and had she married a madman? At daybreak under a cloudy sky above the melted snow, a cart driver from Esquivias took you to Illescas. There you would take the post to Madrid at the hour of the Angelus. You wanted to clarify whether or not the Chancellery of the Royal Seal would entrust you with the collection of some vaguely promised taxes. Then you would take the road of Toledo and Ciudad Real to enter Andalusia through Despeñaperros.

"I understand you very well. At least now."

"Everything is diminished except for the truth, Catalina. In spite of our wishes, I will leave again, although this time I am not going to collect taxes nor to write a book. In the name of the same truth, I want to repeat the same question I asked once before. . . ."

"It was the afternoon when the king stopped his carriage to talk to you. Before you told Santafiore that he was only deceiving himself by trying to deceive us because you did not believe that he was blind. I also lied to you then. Several times I had betrayed you with another man and that man was Lope," whispers Catalina with her hands open on her skirt. "In your absences, he came to visit and presented me with tokens of affection. A plate of candied figs or a bouquet of hyacinths from his garden. I accepted a yellowish lace handkerchief because he said it belonged to his deceased mother. Since he had definitely joined the priesthood he did not have anyone to give it to. Then I refused a golden bracelet, asking him if it was also his mother's. He ignored my sarcasm and replied that he preferred the bracelet to the life that she had given him because there was no heavier load than human existence."

Although eaten by jealousy, which in another parcel of your spirit you may consider irrational, you would deduce that Lope was right. Because he desperately wanted his existence to be bigger, more intense, and his own, life overwhelmed him. You will also remember that afternoon when you and Lope took a stroll through El Prado and he took you by the arm as if he were your mentor or your guide. He admitted then that he hurt others for the same reasons that he wrote. Eager to feel alive, he outdid himself one way or another. Almost immediately, another Lope would emerge in front of the Palace of Maqueda. There, he cheerfully shouted, there he had met the Flemish lover of his youth: the one who surrendered as soon as he lightly touched her breasts. There, they should erect a shrine to her statue, and he would kiss the dew on her feet each morning.

"I asked him why a dissolute person like himself chased women all the time if life was so hard for him to endure," proceeds Catalina in an even softer voice. "He answered that he enjoyed them in order to forget his pain for a fleeting moment. Then he started talking about his dead children and immediately succumbed to grief. He sobbed in silence with his head held high and his arms crossed. I was crushed. I would have imagined any man crying except for Lope or perhaps you."

"Once I saw a woman cry silently in his arms. That was long ago."

"I felt compassion for his sorrow and agony with his ill-fated children. By his misfortune, he had lost nine to heaven's rage. Barely an adolescent, he had a son with a lover and the child died in infancy. Then he had two girls by his first wife who hardly survived their mother. Out of the seven that Micaela Luján bore him, five sleep with the Holy Innocents. By his second wife he had and lost forever his sweetest, Carlos Félix, the most beautiful lad he had ever conceived," proceeds Catalina very softly and almost unmindful of your presence. "In a fit of compassion I started kissing him like someone consoling a child in his affliction. Suddenly, I also felt the rebirth of a desire which I had restrained since your departure.

That afternoon I gave myself to Lope for the first time. I do not want to lie by implying that he forced me. I surrendered willingly to him and did not stop him when he tried to return my caresses."

Impoverished and ruined through your own fault, Catalina nearly starved during the last of your absences. Juan had told you that he had taken her a bottle of water from Alcalá and a sucking lamb. Thorned by a belated jealousy, you asked him if he had suspected her infidelity on that visit. He replied that if he had any suspicion it did not really matter. After all, he was not your keeper. Perhaps, you now conclude, you and Juan were possible variations of the same person in someone else's book, and, also, Lope could be shuffled in with your shared identity.

"What else did he tell you?" Catalina turns as white as the snow of Esquivias. "Another afternoon, Lope could not perform but his failed manhood did not frighten him. Seated on the edge of the bed and naked as the day he was born, he shook his head, smiling. He said that it had to happen to him sooner or later. Perhaps his failure was merely a warning, but death always begins where you have sinned most. I asked him if guilt for our betrayal brought his impotence. With sudden and irrepressible anger he replied that if someone was betraying someone else that one had to be you and not us. You pretended to be a man of flesh and blood, he said, when in reality a demon possessed you. One day or another you would write a work beyond compare. Perhaps you were conceiving it while we thought we were deceiving you. Only for having known you, would you immortalize us with your book. No one transcends his fellow beings so much without betraying them, he shouted, beating on the blanket with his fist.

Memory will take you back to the night when Miguel Cortinas waited in the street for your return from the garden of Janus. *I have prepared Your Grace a nice lettuce salad a la vinaigrette and half a young pigeon.* The same night that you brushed your cheek between Catalina's legs as she slept, while your impotency scoffed at your desire tinted with sleep. Licking her, you exhausted yourself trying to enjoy her in the dark. Besides your common inability with Catalina, other details now tend to confuse you with Lope. All the pieces of this puzzle are finally falling into place. Lope had anticipated the book that you would write before you finished it. Likewise, he foresaw that you were going to conclude the second part when you had decided to abandon it. To impose, in this case, only one will—his, not yours—Lope entrusted the apocryphal version to the supposed Avellaneda. In a vicarious way, Avellaneda tried to appropriate the fable that made Lope envy you so much, although he would say the opposite in public.

"What happened to us?" asks Catalina. "Whatever happened to the man and the woman standing together by that frozen Bobadilla that looked like a hare?"

"I do not know. I suppose we are the aged mockery of that couple. They are gone and only we remain, though very little is left of me in this world."

Actually, you know very well where the young Catalina dwells. She lives in your novel, transformed into the Hidalgo's love. Through twists and turns, there she personifies that man's dream. Nevertheless, you had to diminish her by mockery to then bring her to the crest of an impossible dream. You converted Catalina, the woman you married and who used to recite ballads from La Mancha and prepare the *coniglotto con le olive*, into a poor peasant in the novel. You called her Aldonza Lorenzo, daughter of Lorenzo Corchuelo and Aldonza Nogales, neighbors of Toboso. You deformed her on purpose into a dim-witted and ferocious lass who could labor in the fields as well as the strongest farmer and whose shouts from a bell tower could be heard half a league away. In this manner you parodied not only her but also your lost love. Years and absences changed Catalina into a near stranger in contrast to that young girl with whom you fell in love in Esquivias. The Aldonza Lorenzo of your book, described by the Squire as withered by the sun of the fields, was the last variable of another of your bitter and unavoidable disillusions.

But Catalina is also your remorse. You cannot forget that you impoverished her and that you uprooted her from Esquivias. Nor do you feel less guilty because she freely agreed to guarantee the unfortunate business of the taxes which ended with Freire de Lima's theft. After ridiculing her in the novel, you tried to compensate for her ruin and your satire through paths so hidden that only you were able to follow. With written words that were no doubt your best asset, you wanted to pay Catalina all that you owed her. If the Squire tried to deceive his Master saying that he had seen Aldonza sifting two fanegas of wheat in the yard of her house, the Hidalgo would argue that the grains of wheat would be pearls in her hands. If the Squire referred to her rough and mannish odor, the Knight would reply that she smelled like distilled amber, lilies of the valley, and roses among hawthorn. You know, however, that reality is the most irreducible of all disenchantments because time does not cloud nor tarnish it. Already into the second part of your book, you imagined a very sad passage. Master and Squire suddenly met three peasant girls riding their donkeys. The Servant assured the Knight that one of them was his Master's lady. The deceived, enamored Hidalgo fell on his knees at the feet of the rustic. *And thou, who art all that could be desired, the sum of human gentleness and sole remedy of this afflicted heart that doth adore thee!* But laughing and mocking such importunity, the girl spurred her donkey onward at full speed through the field. *Just listen to him run on, will you? My grandmother! Whoa, there, she-ass of my father!* The Knight tried to assist her as she was sliding from her saddle and before she rode astride with a quick jump. By his misfortune the girl had a foul odor of raw garlic on her breath that penetrated his soul.

The villager slips away and along with her, your Paladin's sweetheart and the young Catalina whom you had met in Esquivias. Your pathetic Hero blames one of his enemy enchanters for having tumbled down and degraded his Dulcinea. But also Catalina grew older, and your forlornness threw her into Lope's arms while you were losing your love for her. Your Knight's efforts to rescue his Dulcinea would be as vain as yours to sprout again your desire and love for Catalina, however much you regret having impoverished her. You would like to talk about all of this with the ghost of the Hidalgo in the garden of Janus. But also his shadow, along with his Squire's, disappeared and abandoned you. Azán Bajá was right when he said that sooner or later all dreams diminish and the pleasures of the flesh end in disillusion. The creations of imagination are not as elusive as the memory of life past.

Neither Ana Franca nor *la Zeffirina*, mothers of your children, entered your book. Only Catalina remains there and transforms herself through several avatars. She is the stinking peasant girl who escapes on her donkey through the prairie, at the same time, she is the country girl who sifts the wheat in her yard; but also she is the cynical Duchess, the beautiful huntress. Thinking about all of this, your legs cramp and your knees creak and tremble beneath your blanket. Your eyes water and blur as you say to your wife in a thin voice:

"Catalina, I have chills and I feel very cold. Ask Miguel Cortinas to bring the fire pan right away."

❋ ❋ ❋ ❋ ❋

As soon as Catalina leaves to fetch the servant and the brazier, Your Grace remembers those envelopes, so long forgotten, that the sorceresses gave you at the top of the scaffold. Squatted and wrapped in their dark cloaks the three of them had the same screechy and broken voice. *Welcome he who comes in the name of*

Janus. Welcome he who comes from his own book. Welcome he who comes in search of himself. That was the evening of the day of the auto-da-fe, before Góngora would say that the furnace of Fuencarral would be sixty square feet in base and eight in height. "They must have brought green or humid brushwood," he said, shaking his hawkish profile, "because it took a long time to flare up in spite of much effort to kindle it with bellows and blowing fans. Thus the infidels burned on a low fire amid a chorus of howls." Lope had covered himself with a cape and only from time to time did he look out, coughing. No one knew whether he cried because of the smoke or because of despair. Without saying a word or uttering a complaint, Catalina continued facing the flames. Góngora also stood there, and later on he would give a complete account of the events.

Still shivering, you open the drawer of your desk in search of the forgotten letters. With an uncertain touch, you cut them open with a Toledo letter opener that had belonged to your father. Each envelope contains one sheet and the three of them seem to have been written by the same hand in a spidery penmanship. Your fingers tremble as you unfold the papers. Then you put on your glasses and begin to read the first message. It is the one presented to you by one of the old witches as she assured you that he who comes in the name of Janus will always be welcome.

The emperor was desirous of seeing the famous temple of the Rotunda, which in antiquity was known as the temple of all the gods and today is more appropriately named All Saints'. Of all the pagan edifices in Rome, this is the one that comes nearest to being preserved in its entirety, and it constitutes a fitting tribute to the grandeur and magnificence of those who built it. It is constructed in the shape of a half-orange and is very large and well lighted, the only illumination being afforded by a window, or better, a rounded skylight at the top, and it was from this point of vantage that the emperor surveyed the building. At his side was a Roman gentleman who explained to him all the beauties and fine points of the huge and intricate structure with its memorable architecture. As they made their way down from the skylight, the gentleman turned to the emperor and said, "A thousand times, your Sacred Majesty, I had a desire to throw my arms about your Majesty and cast myself down from that dome in order that my fame might be eternal in this world."

You immediately remember all of those lines as the first paragraph that you wrote in your book, as you commenced the last part so many years after you had abandoned it. Shortly after meeting the man in the plumed broad-brimmed hat, you drafted and corrected that gibberish as a sample of the Hidalgo's ridiculous erudition. Concealing his face at all times, the man in the soft hat had offered you five hundred escudos to conclude your novel. He said that you had to finish it as soon as possible because the days and hours were dwindling. He did not want to die not knowing your entire story, although he feared that a sudden death would come to him right after he finished reading it. Your unexpected protector called himself Nobody and he added that he did not know whether he was the shadow of a man who had already existed or the presager of another man who would live in a faraway future.

Your Grace wrote the reflections about Charles V and the skylight, just before you penned the adventure of *The Courts of Death*. Memories overlap and you now remember Gregorio Nacianceno Patriarca. You met him in the oak grove on the day of the auto-da-fe. Dressed in his purple coat, he told you that he was attracted by a spectacle where death was real and piety was as certain as death. For an actor there was no higher drama. Patriarca was a Christian and a comedian. As a devout Catholic, he did not want to miss the indulgences promised to those who witness the burning of heretics after their conviction.

At dusk, one of the veiled sorceresses gave you the envelope with the quote from your book. Prodigiously, that depiction of man's thirst for glory foretold your own novel. You would not even conceive or write it until several weeks or months after the auto-da-fe—time unravels in the past like clouds in the sky—. Someone, you will never know who, foresaw your own words. Or perhaps Your Grace inadvertently plagiarized what he had so fluently composed. You would have liked to share all of this with the muffled man, but you would never cross paths with him again. He came to see you to pay the last two hundred and fifty escudos once the last part of your book appeared and people began to restate their praise of your wit. He left the money bag on this very desk where now the three messages of the witches lie open.

"I came to settle my debt and to bid farewell. We are even and everything fits together. Although Avellaneda came ahead of you no one remembers him any longer."

You must have been tempted to ask him to reveal his face, even if it were burned or consumed by canker. Or even if he had no head at all. But you kept quiet, shrugging your shoulders. The same as Avellaneda, the man in the plumed broad-brimmed hat would never have a face or a real name.

"I am surprised to be alive after reading all of your second part up unto and including the *finis operis*," proceeded your protector.

"At times, I even suspected that I was immortal and that Your Grace was hinting at my immortality through the twists and turns of your book. How startled I was by the epitaph of the Hidalgo stating that death never triumphed over his life! I am delighted that you were mistaken when you feared that you would go mad once you had definitely sealed the book.

"You answered that, sane or insane, there were mornings when you awoke with your legs frozen. That chill would torment you until the ringing of bells at sunset when you would finally warm up. But afterwards you were left in a disquieted state, even more disturbing than your helplessness, because Your Grace could not pinpoint what caused it.

"At any rate, count the escudos and invest them in a profitable land purchase. Do not let them fade away like the Devil's monies. Although, needless to say, I am not the Devil."

Your Grace replied that he tempted you to finish *Don Quixote* when you had already abandoned it. You added that now you felt very lonely. Lately, you have lived to work on your book and to speak to your ghosts in the garden of Atocha. But no more were they to be found in the orchard, the tapestry, or the mirror. After your novel was completed, they vanished forever because you buried them in the book.

"I am afraid I am also going away," whispered the muffled man stretching his cape with his gloved hand where he wore the seal of *Janus Matutinus.* "As soon as I leave, I will melt from the sun, like wax, along with my sedan chair and my lackeys. I have no other destiny. But perhaps I will return in that other book of tomorrow where I feel I belong. If fate has it, we will meet there again and I will repeat then what I am saying to you now. May God be with you, my dear friend."

He departed without another word, casually nodding his head beneath his hat. Although his money was not the Devil's but only minted escudos, you would never see him again. As soon as he left, Your Grace hurried to the window. León Street was empty but you could hear the vendors around the corner of Cantarranas Street. In time, you would almost forget about him. Smiling, you must think now that if tomorrow you met him in another book, you would not recognize your protector. In the midst of all these memories, you sense that your chills have ceased. Shrugging your shoulders, you begin to read the second letter of the harpies.

However, as it is rare to cure insanity, people say that when he left the Court he went back to his mania, bought another and better horse, and returned to Old Castile. Stupendous and unheard-of ad-

ventures happened to him there, for he took as his squire a "working girl" he found by the Tower of Lodones. She was dressed like a man and was fleeing from her master because in his house she became, or they made her become pregnant unwittingly, although not because she didn't give plenty of cause for it. She was roaming around in fear, and the good knight took her without knowing she was a woman until she gave birth in the middle of the road and in his presence, leaving him highly astonished at the birth and imagining the wildest fancies about it. He turned her over to an innkeeper in Valdestillas to take care of her until his return and without a squire he went through Salamanca, Avila, and Valladolid, calling himself the Knight of Hardships, for the celebration of which hardships a better pen will surely not be lacking.

You recognize the passage immediately. It is the last one written by Avellaneda: another nameless man who concealed himself behind a book. That impostor had left his plagiarism open to a possible continuation. In his arrogance, he could not imagine how soon his book would be forgotten. You must feel tempted to tear up the letter, written in the same spidery handwriting as the others. But you hide it in your desk, meditating on its ironies. Here they foretold what the thief of Avellaneda would later write. At least a year passed between the auto-da-fe and the publication of his forgery. Neither would know that someone had foreseen that passage, as they had anticipated Your Grace's other paragraph about man's suicidal urge for immortality.

Memories follow one another like beads in an abacus. Avellaneda's quote transports you to the last encounter with the ghosts in the garden of Atocha. The mountain gale that swept the birds and the clouds was blowing papers and the late summer leaves in the street. The polished sky of Madrid had turned the color of jade. *The air is whirling and our souls are being blown away to a cattle selling fair;* Catalina used to quote an enigmatic country proverb that you never understood. Your Grace held on to your velvety beret with your good hand so that it would not be blown away. It was Tuesday as the saying goes, when if you travel do not tarry / do not let your daughter marry / and of your tailor do be wary.

"Nothing like a good hurricane to cleanse your conscience," you said to your phantoms. "At least that is what the Muslims believe and they know more about high winds than anyone else."

It took them a while to respond. The gale stretched the ghosts and made them look thinner. You must have originally conceived them as looking like scraps or flames before you created their bodies in complete detail. In other words, before you perceived them in the depths of your soul as clearly as you would see yourself reflected in the pond of Buen Retiro. *You described the Hero that you had imagined as vividly as if you had come from his house and not from a dungeon. You made me see him with more lucidity than I could see you, as you talked next to the apple tree planted by my grandfather. How you painted his pointed-nosed hound, his nag, his lance in its rack, his fluffy slippers, his stockings, his Saturday suppers of eggs and fried bacon, his lentils on Fridays, and even the pots, the ladles, and the skimmer of his kitchen!*

The greyhound had disappeared but the hack's profile sharpened beneath the barely outlined horseman. The Hidalgo struggled to halt the horse and pressed his pointed knees against its flanks as if he feared that a sudden blast would dissipate the nag or a stronger gust would carry it off to the Devil.

"Did you by any chance see in your wanderings a mysterious man who goes around muffled and with his plumed hat pulled down to his eyes?" Your Grace yelled to make yourself heard though the storm.

Almost miraculously, the gale quieted and silence descended upon the garden. Frowning and amazed, the ghosts stared at each other. The Squire shrugged his broad shoulders and his Master shook his head. The blackberry brambles smelled like fennel and rosemary. The double profile of Janus on its pedestal of Peguerinos enhanced the calmness of the orchard.

"I never saw anyone in such attire more becoming to a comedian than to a God-fearing Christian," said the Hidalgo as his Servant nodded. "As you describe his appearance, I do not find such a character very acceptable."

"No, we never encountered anyone like that, at least in the first part of a novel as truthful as the one you wrote with the chronicles of our wanderings," the Squire remarked.

"You are right, son. And your memory has always been excellent," his Master praised him again, like that day when they first told you of their mutual premonition. Then, they said, the undeniable existence of a plagiarist who was weaving another ending to your story had been revealed to them.

"I bet you two-to-one such a scarecrow would not even appear in the new part of our tale," proceeded the Rustic. "That is, if Your Grace abides by the truth, as the priest faithfully follows the words of the mass."

You wanted to reply with what would be your secret forever. To tell them that you lost yourself within your book amid your own turns and ironic resources. You began by attributing to your novel

a multitude of supposed authors, as the Gospels of the true faith
had been multiplied by four, next to the apocryphal and heretical
versions. You said you were the reader of all versions, and chose
one among all the chroniclers whom you called Moor.—A Moor,
although all men of that race lie like the old Cretans—. As a conse-
quence, there was the possibility that such a fabulist would not be
a Moor or perhaps would not even exist. Thus the text that you
claimed to have read would not belong to anyone. In that jail of
Seville, as you looked at the clouds through a skylight and designed
in your mind the countenance of your characters, not only did you
pretend to be a reader of your unwritten text but also the interpreter
of all its interpreters.

Feigning not to know Arabic, when in fact you read and jabbered
it since your captivity in Algiers, you invented another translator in
and for the book. It was a Moorish lad who for a couple of bushels
of wheat and fifty pounds of raisins would put some newly found
chapters into Spanish. Thus, as an author, Your Grace would hide
behind interpretations, translations, and a mirage of authors, real
and imaginary. However, the whole thing—Moor, translations,
pounds of raisins, and bushels of wheat—would still belong to the
future.

When the wind so sharply ceased that morning, you could only
think of your own paradoxical destiny. The batches of papers, translations, interpreters, historians, and storytellers so extenuated and
distracted you that it was possible and presumable that another
impostor, one who came from reality and who concealed himself
behind a pseudonym, would be tempted to take possession of the
delayed unfolding of your novel. But you did not say anything about
any of this. On the contrary, and in a surprisingly cold and indifferent tone, you unexpectedly asked the ghosts the first thing that came
to your mind and to your lips.

"In the limbo of this orchard, where you came upon leaving my
book, did your Graces meet an elaborately dressed and presumptu-
ous non-entity who calls himself Alonso Fernández de Avellaneda?"

Shaking your head, you now dispel all those memories and dispose yourself to read the last message of the sorceresses. Then you
nearly utter a cry of astonishment. The epistle startles you. It seems
to anticipate a letter from your plagiarist to Lope, written soon after
the appearance of the outrage that wanted to pass for the second
part and the conclusion of Don Quixote, in other words, Avellaneda's
book. Your Grace immediately recognizes the penmanship since it
is the same as the other papers. Holding on to your desk to keep
your soul from being wrenched away, you pushed your glasses up

on your nose and briskly read your letter. Suddenly you must feel very close to a truth that until then you had believed improbable.

Don Félix Lope de Vega Carpio
Phoenix of Wits, Father of the Theater, and Familiar of the Holy Office.

In different passages of his novel and as Don Luis de Góngora showed me, Your Grace and I coincided with our maimed friend of unmentionable name. We coincided, I say, through paths as hidden as those that unite the stars and constellations in the firmament.

No one before noticed such a curious similarity. If in my book some comedians are ready to rehearse Your Grace's play, *Testimony Avenged,* in his and by the eighth day of *Corpus* the company of Angulo el Malo is going on a tour with another of your theatrical pieces: *The Courts of Death.* I never figured out how we came so close in this matter. Perhaps, he and I resemble each other more than we are willing to admit, although I am only his living mockery, as a shadow is to a body.

At any rate, once his continuation of *Don Quixote* was published, no one remembered me. Although much was said about my book when it first appeared, the novel that you entrusted to me and the pen name that I used fell into oblivion. Since he published his work, the greatest of silences fell over mine. I even thought that if I were to appear at the poets' tavern and proclaim myself to be the one and only Alonso Fernández de Avellaneda, everyone would stare at me without knowing who I was because even my readers have forgotten my existence.

From the publication of my novel to the release of his, I thought I was somebody beneath that pen name. I was pleased then to see my book in the hands of strangers and to hear their comments, even if almost all of them denied its merits when they compared it with the first part by the maimed man. They said: "this Avellaneda simply does not have it," "he lacks wit and talent; he yearns to surpass the insuperable." Or "poor Avellaneda, whoever he may be, because he wanted to challenge someone who is a thousand times better than he would ever envision himself to be."

In those days I persisted in timidly attending the literary taverns. I enjoyed the debates on who I was, in other words, who the supposed Avellaneda could be. Some even attributed the authorship of the book to Your Grace and to Don Luis de Góngora. "Only Góngora or Lope could have written such a satire," they said and then added, "but if they had dared to sign it with their own names they would have lost face. Anticipating the failure of their fake, they decided to use a pseudonym." I was delighted, thinking that through my pseudonym I was being confused with writers of such high stature as yourselves.

On another occasion, Don Francisco de Figueroa himself compared me to the one whose name I shall not say. Like him, Figueroa was also born in Alcalá and was the author of well-known verses like: "Leave me alone, oh Love, I already gave thee the fruit / of my tender youth." Don Francisco would assure in San Felipe: "Only my trickster friend from Alcalá would have been able to write that mockery of his own fable. He would not have pursued his second part without first anticipating it in a parody of the first, in the same way that his real misfortunes as a soldier and as a captive preceded those of his Hero in the novel."

But once the last part of his story appeared, everyone forgot mine as if it had never existed, or as if I had not been Avellaneda. Perhaps my work only served to entice him to finish his. Or perhaps sooner or later he would have concluded it anyway. We will never know for certain. But, unfortunately, I do know for sure that I am a nobody. After having been Avellaneda, I find it impossible to go back to the man that I was before. The world will never know who Alonso Fernández de Avellaneda was, even though his name was once well known. When the wind that sweeps away all ashes sweeps us too— Your Grace, Don Luis de Góngora, and me—they will vainly continue wondering about the truth. I do not anticipate the future, least of all can I prove it, but this is how I foresee it.

This servant of yours does not want to bid you farewell without confessing another intimate and profound certainty. It was not Your Grace's intention that I write a false *Quixote,* so that he would, in turn, complete his. Perhaps this was Don Luis de Góngora's purpose, but I am sure that it was not yours. You envied the maimed man so much that your desire was actually the opposite. You wished me to destroy him with my plagiarism so that he would never finish his long-awaited conclusion. His book would have remained incomplete just as life is always a baffling mosaic of frustrated dreams. Your Grace thought that perhaps this last blow would overflow his cup with disillusion and he would let himself die. May Heaven forgive your vain and venomous envy. In the end, everything would turn out to be just the opposite of what you had devised. It is God's will that his name bury ours.

Please accept my most respectful regards as I sign this last letter and say goodbye to you forever.

—Alonso Fernández de Avellaneda

Catalina and Miguel Cortinas had not yet returned with the bra-zier, nor did you hide the letter. Looking at the signature, your memory repeats the same question you asked the specters in the garden of Janus:

"In the limbo of this orchard, where you came upon leaving my book, did your Graces meet an elaborately dressed and presumptu-ous non-entity who calls himself Alonso Fernández de Avellaneda?"

It was a clear Tuesday, and the morning wind made the Hidalgo look thinner and older as he sat on his nag. Perhaps, in a flash of your memory, you recall Catalina telling you that in her dreams she had loved your extravagant Hero whom you had described to her so vividly upon your return from Seville. Before printing the book where you gave him life, you would be dishonored by your own creation. In fact, and if we are to be precise, she would not deceive you with the ghost but with your previous sketch of him, fancied while in jail. In Catalina's dream, the phantom touched her nude body with trembling hands and listened to her confession: *I never missed him in all the years that he was gone. Now he has returned and he is only a shadow.*

"No," the Knight finally replied. "Truly we do not know anyone by the name of Avellaneda."

"Is it by any chance someone of importance with whom we will share after-dinner chats in the next part of your story?" the Rustic sighed, scratching the back of his neck.

His question almost anticipated the last chapter of your novel, as you saw it in the depths of your consciousness and, contrary to your habits, you had sketched it on some paper. In the throes of death, his sanity recovered, the Hidalgo spoke or would speak with such wisdom that it took or would take people a long time to recognize him. If that epilogue anticipated the impostor's book you would make Avellaneda and his impostors come to his death bed. They would not only go to sob next to the Knight in his crucial hour, as everyone was already mourning, but also to confess their remorse for their vain pretensions of imitating your celebrated protagonist with that pair of scarecrows. In other words, with shadows of shad-ows that did not resemble the originals at all. With sardonic mag-nificence, the dying man would absolve the pretenders, and to make matters worse, he would bequeath to Avellaneda fifty pounds of raisins and a couple of bushels of wheat from the next harvest.

"Avellaneda has not yet appeared in my writings. But he will come at the end of my second part, with which I am already making headway and will complete for sure. Meanwhile, you should forget him as if he did not exist," you suddenly exclaimed as you perhaps remembered the two hundred and fifty escudos from the muffled man and your old debt to the hosier of Santa Polonia which you had just settled along with other overdue bills.

"It will be very easy to ignore him, since we do not know him," replied the Peasant. "But, confound it! I swear by the bones of the midwife who attended my birth that we cannot forget the dreams that had begun tormenting us. These dreams of ours coincide and repeat themselves as we both had the premonition that someone, very different from Your Grace, had proceeded with the false account of our story."

"What dreams are you talking about? Dreams that repeat themselves?"

"In truth they are, and besides, they fit together like jam and bread. At daybreak, when my Master and I appear here on our saddles, we tell our dreams to compare them."

"My nightmares are so terrible that I would really go crazy if I could not share them with someone."

"What my Master wants to say is difficult and painful. Not only do we suffer the same delirium as soon as we fall asleep but we also transform ourselves into our own copies from the other book."

"You do not dream about yourselves as you are, but see yourselves like that man weaves you in his plagiarism?"

"In dreams I stop being the Knight whom I had wanted to become by dint of my deeds. Instead, I turned into a decrepit madman. I will only say that in my nightmare last night, as I arrived in Saragossa for the jousts, I was confusing that city with Homer's Troy, and I believed that I was Achilles himself. I do not want to become a scarecrow, a wild lunatic. I do not want to be the laughingstock in the streets of a novel."

"As soon as we entered Saragossa, through El Portillo, a crowd of scalawags, hags, and vagabonds chased and ridiculed us," said the Squire, visibly shaken. "Some shouted that my Master had lost his mind and was raving mad. Others would reply that he was a cunning old fellow who, with his knavish acts and clownish ways merely kept from starving. They added that I would later pass a cup, like the monkey of an organ grinder. A plague upon all of them! I blush when I remember that in my dreams I spoke to them in such an ill-bred speech: *Gentlemen, you should say nothing about my Master because he is one of the best knights you could ever meet. I have seen him with my own eyes in the warrings of La Mancha and Sierra Morena, which if I were to describe them to you I would need the pen of Golías the giant.* As if I did not know that there is no such word as *warrings,* and that it is not Golías the giant but Goliath. I have known this since I learned to speak like my Master! And keep in mind that I am talking about Goliath, the one who was felled by a young Jewish goat herder, according to the Catechism."

Although you never anticipated your ghosts' dreams in the garden of Janus and, least of all, that in their dreams they would change into the parodies, you were pleased to see that the imitations of your characters in that other book were naught but badly made deformities. If in fleeting moments, you feared that Avellaneda would overshadow you with his book, now you had a hunch that people would make fun of his imposture. Also, the extravagant buffooneries that the Hidalgo and his Servant were describing discarded Góngora as the presumed author of such a distasteful account. Contrary to all these excesses, Góngora advised you to diminish your Knight's vision of the world. *The power of your Hero to transform reality according to his own free will is going to decrease in time. In the end, it will be up to him to see huts in huts and perhaps it may be that his Squire starts calling them castles.* Your Grace had asked him how such advice from him could agree with his own poetry, so boundless and entangled in its concepts. Góngora shrugged his shoulders beneath his cassock. *Man's creations as well as men of integrity answer only to themselves,* he replied in a rather vague manner. *That is, if life is life and not a dream.* Mockingly, he blessed you and jokingly you knelt down to kiss his hand when he bid you adieu. *If Lope saw us, he would take us for a pair of faggots,* the lame prebendary replied.

With his brown eye beneath his grayish brow, the Rustic's ghost, standing in profile, contemplated you. A cloud of sorrow and anger veiled his iris and half his pupil. Nevertheless, more than the ghosts' determination to keep their sanity in those dreams, you were more amazed by their cold indifference. Towards the end of your life in the antechambers of your soul, Your Grace may have thought that perhaps you then decided to take your characters to Barcelona instead of Saragossa. You did it to contradict Avellaneda, although you were well aware that by changing their itinerary you were going against your own free will. Almost at the end of the first part, you had quoted some hypothetical memoirs, where it is mentioned how your Paladin went into battle at the jousts of Saragossa. However, you plagiarized the impostor with the idea of the entire city—Barcelona, not Saragossa—making fun of the Hidalgo and his Servant, to the sound of drums, flageolets, and great clamor. They all pretended to be dying to honor your Hero, whom they considered to be the mirror of chivalry, while some rascals put gorse in the behinds of their donkey and nag. Pricked with thorns and in pain, the mounts kicked wildly into the air amid neighs and braying. Instantly, and as a matter of course, the horsemen fell flat on the ground, more hurt by the public shame than by the fall.

"My good Squire is not telling the most embarrassing of what happens in Saragossa," proceeded the Hidalgo. "In our nightmares, as soon as we cross the gates of El Portillo we meet a convicted thief. On a donkey, half-naked, and with a rope around his neck, he is brought forth surrounded by actuaries and constables. Among the clamorous delight of street ruffians, they take him to the executioner to be whipped. I speak nonsense and act crazy upon hearing the screams of the condemned man. I yell in order to convince them to free him right away."

"My Master screams in his dreams for the release of that defenseless man who was apprehended while he was taking a siesta under some alder trees. Since in their bewilderment they do not know how to reply to him, my Master charges against the guards and pettifoggers. It is by a miracle that he does not pierce a couple of them as his lance passes beneath their armpits. In their outrage the people from Saragossa call him daft and possessed. Finally, the constables subdue him with kicks and punches. They drag him, unarmed, through the creek while he implores the favors of Esquife the wise and Orlanda the evil . . ."

"It is Alquife the wise and Urganda the unknown," the Knight corrected him in a low voice.

"Whatever! For two names, I am not going to lose the thread of my dream. They put him in the stocks, handcuffed and with a chain around his neck, in a jail they called Mercy. I cry in the streets, and so that my penance may redeem my Master, I promise Heaven to crawl on all fours like a bear, eating snakes from here to the Indies. Some ask for his head. Others burst out laughing when they hear me. You judge for yourself how low we have fallen in those nightmares."

"And we will sink even lower if you do not save us from those dreams that change us into the mimics of that fraud," the Hidalgo insisted. "If Your Grace does not finish your book, the madness that is overtaking us in our nightmares will become all too real and we will be transformed into our own parodies."

"Only Your Grace is responsible for our destiny. If you had not imagined us, we would not have ended up in this garden. Nor would the impostor transform us into our own satires. What pitiful and sorry luck we had! It would have been better if we had not been created rather than to have had our brains pulled out and to be made into a pair of knaves. We are that badly treated. If we do not deserve to submit ourselves to the whim of he who is pushing us to the edge of madness in our dreams, less do we merit that a bastard change us into two idiots. By my God and my faith, you will be the cruelest man ever if you do not spare us that torture!

The gale from the sierra came again with a new impetus. One could say that it had been conjured by the Knight as he shook his sorrowful grayish head. The wind brought heavy clouds and pushed them towards the hermitages of San Cebrián and The Evangelist. Your Grace was reminded of another similar afternoon of long ago, when a sudden shower caught you and Lope near the Palace of Maqueda. You were tortured with the suspicion that he was the one proceeding with the imitation of your book on his own and secret account. Oddly, you dismissed your fears when Lope started talking about building a shrine to his Flemish lover in a place none other than El Prado. Inside he would put a statue of his mistress so that he could kiss her feet on Easter. You also suddenly recall what Lope said on the porch where you found shelter from the storm. It was a peculiar reflection which you did not consider at the time, while, due to your crippled hand, you clumsily tried to shake your cape and dry your beard with the end of your cloak. *The end of the world will come with a flood greater than the one in the Bible*, reflected the Phoenix of Wits and lascivious Chaplain of the Holy Office. *As soon as the waters dry up, the world will be recreated by the Devil. Everything will be repeated exactly and you and I will be sheltered again by an identical porch. In that new edition of the universe, however, we will not know that we are not ourselves but copies made by the Devil.*

The wind tore the shadows of the garden into strips. The Squire, his Master, the donkey, and the nag faded as at each sundown they vanished in the dark. In a loud voice, Your Grace asked yourself whether they were dreaming or whether you waited for the hurricane to give way so that they could return to the brambles and myrtle in the garden. With your cap jammed on your head and with your cape held tightly so that it would not be blown away by the wind, you hesitated between finding refuge in the house of Atocha or returning to your own. A sudden blow forced you to put a halt to any decision, and it threw you against the iron railing. Exasperated and holding on to the rails with your good hand, you cursed your luck, swearing like a harquebusier. Almost immediately, as if the air were appeased by your blasphemies, the storm mitigated. In the nunnery of the Sisters of the Third Order, the bells were calling the pious to the rosary.

As you return the letters to a drawer, you want to forget the garden, the old witches, and the ghosts. And also Lope. If the letter from Avellaneda was true, it hurts you to think that besides deceiving you with Catalina, Lope wanted you to be destroyed by a final disillusion upon the publication of the plagiarism. But for better or worse, you could not resign yourself to hate him, as Azán Bajá could not love you carnally when you were a captive in Algiers. Instantly, as white and as vast as if you were looking at them from your balcony, your memory evoked the snow fields of Esquivias crossed by that reddened Guadatén between la Parla and Torrejón—.A river that looked as red as the cape of Lope or as an omen of spilled blood.—

Meanwhile your wife and your servant come back. Miguel Cortinas carries the lit brazier by the handles. He puts it by your feet and revives the coals with a bellows. Catalina sits with her hands crossed on her skirt. With a backdrop of chirping black martins by the window, the three of you keep quiet as if posing for a painting. As soon as they leave you alone, you will burn the letters from the witches. If they surprise you and ask what you are doing, you will tell them that you are destroying some worthless rough drafts. Papers that one can do without as though they were human beings. You want your remains to be buried at the Trinitarians'. Catalina agreed to pay for no less than three masses for the salvation of your soul. They will bury you with your face uncovered, your beard combed, and dressed in the habit of Saint Francis. It was Heaven's will that before your death you concluded the forsaken second part of your novel, under the sign of Janus in the garden of Atocha. In your final epilogue, you affirmed that you and your Hidalgo had been born for each other. It was for one to act and the other to write. By order of the General Vicar of Madrid, the lawyer Márquez Torres approved the edition of the new part of your book. He did not change even a comma and even requested in his report that the country support a genius like you with funds from the state. You smiled to yourself thinking that if you had been your own censor, you would have cut out those phrases of the epilogue which seemed dictated by a sinister love. *We two are one.* You would then remember again the son and daughter of your own flesh and blood, both illegitimate, and your son never recognized. You were almost amazed by the coldness of your soul when you wondered for the last time if Promontorio were alive and, if he were, what had become of him and his mother. Then, once you lost all hope that Isabel would visit you in your agony, you were certain that your only heirs before eternity would be the Rustic and the Knight. In the name of those pieces of your spirit and as if voicing their joint demand, you ask Miguel Cortinas:

"Why did you write the fake continuation of my book? What did I do to you, why were you so merciless with me and why wound me as you did in the prologue?"

Still on his knees and with the bellows in his hand, your servant raises his head to face your stare.

"I was not Avellaneda," he replies gently but firmly. "But if you, Señor, want to listen, I will tell you who he was.

Staring at her open hands on her lap, Catalina nods. From the snows of Guadarrama through Monte del Pardo will soon come the April showers. *If the clouds were full of rain, they would spill onto the earth: and if the tree were to fall in the South or in the North, whatever the place, there it would remain,* your wife used to say reciting from Ecclesiastes. Through the plains of Fuencarral, where they burned the heretics with green kindling, the showers will come to the city. Beyond El Prado of the Hieronymous, the afternoon thunders, beneath a sky still very clear.

* * * * *

No, I was not the supposed Alonso Fernández de Avellaneda: the one who dared to proceed with your novel, Señor, at someone else's request. I was not the one, I say, but it was my only son, the tailor, who is also my namesake. The impersonation was entrusted to him by their Graces Don Félix Lope de Vega and Don Luis de Góngora, although my son still thinks that the money for the payment came from someone with a larger fortune than those gentlemen's. I believe he was referring to Don Luis Fernández de Aragón, the present Duke of Sessa, whose chaplain and confidant and procurer of illicit love affairs is Don Félix Lope. At least so the rumor has it, and may God help me for repeating it even if it is beneath the roof of this house.

You look at me in silence. But it is as though your eyes are piercing mine. You must be wondering about my faithfulness if I kept to myself what was being plotted behind your back. However, you are also a father, Señor, and you must understand that I was obliged to be loyal to both of you, to my master, and to my son. How could I betray him whom I begot, when he confided the intrigue to me on his own account and without my requesting it. I hope that through your mercy I may find forgiveness.

The idea of the plagiarism was my son's, who, as you Señor may remember, sews for Don Félix Lope de Vega and for the Duke of Sessa himself. While Don Félix was trying on a cassock, my son, in friendly chatter, started telling him how during his idle hours he imagined new wanderings for your celebrated Hidalgo and his Squire. The continuation of the first part was taking you so long that my son amused himself imagining how he would have carried on the story if he had been its true author. After all, did Christopher Columbus himself not say, when he had fallen into disgrace, that in the decadence of his time even tailors made themselves discoverers?

Listening to all of this, Don Félix Lope de Vega remained speechless and immobile in front of the mirror, unmindful of his own reflection and his basted clothes. Absorbed, he did not notice my son's reflection in the mirror with the pincushion hanging from his elbow and a piece of blue chalk between his lips. When he finally spoke, after an almost endless silence, it was to propose the plot that would give birth to Avellaneda. He remembered the humorous pastoral eclogues that my son had read to him as his own parodies of Garcilaso and the Sevillan poet Baltasar de Alcázar. He sincerely praised him for his verses because Don Félix Lope was as generous with the unknown poets as he was severe and biting with the celebrated. If the tailor agreed to show him and Don Luis de Góngora what he had tacked and basted towards the false continuation of *Don Quixote,* Don Félix Lope was almost sure to promise him some fixed and punctual payments till he stitched the very end of his satire. All of this assumed that the parody was acceptable and in no way contrary to the Christian faith and morality.

More playfully than seriously, my son promised to read to Don Luis de Góngora and Don Félix Lope what he had scribbled so far about the new outing of the Knight and the Peasant on their way to the tournament in Saragossa where you, Señor, insinuated—at the conclusion of your own first part—that one day perhaps they would go and joust. *It is hard to understand how two great poets like Your Grace and Don Luis de Góngora became so interested in the fable so frivolously set forth by a tailor,* my son asserted and insisted before Don Félix Lope. *Read for us what you have written and the three of us will see if the mockery is truly a mockery,* replied Lope, the Monster of Nature and Phoenix of Wits.

One evening my son took his papers to Don Félix Lope's house. There he met Don Luis de Góngora, whom he had known only by name. Urged by Don Félix Lope, my son read his rough drafts. Both of them liked my son's imaginary account very much, although Don Luis de Góngora was more reticent with his praises since he is by nature reserved and inclined toward melancholy. Both of them, however, gave their word to pay my son a small retainer so that he would resume your book in its false continuation. All they needed was to sign a secret agreement, with Don Luis de Góngora as a witness and before a notary public for Don Félix Lope to hand deliver the first of the promised payments. As a marginal comment, the Phoenix of Wits added that my son should not neglect his work as a tailor, nor should he delay his cassock and clerical collar for as long as you have been postponing the culmination of your novel.

My son resisted their offer insisting that he did not have the time to accommodate such a demanding enterprise along with his many responsibilities as a tailor and maker of doublets which were so fashionable in the city at that time. He also argued that you, Señor, had been very good to me. While you were at home and during your absences, you always shared with me the little that there was in this house. To betray my master, my son added, was the same as to sell his own father. The two chaplains replied that they did not mean any evil or deceit. On the contrary, they intended to help you, Señor, by not revealing the identity of his protectors. So much time had been wasted since the publication of the first part, so many years had passed that only an unforseen apocryphal second part would challenge you to continue and finish your novel.

My son then accepted. But later he also clarified that the insults to you, Señor, in the prologue of the unknown Avellaneda where you are called old and maimed, were not his. In that matter of honor, he gave me his word. It was Don Félix Lope himself who composed the offenses and objected to the protests of my son and Don Luis de Góngora. He then maintained that if the parody did not induce you to write the conclusion of your own novel, those affronts would. The lower and more vile the offenses, the better they would accomplish the purpose of spurring your concealed pride, because as far as vanity was concerned, you, Señor, harbored more than anyone else in the world. At least in Don Félix Lope's judgement.

All that remains for me to tell you is how the name Alonso Fernández de Avellaneda came to be. Shuffling through several others, together the three of them composed the pseudonym. Don Félix Lope de Vega considered it a subtle and effective choice to call the author of the plagiarism Avellaneda. If you, Señor, were a paragon of arrogance in everything related to your family names, then by contrast, it would fit that your mocker and copyist be called Avellaneda—a sort of hazelnut tree. Any tree name would do fine among those from whence acorns and other dried fruits fall when shaken, avoiding of course, the cork tree for the blockhead insult that it so obviously suggests. Such sarcasm—that of mocking oneself—would cause no little bewilderment in an ironist like yourself.

This is the entire truth about that intrigue. If there were more, I did not know because I never spoke again about the matter with my son. When, soon after the publication of Avellaneda's book, and even before its release, you dictated passages of your own continuation and stared at me as you do now, I was tempted to tell you everything: "I am not who you, Señor, think that I am. I am only the father of my son. If, as Don Luis de Góngora affirms, there is no one on earth who knows for sure who he is, at least I can assure you that I have never been who you, Señor, thought that I was."

But I cannot end without adding that my son liked the pen name Avellaneda and the reasons that Don Félix Lope had to sponsor him. As my son then reasoned, there was in all of that a sort of obscure retribution because long before you and I met, Señor, you renounced our common last name when you changed your mother's Cortinas for the more high-sounding Saavedra. If you had not been from Alcalá, but from Esquivias like your wife, all of us—masters and servants, tailors and poets—would have been taken for blood kin. It is a known fact that at least in Esquivias all the Cortinases are related, as also are the Salazars and the Palacios.

Also everyone in town knows that all of us, Palacios, Salazars, and Cortinases are of Jewish descent. Our ancestors passed away and fear buried their beliefs in oblivion. After so many persecutions, we are now Christians in appearance, although very few of our people ever served in the Church. Many were true Christians because, at times, faith is as contagious as black cholera. We have zealously kept hidden the Romance Ladino language of our forbearers as they had kept hidden the law of Moses. Our tongue is concealed beneath "the force of our blood," as you, Señor, if I am not mistaken, entitled one of your exemplary novels. We could lose, and in fact we lost our religion, forgetting those who ended their lives at the stake defending their faith. In our secret language we maintain the veiled meaning of our true being as if it were an obscenity or a sin. We are only what we speak in secret and among ourselves. You, Señor, probably understand it better than anyone else because your identity is also reduced to what you said in your book. Perhaps you wrote it to feel that you were alive, and you even delayed its continuation for so many years because you feared you would lose your identity upon finishing it. Besides, you convinced yourself that you could live for only as long as the epilogue of your novel did not appear; thus your work would not be completed. Perchance it would be better to have left your book like that, as unfinished as certain cathedrals remain whilst time reduces other temples to ruins. Perhaps to remind men that they should never

have concluded them, if they did not want to fall into the sin of
Satanic pride. To tell the truth, I do not know.

You, Señor, survive or grow more feeble in your delirium. At
times you believe that Miguel Cortinas made a long and astonishing
confession to you in a recently lost past. *The idea of the plagiarism
was my son's, who as you Señor, may remember, sews for Don Félix
Lope de Vega and the Duke of Sessa himself. While Don Félix was
trying on a cassock, my son, in friendly chatter, started telling him
how during his idle hours he imagined and wrote new wanderings
of your celebrated Hidalgo and his Squire.* At times, you imagine
Catalina asking if you remember yesterday's visit by Lope, Figueroa, and Góngora. Your Grace stares at her without replying because
if there were such a visit, you had entirely forgotten it.

Instead, you remember your doctor. The one who lives only a
stone's throw from you on Franco Street, with his blind spaniel, his
eyeglasses, and his copious beard. He comes, massages and bleeds
you, and applies cuppings on your stomach and cold compresses on
your forehead. At other times Your Grace shivers, shakes, and your
teeth chatter with the chills of a fever. Then, Catalina and Miguel
Cortinas fill your bed with hot water bottles and hot bricks wrapped
in the rags of a blanket eaten by moths. Little by little, you become
quiet and calm down. You smile at your wife and your servant
although it is getting harder for you to recognize them. By contrast,
you have a very clear memory of the Atocha of your adolescence
where your father tried to establish himself as a surgeon. That was
an Atocha still surrounded by walls with tents, sheds, and eating
houses along the riverbank. The Atocha of esparto grass and hawthorns around the sanctuary of the Virgin of Antioquía.

Then you fall asleep and dream of the Guadatén. Upon crossing
Torrejón de Velasco, that trout creek becomes as bright as shining
gold. In your dream you see the swarthy shepherd of Esquivias who
seemed to have the same gaze as the muffled man. *Truly I say to
you that the golden age is now here,* he assures Your Grace, *because
your book is no longer yours but belongs to all men.* Knowing that
you are dreaming, but very aware of the truth of such words, you
reply that you are not pursuing a Guadatén of gold. Nor do you
pursue a river of blood that would be nothing but Lope's red cloak
meandering among the vineyards, since in dreams everything is an
allusion or a symbol of the most distant and opposite. *I go after the
river that I once saw suspended above Alcalá de Henares where I
came into the world. At sundown, it ran from east to west. There in
the firmament, like on the back of a mirror, the olive trees and the*

fences of those lands were reflected. Above the church of Santa María la Mayor, where they christened me, the screeching crows circled. In that corner of the sky and above the bell tower, the birds were probably scared to see a sand field covered with gladiolus and a small boat tied to a dead poplar.

Your Grace realizes that for just a fleeting instant you saw the river suspended across the firmament. However, you have the certainty that you have only witnessed a mirage and you know that somewhere on earth you will find the true river and that it cannot be the Henares. The shepherd shakes his head *I do not understand anything about rivers hanging from the sky. I only know that the golden age is finally here because a book, that before was yours alone, is now shared with all humanity.* The shepherd vanishes and, as if on cue, Lope emerges in his place. Looking down at you in your bed, he wipes the sweat from your forehead with a handkerchief. *Tell me whether you and I exist or if I am merely dreaming about you, as I dreamed before about a shepherd from Esquivias.* Lope replies that it matters very little who dreams about whom or if both of you are asleep or awake. What is significant is that you are conversing and one hears the other, while he, Lope, was never able to do that with God Himself. *Tell me then if you entrusted Avellaneda to write his book to force me to finish the second part of mine. Or did you intend that I never complete it?*

Lope shrugs his shoulders. He is not sure of his true motives in that affair. All men are unaware of their old intentions because they cease being who they were in the past. At any rate, all of this matters very little because neither of you knows for certain if one dreams of the other or not. *Whether our dreams are imagined or real, death is the only unfathomable truth. And I am dying,* smiles Your Grace. Lope shakes his head. He had not come to hear your confession this afternoon but to speak with you as a good friend. *We so degrade death that we transform it into a venial or a scrupulous sin. I know that you never believed a great deal of what I said. But I assure you that nowadays, dying is not worth it. It is not morally profitable,* utters that priest and member of the Holy Office.

My father told you, Señor, that I was Avellaneda and that by the request of two great poets, Don Luis de Góngora and Don Félix Lope de Vega, I composed my false *Don Quixote*. All of it is in part true and also in part false. To say it better, it started out being true but ended up being a sheer mendacity. As it is, my father never wanted to deceive you, not when he kept silent, nor when he attributed the authorship of Avellaneda to me. He only knows a half-truth, and I was not going to allow that because of misinformation he would, unintentionally, lead you to take as true that which never occurred. Neither could I permit that perhaps you might find out from other sources something that not even Don Félix Lope de Vega and Don Luis de Góngora know. Finally, and above all, it is fair that you, Señor, be aware of the entire truth by the mouth of the only person who can tell it. After all, if this interlude of our lives were authentic theater, you, Señor, would be the protagonist on stage and we would be your bit actors: your shadows or your reflections in the water.

The hardest part is to find a proper way to begin my confession, because in real life facts are entangled in more intricate ways than they are in chivalric novels where everything follows a more reasonable and convincing pattern. Nor would I dare to reveal what happened if it did not concern the good name of my father and that of my own. Be assured that he was always loyal and never betrayed you at someone else's request. If it happened that I felt tempted to impersonate you as a writer it was more from admiration of your genius than from envy of your talents.

More out of my desire to be you than out of a need to cease being who I was, I agreed to become Avellaneda when Don Félix Lope asked me to become a man who never existed. A client of mine for many years, Don Félix Lope has also been my confessor for quite a while. Out of respect for the sacred vestments that I cut for him, and out of devotion to his consecrated hands that I kiss when I bid him farewell, I took the identity of Avellaneda. Generous, although not extravagant, my payment had little to do with my fraud because from the start I saw it as the devil's money. At an ill-fated moment, I accepted Don Félix Lope's proposal to proceed with the tale of your novel. I had already begun writing for my own enjoyment, as I unfortunately confided to my spiritual father that afternoon. After reviewing several pen names with that pair of gifted poets, I chose that of Avellaneda. As soon as I assumed it, along with the task, I had a change of heart. I wanted to give it up as an unfit priest gives up the cloth. This is, however, another story and I do not wish to go into it now if you, Señor, have no objection. Instead, I would like to go back to the very origins of my existence.

Although my father does not know it yet, and I hope that he never will, I am one of those who was born with the spirit of a woman in a man's body. I did not chose the abominable love that possesses me as I did not chose the existence that was thrust upon me. There were times when I was desolate because of my deviation until I learned to accept it as my very nature, that is to say, until reconciling myself with who I was, since I had not been born a sodomite out of my free will.

Needless to say, Don Félix Lope is aware of my secret. But when he became my father confessor and I tried to reveal it to him, he interrupted me right away with a gesture of impatience. He did not want to hear of my pederasty at the confessional because there he was subject to secrecy and he feared that in other circumstances he might denounce me as a faggot. My own fear would render suspicious the repentance of thousands of sins and the sincerity of my remorse at the same time that it questioned his personal dignity. If I wanted to talk to him about my deviance, I had to speak to him man-to-man with all the cards on the table. Otherwise, he refused to listen because my confession would be a waste of the precious and dwindling time that he needed to write his comedies. *Know that I absolve you of the rest of your sins,* he concluded, *in hope that you sin no more and with the condition that you pray for me so that I do not relapse into the sins of the flesh. I am convinced that by my own free will I cannot refrain from lascivious pleasures,* he insisted without apparent false modesty. *If I am not redeemed by someone else's prayers, I will not be saved.*

Far from the confessional, in my shop and while taking his measurements for some shirts, I finally told him about my perversion. Smiling beneath his short mustache, curled with a curling iron and beginning to gray, Don Félix Lope shrugged his shoulders. *You were born effeminate as I was born a womanizer,* he said. *To make matters worse, we are unable to control our nature. I am not one to give you advice, but perhaps you should bathe yourself in the cold water of early dawn, exercise strenuously, play ball, and pray to the Most Holy Sacrament and to Saint Sebastian, martyr and patron saint of all homosexuals. To conclude, let me make clear that my duty as a Christian Inquisitor is to denounce you to the Holy Office. Reproachably, I will not do it because I do not want to lose my good tailor and habitmaker, if you see what I mean.*

Long ago, Señor, I met the man who is still my lover. As a youngster, he had inherited some farmland that later sold at a handsome price. With new pasture lands and flocks, he multiplied his earnings as if by magic. In each dry land that he bought the diviners found water. Like Midas, he changed all the fields that he acquired into gold. He owns a house at El Prado of the Recollect Friars with an entrance hall of cobblestone and with room for two carriages, not to mention a patio adorned with blue tiles and a marble fountain in the middle. When he is not busy adding his profits, he dissipates his tedium by reading his many books. He is so devoted to them and to the theater that he would have given an arm and a leg to have been a playwright.

For a long time, Señor, my friend has admired you and Don Félix Lope de Vega for your writings. When I committed the indiscretion of telling him that Don Luis de Góngora and my spiritual director had entrusted me with the false continuation of *Don Quixote* and adding that I was as stuck as a sparrow in a bramble bush without being able to make much progress in a task that I should have never accepted, my lover was filled with joy. Grabbing me by the ruffle of my shirt and shaking me, he begged that I allow him to proceed with the work, thus becoming truly and secretly Avellaneda. All of this because of entangled motives which on another occasion and in due time he would reveal to me.

If I consented to entrust the task to him, he would be forever grateful. Our deal had to be kept so quiet that neither Don Félix Lope nor Don Luis de Góngora would ever know about it. He refused to accept the payments when I offered them to him. His reasons to be Avellaneda were private and he did not pursue any profit. After all, a monetary reward would not mean much to someone as wealthy as he. He did not tell me his most secret motives until much later.

Señor, you frighten me with your silent stare. I believe I am reading a question in your eyes: Who is the man I love? Who is, therefore, Avellaneda? Perhaps you have anticipated who he is and you are only waiting for me to tell you in my own words. Actually, you, Señor, met Avellaneda long before I did myself. You must undoubtedly have guessed it. I am talking about Gregorio Nacianceno Patriarca. He told me that he had seen you several times in the tavern of the poets where, because of his timid spirit, he did not have the courage to talk to you. About the same time that he received his inheritance and left the company of Angulo el Malo and Romero Retama, he crossed paths with you at an inn. Since then many rains have come and gone and much water has passed beneath the blind eyes of the bridges.

He did not dare to speak to you at the inn either. He was overwhelmed by his own bashfulness and he only gained confidence when he caught up with you on your way to Madrid. As my father says that you do not ever miss or forget anything, you must remember that he was wearing a purple coat and his hair was as blond as the wheat of the fields although now it is graying around his temples. You must also remember how he knelt down at your feet to kiss the hand that had written *Don Quixote* and would have succeeded had you not pushed him aside.

Gregorio Nacianceno Patriarca himself confessed to me that only by pretending that he was not who he was and by exaggerating his role, was he able to overcome his timidity to follow and speak to you at the holm-oak grove among strawberry and raspberry bushes. As you may not have forgotten, that morning he proposed that you write a play together: a piece where your Knight and the Squire of your novel would be on stage telling their story while other actors, all as mute as mimes, would act it out. In fact, Gregorio Nacianceno Patriarca himself would have played you in your youth, and no one else more appropriate than you, Señor, would have represented yourself in your venerable maturity. He was ready to cover all of the expenses for that adventure, thanks to the profits from the sale of his inherited lands between Villanueva and Quijorna.

You seemed to be pleased with his offer. You even invited Gregorio Nacianceno to visit you at your house, at this house, where you would discuss it carefully. Anyway, you added and warned, you could not take the project seriously until after concluding the last part of your novel. Gregorio Nacianceno then exclaimed that you would never finish it, but your doubts and hesitations could also be represented in the play. In the end, he never had the nerve to see you again. From that moment on he became resentful, which was nothing more than anger at himself because of his failure to overcome his fear of facing you again. At least this is the way I see it.

Only God knows up to what point and with the passing of years how a poisonous seed such as that would germinate and deepen in a man's heart. If it does not find a way out, it ends up by pricking him inside, awake and asleep. When my lover saw the opportunity to become Avellaneda he thought that the day had come when, through such a twisted and unforeseeable path, he would approach you again. Also, behind the mask of a pseudonym he could avenge the many occasions when he stopped at León Street and did not dare to speak to you. The spite that he had for you for hating himself was the backdrop of his derision in his apocryphal novel. If Gregorio Nacianceno could not be you, Señor, he would be your shadow or reflection on a concave and deforming mirror. A shadow almost erased today because no one remembers Avellaneda or his book any longer. A shadow so vain that not even I have the courage to mention it to the one I love.

You, Señor, may wonder why I did not tell you before what had happened. My reasons to postpone it were no different from my father's. Perhaps I would not have revealed it to you now if he had not told me that yesterday afternoon he confessed to you who Avellaneda was. He had kept silent until then because he felt obliged by our blood ties. I was silent for other reasons, for reasons of love, which forced me to hide the truth. I could not denounce Gregorio Nacianceno, that young lad in the purple coat who followed you to the helm-oak grove, although I also refused to read what he was writing under the name of Avellaneda.

When the apocryphal novel finally appeared, I devoured it entirely but it held no further interest for me. The novel was like dead leaves and ashes. My lover composed it for nothing because, instead of your parody, Señor, he wrote his own unintentional mockery. The novel of the false Avellaneda would have remained as a regrettable waste of time if it had not spurred you, Señor, to finish yours. Don Félix Lope said that this had been his intention when he proposed the fraud to me. Today I am not sure of it, and I will probably never know for certain, nor will Don Félix Lope be able to clarify it to himself in the depths of his soul. There is no more to tell. As Heaven and the Most Holy Trinity are my witnesses.

Once again, and as in the midst of another dream, you think that Mateo Vázquez suddenly appears at your bedside. Vaguely you distinguish his mouse-like profile always ready to pry into others' affairs, his inquisitive eyes, and the vertical wrinkles from his temples to his chin so very deepened by time. *For the last ten years I have served that great Filipo of ours, / now rested, now tired and exhausted.* Your Grace does not resent his ignoring the rhymed epistle that you sent to him during your captivity. When you want to get rid of part of the present, let us say of the daughter who refuses to see you in your last days, you mitigate the pain by pushing it into the past as if you had lived it in another life. Then you displace the past itself even farther: to the reign of myths, lies, and the void.

But at every moment others force your memories and urge you to bring them back to the most recent happenings. They ask Your Grace to break that silence in which you find refuge and perhaps even solace. They ask you to answer and share your remembrances with those in this bedroom. *Do you know that Mateo Vázquez came to see you?* Catalina insists with her elbows resting on the fold of your sheet, staring into your eyes as if trying to pierce your soul. *You could not have forgotten Mateo Vázquez. He was riding in the royal coach when it stopped at El Prado because Don Filipo Hermenegildo wanted to talk to you.* Your Grace remains quiet and stares back at your wife. Perhaps you are evoking Mateo Vázquez's visit but you do not know what he said because you simply refused to listen to him. You did not reply because since before the visit of your family doctor—the one with the spaniel and the copious beard—you had firmly decided not to speak to anyone. *Someday you will see that the greatest wisdom, that the most supreme knowledge does not reside in books, nor in war, not even in love. Supreme knowledge has no name and resides in silence,* said Azán Bajá on the beach of Algiers. Perhaps in these days, bedridden and slowly expiring, you are beginning to understand him.

Catalina persists, adds, and proceeds. *You could not have forgotten Mateo Vázquez who was here just yesterday. Neither can you ignore what he said because it was so grand and extraordinary. Your Majesty wants to come here and visit with you. Do you hear me? Do you understand me? The King, our lord, is going to honor us with his presence.* Many days of haste, hustle, and bustle follow. Catalina and Miguel Cortinas leave the house as neat as a pin. They call a cleaning woman from Lavapiés to give them a hand. They get up each day at dawn, dress themselves in their best attire, change your night shirt and your sheets, sweep the floors, chase with foxtail and feather dusters the nonexistent dust, touch up the windows that had been cleaned the day before, fill the flower vases with new bouquets, and even change the strawberries and grapefruits in the fruit bowl. Then they let time pass and wait the entire day. They run to the window each time that a coach stops at León Street. At night, before going to bed, Catalina sits down in the alcove. Sad, she shakes her head and sighs. *The King did not come today. But I have the feeling that he will come tomorrow.* Then, she undresses by candle light. She lies down at the edge of the bed as far as possible from Your Grace. Perhaps she fears that before daybreak and while she sleeps you may die on her.

One afternoon Your Grace has dozed off when Miguel Cortinas at his wits' end with excitement wakes you up: *Señor! Señor! His Majesty, may God keep him, has come with the Duke of Sessa, Don Félix Lope de Vega and Don Luis de Góngora. Doña Catalina is now kissing the King's hands.* It is hard for you to understand what is going on. You are tempted to speak for once and ask them all— Miguel Cortinas, Catalina, Lope, Góngora, the Duke, and the Monarch—to leave you alone with the dream that you were having before you forget it. You were dreaming about Ana Franca, resurrected and running barefoot up the hill of an old meadow, while she was holding the hem of her skirt with the tips of her fingers. She was laughing loudly and merrily when you reached her. Then you enjoyed one another and conceived Isabel. Perhaps you may even think about what would have happened if on that day, lived or dreamed, you had not given life to anyone in Ana Franca. Isabel would not exist and you would not be waiting for her in vain. Perhaps Ana Franca would still be living since she started to languish right after giving birth and never recovered. Maybe you would have married her instead of Catalina, once that husband of hers died as he did in the Indies, and now it would be Ana Franca and not Catalina who would be kissing the hands of Don Filipo Hermenegildo, *Señor! Señor! The King has come and he says that he only wants to greet you if it is not too tiring for Your Grace!*

Since we saw each other in El Prado, I have had no peace and I believe that I am slowly losing my mind. I lock myself in my private chambers and order fines for those who disturb my slothfulness. The matters of government, which I have always despised, are completely abandoned. I say to everyone that if I reign it is not to take care of tedious business that does not concern me. To be idle seems more honest and I shamelessly confess it. I will answer to God for my conduct when I appear in his presence. I am afraid you will have a lot of explaining to do yourself for having delayed the continuation of *Don Quixote* for so long. Your indolence is worse than mine because your book is worth more than my kingdom.

My madness comes down to a few questions for which I have no answer. I ask Heaven at times but I receive no response. If man is created twice, as you said in your book, who creates him first, God or nature? If you think about it seriously my question is no trifle and it leads to other no less overwhelming matters. For instance, is it possible that nature creates heretics, murderers, imbeciles, and the depraved, since their mothers gave them birth, although, for unknown reasons, God forgot to create them too? Or, on the contrary, could it be that the entities conceived in the imagination like your Squire and your Hidalgo are woven by the Supreme Maker in the loom of a spirit like yours and nature never creates them again?

By the same token, since we are indeed twice created, as you say it, and I do not dare to argue, how many times will we die on earth? I suppose that our first death—the one of dust, ashes, and nothingness—is nature's order. But later there will be another imposed by God. One day or another, everything passes, transforms, or destroys itself. Saying it differently, oblivion corrupts or changes the name of things. The horrifying aspect is not to ponder where are those who once existed, *ubi sunt,* but where the memory of those who loved them might be. How many centuries will pass until everyone has forgotten that you wrote *Don Quixote* and that I, at least in appearance, reigned in this strange country?

Since that book of yours is the cause of my worries, you will understand perfectly why I turned myself into a slothful King, as everyone calls me behind my back. Thus they say, because they are far from understanding me, although their misconception does not bother me in the least. I hold concerns greater and longer than my empire and to make them worse you published the second part of *Don Quixote*. At the end of the fable I read that death did not finish the Hidalgo's life. Nor will our physical disappearance end your existence or mine, forever. To be completely sincere I admit that I doubt that neither you nor I will live much longer on this theater of Chinese-like shadows. For what remains to be seen on the stage, my demise leaves me almost indifferent. However, I have no peace wondering how long I will be remembered after my death. Until what point in the future they will remember that I, Filipo Hermenegildo—the third Filipo of my line—, existed and reigned, although throughout my rule I accomplished absolutely nothing?

I am more overwhelmed when wondering if I was created once or twice. I almost do not dare to ask myself if the Lord was my maker or if I owe my life solely to nature. From time to time, I would say that, the same as the incurable madmen, the pervert, the criminals, the heretics, and the obstinate Jews, He forgot to create me, and my life is a limbo between the existence that nature granted me and the being that God has not yet given me.

As I am caught in all these doubts, it matters very little to me what happens in the circus they call my Empire. Overwhelmed in his agony, my father said: *God who has given me so many kingdoms has deprived me of a son capable of ruling them.* He, who was so dedicated to the art of governing, did not ever understand why I wasted my youth in the theater, in hunting, in dances, in ball games, in all-night fiestas, or simply in praying. He was never able to comprehend that, since my early years and even before I discovered your disturbing book, I already had the feeling that everything was nothing and that there was not a greater emptiness than the royal power in this damned dream that they call History with a capital letter.

Next to such questions, for which I will never get an answer, what do I care if at the end of the world they find a continent and call it Australia in honor of my family? Why do I care if there is war in Flanders or not. If the Moors are or are not expelled from my Kingdom. If the British defeat us or if we defeat them at Gibraltar. What do I care if the Duke of Osuna in Naples conspires or not to take the Crown away from me. All of this, I dare say, has so little to do with me; it is as if it happened to another King, different and distant, in a star still unnamed. Or perhaps even farther: where the star gazers can no longer distinguish the firmament.

Coda

Your Grace will never know if all of that was reality, delirium, or the tale of someone else's dream. You will not find out because time is running out and you pass the days in opaque lethargies, waiting for the moment when eternity will come tiptoeing in to claim your soul. One afternoon of incredible lucidity, you made your will and dedicated to the Count of Lemos a long forgotten novel—*The Trials of Persiles and Sigismunda*—that Juan de la Cuesta made you publish. A year before, you had also dedicated to the Count the second part of *Don Quixote*. Lemos, who was also the Count of Andrade and Villalba, as well as Marquis of Sarria, Gentleman of His Majesty's Chambers, President of the Supreme Council of Italy, Knight-Commander of la Zarza, and Knight of Alcántara, did not deign to write and thank you. In the *Persiles,* Your Grace said to him that if by any miraculous chance heaven would lend you a longer life, you still nestled in your soul the first glimpses and traces of another book that would be called *Weeks in the Garden.*

All of a sudden, April days brightened as if it were June and you woke up feeling better and in high spirits. Catalina and Miguel Cortinas were delighted to see you regain your appetite. You ate half of a boiled chicken thigh as easily as you ate the marmalade from Esquivias, preserved in smoked glass jars in the pantry. You also enjoyed hearty soups as long as you had not lost your appetite, and then you preferred a light cream of celery soup and mint tea. Your sister Luisa of Bethlehem wrote to you from her convent and attributed your health improvement to your recent entrance in the Venerable Third Order of Saint Francis. Heaven had blessed you since the second of April of the year of our Lord when you had been admitted to the fraternity.

As soon as you noticed that your knees would hold you up, you insisted on going for a stroll alone. Firmly, you declined Catalina's support as well as your servant's. But you allowed them to dress you because your good hand was trembling. Following the hubbub of children, you went down León Street helping yourself with a cane and wearing your cap from the hat maker in Redondilla, so that the sun would not blind you. The urchins were having pretend jousting tournaments with some riding on the others' backs as if they were horses and paladins. Next to a portico a lizard was sunning himself and a girl played a melody on a sweet flute. Captivated by the music, the creature raised his head to look at her with his jet black eyes.

"Stop your yelling for a minute and tell me if you have seen the blind man Santafiore today."

The astonished children stopped and stared at you. Either you were speaking in an unknown language or the so-called Santafiore had never existed for them. Only the measures from the flute disturbed their dazzled silence. Vaguely you recognized the tune of an old ballad from those that you had heard once upon a time along the roads of La Mancha. *Now that I have known love / you made me a nun against my will / now that I have known love / in the wheat fields / scented with rosemary.* In an oblique frieze beneath an indigo blue sky, the olive trees twisted in your memory. Here and there a brownish inn. A pond and a mill. The smoke from a house. Beds of thyme where swarms of bees buzzed. The lands that you crossed so many times on your way to Andalusia. *Now that I have known the love / of my sweet gentleman.*

"A very tall blind man who begs while singing in Italian. You used to run him off by throwing stones at him."

Little by little, the children moved farther away from you as if you were leprous. The sweet flute fell silent and the girl disappeared. The lizard drifted off to sleep beneath the sun. Shaking their heads the youngsters left you. You first called them in vain and then ignored them. Suddenly you were overtaken by an immense compassion that ironically would not be too far from indifference. Perhaps you felt sorry for yourself because you would not see the Hidalgo and the Squire again since you would never go back to the house of Janus that must have vanished through the mirror along with the tapestry, the bust, and the orchard. The same as one of those high waves that, once broken, left behind big shadows on the beach of Algiers—gigantic horses, albatrosses, octopuses, giltheads, swordfish—, you extended your pity to Catalina, Lope, and Góngora. To Lope and Catalina because they tried to love one another behind your back but they were merely able to give each other pleasure. Perhaps in vain Lope tried to conceive another child in the woman who could not bear, even for you. Catalina must have been condemned to love you—old, idle and ailing—in the same manner that you were compelled to love your Hidalgo and his Squire more than you loved your lost illegitimate children. And above all, you felt pity for Góngora: for that chaplain who must have acknowledged your existences in his infinite and very peculiar erudition. But each time more oblivious, soon he would profess never to have known any of you.

Your commiseration dissipated as promptly as it had overwhelmed you. You felt such a melioration in your mortal body, sack for your sins, that you decided to ride forth into the countryside through Puerta de Toledo. With the profits from the second part of *Don Quixote,* you had acquired a handsome horse and now you did not have to borrow Lope's. No sooner had you bought the horse than you felt sick and you lacked the energy to ride, although Miguel Cortinas would brush and groom the dark chestnut horse every afternoon and walk it through El Prado. Slowly and along a path bordered with early blooming genista, you now rode alone towards Villaverde between the Manzanares and Carabancheles. The fields and the sky started to turn yellow when you began to recite the speech of the golden age that the Hidalgo in your novel had delivered to the goat herders. *Happy the age and happy those centuries to which the ancients gave the name of golden, and not because gold, which is so esteemed in this iron age of ours, was then to be had without toil, but because those who lived in that time did not know the meaning of the words "thine" and "mine."*

Emerging as suddenly as if he had come from the genista in bloom and had come alive in the air, you saw another horseman by your side. Silently, the stranger seemed ready to accompany you. When Your Grace almost stopped to glance at him out of the corner of your eye with half of your face shaded by your cap's visor, you were startled by the visitor's appearance. Not only was his horse identical to yours but also the traveler seemed to be a faithful copy of yourself. Your profiles were so alike it was as if both of you had been minted and superimposed on the same coin. Immediately you remembered that dream of yours, so distant now, when you believed that the Hidalgo and the Squire were taking you through the pages of a book which were destined to remain unwritten forever. They told you then that you were going to meet the one who was trying to steal your novel: someone as close to you as each face of Janus was to the other.

"Are you by any chance Gregorio Nacianceno Patriarca and are you thus disguised so that I may not know even who I am?"

"Gregorio Nacianceno Patriarca?" Your interlocutor seemed sincerely puzzled, although the tone of his voice reminded you of the actor in the purple coat. In passing, you must have remembered then that Góngora had said that no one would be able to identify his own voice, even if it were recorded and kept in a wooden box to be later played back through a tulip shaped trumpet. "Whose name could that be? I do not know anyone by that name."

"You must not know who you are. Lope says that in order to be a good comedian it is essential not to be aware of one's own identity. Now you pretend to be my double and you forget your name. For my part and at my age, I feel totally dispensable for I have lived and performed my role in the world."

"If the world is a theater, what you are saying may be true,," slowly replied the man who was your own reflection. "But if you believe that you are already superfluous, I came only to announce to you that you will die in a few days."

Since you had already resigned yourself to your unavoidable fate, in spite of your apparent alleviation, you almost did not pay attention to his warning. More amazing than his premonitions was the unbroken view of genista fields followed by the golden hues of a horizon of sunflowers. You did not recall having seen such plants and fields, neither on your way to Andalusia nor on your solitary strolls throughout those lands. More than cultivated or grown wild, one would say that they were fields and thickets created by a man's imagination. Translated into words, the landscape would probably be dulled on the paper and imprisoned in a paragraph.

"But if you are neither Gregorio Nacianceno nor my mask, then who can you be?"

"I am your exact replica, but I also have a different name in all languages. I belong to every man and I am inseparable from every human being."

"If you are Death, for certain, tell me if I am now living for the first or the last time?"

"How would I know how many times you have passed through this earth? Death has no appearance and it is merely a human condition. I am your herald, or your guardian angel, and I came to advise you that in a short while you will become the mere memory that others keep of your life. You will be remembered as long as men celebrate your book. In the meantime you are free to proceed as you please. If it is agreeable with you, we will cross the river in that boat and see what awaits you at the other bank. Or we can bid farewell, for the time being, right here."

Suddenly the landscape changed again. With the swiftness of a flash of lightning in a stormy sky, an unforseen river appeared by your feet amidst the genista and the sunflower fields. So clear were the waters that one could see schools of barbels gliding on the bottom behind the genista and sunflowers while the meadow undulated into rolling hills and brownish slopes. New olive groves added shades of gray to the landscape and stone fences parceled it among the hills. On a sand bar, spotted with reed mace, a whitened dead poplar was losing its bark. With a long rope, they had attached a row boat to its trunk.

Silently, you took off your glasses and breathed on the lenses, then you rubbed them on the sleeve of your maimed arm and put the spectacles back on. More than just contemplating a real landscape, you thought you were facing one of your most recent dreams. You remembered how, in your sleep, the shepherd from Esquivias had appeared and said that the golden age had finally arrived. Your Grace replied that you had no need of that Guadatén of gold which in your dream ran along Torrejón. You added that you were in search of another river that you had seen one afternoon suspended in the firmament of Alcalá above the church of Santa María la Mayor where they had christened you. The terrified crows flew away cawing when a boat appeared in the sky tied to a dry poplar near another sand bar where gladiolus grew. *I do not understand anything about rivers suspended across the firmament,* the shepherd had argued before vanishing in your dream. Then, once you woke up, you found yourself facing Lope as he wiped the sweat from your forehead with an embroidered handkerchief.

"What river could this be?" you wonder now as you think of Santafiore. "Is this the Styx that borders the Inferno or is it an ocean estuary at the entrance of Purgatory?"

"Call it as you will and come if you please. I do not know the name of these waters but I will be your oarsman when we cross."

The two of you dismounted and tied your horses to the dead poplar. Hesitantly you stepped into the boat while the apparition held it with his right hand. As soon as you settled in your seats, the Angel of Death untied the boat and took a long starting stroke and began rowing vigorously with his good arm. Perhaps to avoid the rower's stare, you decided to look at the other bank. Long fences crossed it from east to west. At various intervals and beneath the flight of the rooks, there appeared fennel beds and patches of reddish unsown ground. You recognized the countryside of Montiel among the untilled lands, although they were not exactly as you had seen them but as you had described them in your book. On some clayish ground sprinkled with bulrushes, the two of you tied the boat to another poplar. This one was alive but had no birds. Once disembarked, and while you were still contemplating the slithering silence of the river, your mirror image said to you:

"Look at the top of that hill to the south. Clarify for me if the figures silhouetted there are giants or windmills."

Your eyesight which by that time had clouded, felt rejuvenated. Sweeping over the cultivated fields, your gaze cleared the horizon.

Thirty or forty windmills whirled their wings in the wind. Wings that made the grinding stone turn and finely mill the wheat or the barley, as the Peasant had warned the Hidalgo, his Master. You still remember your amazement at the sight of the first windmills that you saw swinging their blades under the north winds. In those days you were collecting taxes for the King, and as Inspector of weights and measures you often traveled to Andalusia. By that time, you had been redeemed from Algiers six or seven years and had been married to Catalina for two or three. When Your Grace was a child and your father—that bloodletting quack who had vainly tried to establish himself as a surgeon in Madrid—moved his family to Seville in search of better fortune, there were, as yet, no windmills throughout those ochre lands which always reddened or became eggplant-colored after the rain. Much later you found out that the idea for such wonders came from Flanders and in no time those machines sprouted up all over that clay wheat land. Still in 1586 or 1587 when you returned from Andalusia as the revenue officer, the stagecoach stopped at several points in La Mancha, so that the travelers could admire the windmills. Contemplating then those clever inventions a strange excitement stirred your soul. Yes, you must have felt the premonition of having stopped at a place in a transcendental moment of your destiny, for reasons that would take you many years to understand.

"This must be the road to Puerto Lápice or its evoked copy as it appears in my book. And those must be the windmills that my Hidalgo attacked at full gallop thinking that they were mighty giants and determined to eradicate their evil seed from the face of the earth."

"You are right when you say that this must be the road to the port and those the windmills. But the Knight has not yet charged against their blades. You foretold all of this in your book, but once dead you will come to live it on this spot of eternity. As soon as you die you will enter your novel to truly witness what you had anticipated in your writing and you will never leave its boundaries. This will be your redemption or your eternal exile."

"Exile or salvation, will all of this not end the night or day of final judgement? Perhaps another angel, different from us, will call me and make me answer for what I did not write. Or for what I deformed, to write after having lived it?"

"I know nothing of other angels because I am only the herald of your fate. Nor do I know of the judgement that you mentioned. But I presume that you will live here among the beings that you created and in the world that you gave them for as long as the other world remembers your book."

Suddenly and before you had the chance to reply, your Angel of Death began to change his appearance. Little by little, as if he were being crumbled like breadcrumbs only to be redrawn with perfect strokes, he was losing Your Grace's old features and adopting the bittersweet air of Don Luis de Góngora. As if emerged from a painted playing card, he ended up by converting himself into the living effigy of the chaplain. He appeared wearing his shiny worn-out cassock that he liked to wear when he was alone at home measuring the Alexandrine verses that never satisfied him no matter how much he polished them.

"When you read to me that episode that you will see here, I asked myself why some visions from a man's fantasy remain in other men's memories," Góngora rambled, or suddenly remembered. "I gave as an example, blind Oedipus wandering with his daughter throughout Colonus in search of forgiveness for his crimes. Then I wondered if that chapter of your book with your eccentric Paladin charging against the giants of his soul by way of the windmills on earth would not become another immortal image. Now I know for certain that this is its irrevocable destiny," he fell silent shrugging his shoulders before continuing in a low voice: "I also said then that I would have renounced all my poetry to have been able to write a passage like the one of the windmills. This still holds true, and if we find ourselves in eternity, I suppose this is my irrevocable and everlasting truth."

"But who could you be, someone between truth and fiction or someone between dreams and eternal life?" Your Grace exclaimed, disconcerted. "As soon as I get used to facing someone identical to me, you transform yourself into Góngora."

The poet did not reply. Knitting his brows above his dwindling pallid smile, he only contemplated you with his half-closed eyes. Looking back at him, perhaps you remembered that distant afternoon in the tavern when the two of you shared with Lope a couple of meat pastries and a pitcher of Valdemoro or Yepes wine. The same afternoon in which Góngora spoke about the shrine dedicated to Janus in the forum of the Empire. An oratory in which the doors would open at the break of war and close with peace; the reason for that rite had long been forgotten by the Romans. Likewise, the clergyman explained that Janus was the father of Dawn and of all the gods, as well as the father of departures and arrivals and of ends and beginnings. In a book of his *Metamorphosis,* Ovid attributed another sacred garden by the fountain of the Naiads to Janus.

"Are you, by any chance, Janus as well as the Angel of Death? A Janus with my face and with Góngora's? Am I now living the end of a book that begins in the poets' tavern or even earlier, in that garden of Atocha with your bust?"

Murmuring and melancholic, the river appeased the afternoon while Góngora unraveled beneath the skies. Little by little, he was transformed into Ana Franca de Rojas. Melting in the light like wax in a flame, his old hawk-like features darkened and vanished giving way to the almond and childlike face of a woman, now dead, whose forehead was half-hidden behind page bangs. Ana Franca smiled at you and Your Grace probably sensed, underneath her clothes, the caramel colored body that you had possessed one afternoon of the past. *Take care, watch out, you seem blind! Your moves are so simple that I guess them before you think about them.* Humiliated and angry because you had been defeated again at your chess game by someone who hardly knew how to write her own name or read the Lord's Prayer in the Catechism, you knocked all the pieces off the board with one grand sweep of your hand. Ana Franca fled like a gazelle when you yelled that it was time to play another game. Then her buoyant laughter would mingle with the chirping of the lark and the ringing of the bells at the convent of the Hieronymous amid a concert of canaries beneath the grapevine of an inn.

"I am offering you a glimpse of the eternity that awaits you," the angel said. "Dead, you will return to this meadow where the characters and landscapes of your book preceded you. On this riverbank, you will share with them the endless flow of eternity."

"Will only my characters live with me in this world? Will I never see again those with whom I lived and loved? Although you are no longer Góngora, nor my double, tell me if I will not meet that Ana Franca who is now so identical to you."

"The world of your novel is almost as real as the world where you lived. It would only be fair that you share eternity with those who lived with you and with those whom you created."

Although tempted, you refrained from asking if you were going to meet Isabel and if she would deign to speak to you in spite of her angry arrogance. The Angel of Death so resembled Ana Franca that it was impossible to believe that the spirit was not the mother of your only daughter. In the end you must have understood that Isabel was still alive and that her arrival would not precede yours. In the meantime the windmills whirled at the top of the hill. But the Knight and the Squire did not appear on that plain. Perhaps invisible, they were carefully spying on you knowing that soon you would join them in the boundless mirage of your novel.

"It is time for you to depart and return to the world. You still have to die and entrust your remains to the Trinitarians."

"Tell me if you remember a very tall man who wears a plumed chambergo hat and a raincoat, although he might not exist at all beneath his attire. Am I going to encounter him in those spots?"

"I do not know anyone who has not existed," that angel, who was the living image of your lost love, replied with some confusion. "Perchance that man whom you are talking about belongs to the future."

"In such a case, perhaps his space and time border mine at some point of eternity. If that were so, I might see him again in someone else's fable."

"You have said it. But let us not waste time with idle words. Your hours are dwindling and you have a lot left to do in just a few days. After your demise, neither I nor anybody else can delay your return to this riverbank. Or to your book, if you thus prefer to call it."

As she spoke, the image of Ana Franca unraveled and effaced in the air. Before dissipating completely she kissed your lips. Or perhaps her kiss was just a puff of wind caressing you. Once alone, you gazed at the horizon and measured the entire landscape. In that world fashioned in the manner of your novel, you recalled another day so clear that your shadow looked as thin as a lance. Ravenous and with your clothes in tatters, you walked all the way back to Esquivias from Seville. As Catalina would not forget either, you found her sewing in her grandfather's apple orchard. When you called her name, she merely raised her eyes and stared at you silently. Little by little her unaffectionate gaze, full of contempt for your ragged appearance and rebuke for your long and unreasonable absence, began to change into a gesture of growing interest as you described to her the Hidalgo that you had conceived while in jail and the household that you had given him. That night she dreamed that she seduced the Knight—like years later María Mercedes del Calvario would attempt to seduce you. Your Hero was still a virgin and Catalina was initiating him in the pleasures of the flesh. But she would never know for certain if that was her true dream, or if she lived in the dream of an imaginary and as yet uncreated lover.

From Catalina in the apple orchard, perhaps your mind meandered to the memory of Catalina describing a winter sunset in the lands of Esquivias. She spoke to you of rainbow trout from the Guadatén and of ghost towns with names long forgotten. *In a village of La Mancha the name of which I have no desire to recall*. When the two of you meet again on the other bank of the river it will be Your Grace's turn to show her the nameless town of the Hidalgo and the Squire. Then you will go together to that house with a back door over the corral, through which your Paladin set forth into the world one early dawn in July, on one of the warmest days of that year of Our Lord. Or you would take her to the Duke and Duchess' castle: the one whose armory grounds border with the green exuberance of the forest. Dressed in colorful clothes, lackeys and hostlers would welcome you, ceremoniously. They will be the same ones who received the Rustic and the Hidalgo in your book. With their identity, all of them will owe you their lives, forever perpetuated with the forest, the armory grounds, and the castle.

But your evocations pertained to the future since you and Catalina were still alive. Shrugging your shoulders, you remembered that your time was growing short. After glancing for the last time at those plains, crowned with windmills, you headed back to the river. You found the boat rocking in the stream amid a swarm of dragonflies and tied to the bare dead poplar. You stepped in firmly and began to row with your good arm. By midstream, a sudden mist covered both banks. *What river could this be? Is this the Styx that borders the Inferno or is it an ocean estuary at the entrance of Purgatory?* Through the fog and through time Santafiore would return to your mind. At León Street and just before his disappearance he was chanting with his beautiful voice the words of Virgil in the *Commedia* urging the souls to kneel down before the Angel of God, as he would be taking them to Purgatory. *Fa, fa che le ginocchia cali! | Ecco l'angel di Dio-piega le mani!* Virgil's angel abandoned the paddles and had no other sail than his own wings. He opened them to the sun and you saw that they were covered with feathers as perennial as myrtle leaves.

Coming from the other bank, a boat crowded with shadows emerged from the mist. Without sails, paddles, or a rudder, it glided over the water. But there was no angel at the helm, instead you saw Santafiore there, standing as tall as life. His eyes lit up; death seemed to have returned his sight. Neither the pauper nor any of the ghosts could perceive you because you still belonged to the land of the living. *Niccolò, credo propio che non mi será possibile di esser soddisfatto con la tua supposta cecità. Deceiving us, you deceived yourself and you became your own metaphor. But I do not believe that you are blind because you see better than I, myself.* It was clear for you then that Santafiore had died—perhaps in the great hall of the General Hospital or in the ward of the Hospital of Passion, two buildings separated by that trough where one night you saw a couple of bay horses drinking water while a young lad brushed them under a light held by a witch. Thus you understood why you had not heard of Santafiore in so many weeks. You also recognized other shadows in the boat that you had not seen in a long time.

Seated at the edge of the boat and with a lute on his knees, Your Grace got a glimpse of the tiny eunuch, may the peace of Allah be with him, who sang the taking of La Goleta for Azán Bajá's greater honor and glory. The capon was accompanied by Don Juan of Austria, conqueror of the Turks and Viceroy of the Netherlands who let himself die in a bleak attic. The same Don Juan of Austria who once granted you an audience and told you that he, the glorious bastard of the Emperor, ought to have died in Lepanto because he would never be the same man afterwards. Next to Don Juan you saw Agustín de Cetina who progressed from pen-pusher and accountant in Seville to big shot on the Advisory Board of Accountants and enjoyed much prosperity only to leave this life like anyone else. Frowning, he was stroking his beard as he did that morning when he proposed the ill-fated business of the taxes to you. Aboard with them was María Mercedes del Calvario, the whore that one night got into your bed. She went looking for you in the room prepared especially for you by the innkeeper. This same innkeeper who from time to time purchased pepper, salt, oregano, cloves, ginger, and red-skinned garlic at the spice shop in town. In the moonlight coming through the open shutters, María Mercedes del Calvario said to you that your madness was not that of a fool or an angry man, provided that you were indeed insane. The courtesan must have died as young as the virgin nun who was also on the boat. Looking at her through your glasses it took you a while to recognize who the nun was. She was the novice who was pushing the noria for the lack of a horse when you went to tell your sister Luisa that Magdalena was dying.

Next to those people who lived in your time, you also noticed others who you knew belonged in your book and whose only existence was the one that you gave them. Between Don Juan and the blind man you saw two equally grayish women, although one could have been the mother of the other judging by their age. The Hidalgo's housekeeper and his niece seemed as imprecise and undefined as you had imagined them in your novel. Nearby and dressed in green satin and with a falcon on her arm, you distinguished the Duchess of your story. The one that your Knight and his Squire saw in the forest among other high-flight hunters. At the back, a clergyman wrapped in his cassock chatted with a red-headed man of an undetermined age who was dressed in a white coat with big pockets. You assumed that they were the curate and the barber from the Hidalgo's town. That town that was never registered in

any census although many places in La Mancha claimed it according
to what some Andalusian travelers said in the tavern of Cantarranas.
Because of his red hair and ruddy complexion the barber could not
be mistaken. In another epoch you created him in the image of your
own father, an ill-starred surgeon who perhaps was nought but a
well read veterinarian surgeon or a simple barber. With a pair of
pruning shears in his hands and seated by the two chatterboxes, a
strong youth remained silent. It was the farmhand whom you mentioned in the first paragraph of your novel and then sentenced to
oblivion along with the Knight's greyhound because you very seldom read over what you had written. You also saw the dog among
the shadows in the boat. With the translucent tongue of all ghostly
dogs, it licked the lad's open hand as he caressed its pointed muzzle.

Your right arm on the paddle and your left against your chest,
you gazed at the boat until it disappeared into the thicket of the
riverbank. Then you let go a sigh and smiled. Perchance your entire
life, although stitched with threads of bad luck and woven with
mishaps, had been for the better. You did not have time to meditate
on it for long and even less to make sure that it was true. At any
rate, it had been worth it to have suffered so many setbacks, blows,
and broken dreams in order to have created a story like the one of
your Paladin and his Servant. A work so superior to the rest of your
writings, that at times Your Grace thought that you owed it to another different, distant, and unknown man.

It would also be worth it to close your eyes and give up your soul,
the angel had warned it would be soon, if you were to find yourself
on that riverbank where your open book became a landscape that
extended for all eternity. Among all the beings who awaited you
there, the real and the imagined, you did not know for certain which
ones were more authentic. Perhaps you had written your fable and
even answered Avellaneda's challenge with your own second part,
only to widen the horizon that would belong to you in the everlasting
hereafter. Before securing the paddles to row to the other bank
where your stay would be brief, you put your hand in the water
and lifted it to the sun. For a few fleeting instants you became
absorbed by the iridescent drops that little by little slipped through
your fingers and fell one by one into the silent river current.

THE GOLDEN AGE

Contrary to the public auto-da-fe, the *autillo* or private auto is celebrated inside the churches. Henry Charles Lea indicates that the Holy Office never invited the civil authorities to those causes and very seldom the ecclesiastic, except for priests from the Inquisition itself. The *autillo*, however, was not held in secret, but it was open to the public, who attended the trial and settled in the audience chambers for as long as there was room.[1]

Two months after Cervantes' demise, on the sixteenth of June 1616, a private auto-da-fe was celebrated in the Madrilian parish of Bethlehem.[2] Six convicts were tried of whom only one, the Father Friar Manuel María del Rosario, was a clergyman. Two culprits worked as notaries in the Ministry of Finance. Another was a bookseller for the Alcalá printing company of Juan García, precisely where Cervantes published the first part of *La Galatea* in 1585. Another declared himself to be an outstanding carpenter of richly decorated cabinets, marquetry, and billiard tables. The last one— a landlord with a recently acquired title of Gentleman and therefore exempted from royal or municipal taxes—was named Gregorio Nacianceno Patriarca.

The secretary, Don Alejandro Murciano, read the process from the pulpit. Seated on low, infamous, stands one foot high and without a back, the convicts listened to the report. Bareheaded, they each held a candle in their hands. Friar Manuel María del Rosario wore his scapulary but not his cingulum or his cowl. The charges for sodomy and other heinous crimes were all opprobrious and very serious. In order not to cause excessive scandal, the reading was shortened to the following text:

The six convicts periodically devoted themselves to carnal sins, much *contra natura*, at the house that Gregorio Nacianceno Patriarca had at El Prado of the Recollect Friars. There, Friar Manuel María del Rosario said to them that lascivious caressing and kissing were not sinful if they were done in the name of God. They all kissed on the mouth and felt each other. Friar Manuel María made himself bleed with a lancet and the others kept his dry and pulverized blood in a small urn as if it were a sacred relic. The friar assured them that upon the demise of his Holiness Paul V, happily reigning, the Holy Spirit would choose him to be Pope and he would in turn appoint each one of them cardinals after his coronation. Together they would launch a new crusade which would definitely conquer Jerusalem for Christianity. The new Pope would move his throne and the Sacred Episcopal College there in order to rule over the entire world from Solomon's temple.

Friar Manuel María del Rosario is condemned to life in prison in a convent that the Holy Inquisition would indicate in due time. Also, he will not be allowed to hear confessions for the rest of his life nor preach nor sing a mass. He will fast on bread and water on Tuesdays and Thursdays, confess his sins to a learned man, and only receive communion on Easter Sunday. The others are punished with exile from the city. The so-called Gregorio Nacianceno Patriarca requests that he fulfill his years of exile at Colmenar Viejo, Torrelaguna, or Guadalajara where he owns land and knows people who would help him in his disgrace. The High Tribunal orders that his request be put on file and it is assumed it will be ignored.

The sentences reflect the relative leniency of the Holy Office towards sins of the flesh but they are far from pleasing everyone. A pamphlet, *News from the Court,* that circulated in those days and was quoted in 1881 by Santiago Sendín y Marañón in his book *Spain of the Last Austrias,* denounced the excessive Inquisitional weakness. "With regard to the convicted for hideous carnal crimes, the desired rigor was not used. No one was ever burned. Gregorio Nacianceno Patriarca confessed on the rack that privately and secretly he had maintained lustful relations with a tailor and doublet maker from Madrid in addition to the repeated sacrilegious acts committed at his own house which were unknown to his tailor friend. The latter must have had powerful connections since he was never called to declare and his name does not appear in the records."[3]

Bringing it up himself, without anyone requesting it, Gregorio Nacianceno denies being the author of the false continuation of *Don Quixote of La Mancha.* He says that, consequently, he is not the pretend Alonso Fernández de Avellaneda who signed that novel published in Tarragona. He adds that the apocryphal text was first entrusted to his lover, the doublet maker. But then he voluntarily took over the task as later he gladly gave it to another person for reasons that are of no concern here and whose name has no relevance. The judges show no interest in those tangent confessions which have nothing to do with the main charges. They appear in the initial declaration but are not recorded in the interrogation nor are they mentioned in the sentence.

Manuel María del Rosario is confined to the old convent of San Gil of Portugal, demolished at the time when the Discalced Carmelites of Santa Ana was also condemned, and located not too far away from the disappearing parish of Bethlehem where the *Autillo* took place. Imprisoned there behind the corrals of Pacheca and Cruz, he dies after one year. His death certificate remains to this day.[4] As far as the fate of the rest of the convicted, there is no available documentation after the trial. *They seem to have vanished into thin air.*

—Reynolds Simpson, *Inquisition in Spain*. Translated by C. R.

Notes

1. Henry Charles Lea, *A History of the Inquisition of Spain*. v.III, pp. 220–21.
2. Manuscrits. Bibliothèque Nationale de France, legado Grenier, 15, folio 158.
3. Santiago Sendín y Marañón, *Spain of the Last Austrias,* p. 473.
4. Archives of Simancas, Inquisition, Room 40, Book 4, folio 531.

INSIDE OUT

Gregorio Nacianceno Patriarca's documented declarations in the *autillo* of Bethlehem prove for certain that the former actor was not the pretend Alonso Fernández de Avellaneda although he must have felt tempted to be. Judging by Patriarca's confession neither of the two Miguel Cortinases, father or son, was Avellaneda. In view of other reasons it seems quite improbable that Jerónimo de Pasamonte, Lope, or even Your Grace—as Figueroa wanted to prove in your time, and as an officer in the Service Corps wanted to prove in ours—would have appropriated the fake continuation of your book.

A greater mystery than the identity of that gentleman and author of the fraudulent novel is for me the time wasted by Your Grace in the ten years that lapsed between the two parts of the novel. An interval that could have lasted forever had not Alonso Fernández de Avellaneda come out with his apocryphal text. Lope himself said that he did not know for sure if he entrusted and requested the false fable to make you continue or abandon yours. I tend to imagine that a tossed coin could have fallen either way. In other words the plagiarist could have forced you to renounce your second part by way of indifference or spite. Or he could have angered your sense of pride, as indeed he did with his slander and insults, driving you to conclude a tale so long interrupted. At any rate, I am not aware of a greater disillusion in the world and its vainglory—realities and appearances, inns and castles in the air, giants and windmills—than that tacit lack of esteem or that silent abandonment of your work, maintained by Your Grace throughout so many years in spite of the success of *Don Quixote* and the renown that it had given you.

In order to measure those lost years, I conceived *The Garden of Janus*. Or at least, I suppose that was my purpose: to suspend myself at the edge of that void in your writer's life like someone stops at the brink of a cliff whose bottom is the center of the world. Nevertheless, other inadvertent motives made me compose my fable. I dreamed that dream between pages 50 and 51 of this fable of mine. I dreamed that upon confronting that double of yours in a duel that would never be, you were also facing me because I was both your replica and the invisible spectator of our encounter. I was the one who told you then that it was not worth it to get killed for a book and I was also the author of this other book where your dream reflects itself after more then three centuries.

Although I cannot prove it, I feel certain of not having limited myself to dream all of that in the twentieth century, for Your Grace had also dreamed, in your time, that which I would write in *The Garden of Janus*. In short, I am convinced that I was Avellaneda in the seventeenth century, although no one knew or will ever know the true name of that impostor. Vainly, in order to recognize myself for who I was in another life, I wrote the novel that I am now concluding.

I thought I was creating fiction when I was only recording history. I could swear that the house in Atocha, the tapestry, the mirror, the orchard, and the bi-frontal bust of Janus existed. Furthermore, I also became convinced that there they truly embroidered and foresaw Your Grace's entire life and every episode of *Don Quixote*. If in the twelfth century Hugues de Saint-Victor speaks of a book that predicts the entire history of mankind from creation to doomsday, why could not the weaving of a tapestry also announce the book and the existence of a man, both to be reflected in a mirror? I am referring to that vast looking glass, perhaps as old as the world, where your life and the parody of your life are reflected in the same way that every novel is the opaque mirror of an autobiography.

I said a tapestry as old as the world because Atocha is a land of marvels, as Your Grace stated at the beginning of *The Garden of Janus*. I allude here to my book and not to the orchard, although the orchard is in the book. I do not know when they built the house nor who laid out the garden since the hawthorns were already overrun with brambles the afternoon when you discovered it with your brothers and sisters. It is not mentioned by such Madrilean chroniclers as Mesonero Romanos, González Ruano, or Pedro de Répide. Unsuccessfully, I looked for the house and the garden behind the station and the hill of Moyano. I do not know whether they intentionally demolished the villa and the bust or if they were devastated by a fortuitous fire. Sometimes I say to myself that perhaps the orchard, the statue, and the building disappeared at the very instant when I began my novel, just as Your Grace was telling the ghosts how Rodrigo discovered the double profile of Janus behind the fence.

Although the tapestry included that scene among all those of your life and your book, it omitted my true effigy as Avellaneda. I was not part of the wall hanging because, after you published your own second part, I was no one, and my novel was nothing. As you may remember, I wrote this to Lope in the letter that the witches gave you. Ironically, I only lived for the purpose of not being. Whoever the man masked with my pen name might have been, I was sure that he would not write anymore under a false or true name. In short, he would not write again until he started *The Garden of Janus*.

If in another incarnation I was the Avellaneda of your days, another character from *The Garden of Janus* would anticipate my time in yours. I am certain that your protector, the muffled individual wearing the ring with the sign of the father of all gods on it, truly existed and that you saw and spoke to him as Your Grace speaks and sees him in this book. But, also, I believe that beneath the cape and the plumed chambergo hat there was no one because that man wandered mistakenly in time and space. Góngora must have foreseen this when he said that the muffled stranger wandered lost between magic and comedy.

Your protector must have had an unclear awareness of his identity in the seventeenth century. In your first encounter he confessed that he believed he was the shadow of someone who had previously existed or the sketchy anticipation of he who would only be in the future. When he disappeared after paying you the last two hundred and fifty escudos, he planned to enter an unwritten book where Your Grace would meet him once again. On the other hand, I am inclined to believe that the escudos were legal coins minted in good gold from the Peruvian Indies. Those escudos rescued the second part of your book like the same sum had liberated you from your captivity. If man is created twice, as the Hidalgo assured you, perhaps a rare destiny caused Your Grace to be redeemed twice for the same price. Once from the prison in Algiers and the other from your own disillusioned lethargy so that you would conclude the delayed renewal of your novel.

In a book already mentioned, *Cervantes, Passamonte, and Avellaneda*, its author affirms that there is no greater nonsense than that of the Knight when he declares that the King should not be served by enslaved men whom "God and nature created free." Personally, I disagree and I understand Philip III's fascination with the supposed witty, yet foolish, reply. I would also have God as a witness that your encounters with the Monarch truly occurred when he came to visit you on your deathbed. I thought I was imagining such notable events, but I was only reflecting what really happened in a very distant mirage through time. *If man is created twice as you say in your book, who creates him first, God or nature?*

Philip III also wondered how many times we would die, once or perhaps twice to correspond to our double creation. Like Avellaneda, I died on a day of the baroque century and perhaps they lost my ashes like they lost Your Grace's remains at the convent of the Trinitarians. *The Prince was buried here. In those days they used to bury people in the churches. They kept throwing dead relatives on top of him. His wife, his daughter, his son-in-law. You know how it is.* I disappeared then like the unknown muffled man under his panache. Again I am alluding to your protector, the shadow who was afraid of dying before they gave the last part of *Don Quixote* to the printers or of going insane if he had had the chance to read it. The man would not have truly lived if he were solely the premature sketch of a character in *The Garden of Janus*. But although such was his condition, he would also be my disembodied shadow precipitated and lost. Let us say the eternal and errant shadow of Avellaneda.

In a way, every novelist who writes in Spanish is Avellaneda since knowingly or inadvertently he is trying to equal Your Grace's novel. In vain, he would pretend to measure up to the most extraordinary of your books which by contrast accentuates and highlights the mediocrity of the rest of your works. While I am writing about books that can be dispensed with, I have only been Alonso Fernández de Avellaneda in the reign of the Austrias even though I do not know the name of he who I feigned to be then. As the snow of another recently born year falls outside, I say to myself that all of it matters very little, and I prepare to conclude this manuscript.

A manuscript which will be published under a pseudonym. I am not he who appears as its author, and I am not about to reveal my name. Today the only certainty that matters is that Avellaneda, such a long time after his passing through the world, has been reincarnated in me. The impostor that I was has been revived to write this novel that ends now. It is also fitting that Avellaneda came to be reborn in me because Your Grace died in 1616 without finishing another book, now lost, under the uncertain title of *Weeks in a Garden,* which perhaps was also the garden of Janus. At least this is what I wish to believe at the break of day on this shivering January morn.